— THE —
ROBOT HERITAGE

Neil Frude

GUILD PUBLISHING
LONDON

About the author

Neil Frude was born in Plymouth, Devon and took a degree in Psychology and Philosophy at the University of Newcastle-upon-Tyne. After an M Phil. in Clinical Psychology at the Institute of Psychiatry in London, he went on to gain a PhD in Psychology at the University College, Cardiff where he now lectures. A regular contributor to a number of academic journals, Neil Frude has also published books in the fields of aggression, family relationships and family therapy. He is the author of *The Intimate Machine* (Century, 1983) which looks at how computers can affect human feelings and understanding.

First published in Great Britain in 1984
This edition published 1984 by
Book Club Associates
By arrangement with Century Publishing Co. Ltd

ISBN 0 7126 0918 0
ISBN 0 7126 0921 0 (Pbk)

Typeset by Rowland Phototypesetting Ltd, Bury St Edmunds, Suffolk
Printed by Guernsey Press Co. Ltd, Guernsey, Channel Islands

Contents

ONE
The State of the Art

What is a Robot?

If we had now to prepare a 'robot' entry for an encyclopaedia to be published in the year 2000, reflecting the 'current' state of the robot industry, a choice of strategies would be available to us. We could 'play safe' and portray the industrial robots of the early 1980s, adding a few developments that are known to be 'on the drawing board'. Alternatively, we could examine the predictions of experts in the field about what will be achievable by AD 2000. The results of these two strategies would be very dissimilar, for much is said to be 'just over the horizon'. But there is a third strategy: to build on the second, taking the sober predictions of the scientists and then considering how such potential might be exploited artistically and commercially. This involves an additional analysis of relevant aspects of human imagination and of likely consumer appeal. This third strategy seems to be the one most likely to reveal aspects of the future, for few would doubt that by AD 2000 robots will have emerged from the laboratories and the factories and will have joined the human throng.

The thesis of this book is that the vast body of 'humanoid' literature—the 'robot heritage'—can be of great help in constructing a vision of the real robot future. This is not to claim that SF can simply be taken literally: SF is a highly unreliable source, an amalgam of speculation, fantasy and nonsense. In an SF story we may encounter time-travel machines, bug-eyed monsters (BEMs) and marvellous potions that make people invisible. Such artefacts and aliens have no parallels in the contemporary scientific enterprise. But in similar sources we find powerful images of humanoid robots with intellect, speech and vision. Here there are clear parallels with serious scientific research. Expert roboticists say that such talents will indeed be given to machines. They promise to provide the potential, but how will that potential be reified? In looking forward to the arrival of such humanoids, not as

1

'scientific demonstrations' or 'industrial equipment' but as commercial products designed for maximum acceptability across the widest consumer market, we would do well to consider the imaginings of SF writers and film-makers. What will such creatures look like? What characteristics and personalities will they display? And how will people react to them?

Science fiction can thus be used to put flesh on the bones of technological promise. But in adopting such a strategy we must remain with at least one foot planted firmly on the ground. We must draw upon the fiction, not add to it. Due regard must be given at all times to technological feasibility. But to limit our concerns to the scientific nuts and bolts (or rather chips and databases) would certainly be to misrepresent the future. For within a couple of decades, at the latest, robots will 'go public'. Chips are the new raw material, capable of being shaped into a million forms. Which of the possibilities see the light of day, receive manufacturers' attention and end up on supermarket shelves will depend on human need and human fancy. How can we assess the whims and desires, the reactions and repercussions relevant to robot products? By a critical examination of the work of those who have thought about such matters over centuries. In short, SF may provide us with more than a glimpse of the real robot future.

What of the robot present? Most of the 100,000 or so robots that now exist in the world are functional devices working in factories. They are generally sedentary machines, without speech, hearing, vision or locomotion. Although they are not humanoid they do simulate human actions, at least of the arm and hand. Their advantages over human operators are that they are tireless and may be highly accurate in their movements, and, although they are often very strong, they can be gentle too. Most are 'fixed-sequence' machines designed to perform a particular task with endless repetition, but some are more flexible and can be easily reset to perform a variety of tasks.

The arm and wrist movements are controlled by a computer and effected by the actions of electric motors, hydraulics or compressed air. The overall movement can be very flexible. Movement in three planes allows the machine to get to any point within the reachable space and it may be able to make complex and flowing movements as if conducting an orchestra. The machine would be capable of managing only the slower musical passages, however, because most robot arms have a maximum velocity of about a metre a second (speedier machines are promised for the near future). Some robot arms have a claw-hand action, and others even have fingers with independently movable digits. A piano-playing robot would certainly be viable, although special problems would arise. The robot would have to be placed very accurately before the instrument. Since most robots have no power of vision and no means of interpreting audio feedback, if the piano were to be placed 'one note to the left' the preprogrammed repertoire would emerge weirdly transposed and decidedly flat.

The piano example can be used to illustrate some further points about industrial robots. One of these concerns the programming. A program could be written specifying the pitch and length of each note; the composition could be laboriously translated, note by note, into a computer instruction. But instructions could be provided in another way. It could be arranged that the piano keys were connected to electrical contacts linked to a computer, so that each time a key was depressed the computer would take note of this and in effect 'record' an analogue of the music played. A musician could then be asked to play a piece. The computer record of the key depressions would then be used to control a robot who would effectively simulate the musician's play. Clearly this would save a lot of time, and the basic set of instructions could then be tampered with to make the piece faster or slower, to change the musical key, or to edit passages.

The basic strategy here is hardly new. A similar technique forms the basis of the 'pianola' or 'player piano', first patented in France in 1842. Some fifty years later another French contrivance, the 'Pianista', used felted 'fingers' to play simple tunes. In principle robots could play music that was either 'language-programmed' or 'replicated' from a human performance and, indeed, the replication technique is already employed with some advanced machines. A human operator's movements, for example in welding, are recorded and then reproduced by the robot. By-passing the need for step-by-step programming, this is a very efficient way of transmitting highly skilled operations to the machine. It is often referred to as 'teaching by doing'.

The current goal of robotics can be simply stated: it is to give machines 'sense'. There are two implied meanings of that term. On the one hand it refers to 'sensory awareness' of the environment and on the other it refers to 'commonsense' knowledge. The two aspects are closely linked.

Current developments in industrial robotics focus on making robots 'intelligent' and 'sensible' of the world around them. So far the machines have little 'awareness'. Few can be said to see, or to hear, or to know anything about the world in which they exist, and there are therefore very strict limitations on their usefulness and adaptability. Robots with 'sense' would be able to make a far more extensive industrial contribution, and there is thus an obvious practical motive for research towards the 'aware machine'. But when such skills are achieved they will find many applications in fields beyond industry. Such systems would have important uses in the business and scientific worlds, and in the home. The task of giving machines such skills is formidable, but few doubt that the problems will prove solvable. Intense research effort is under way and notable achievements have already been made.

Some machines already 'see' in an elementary fashion. It is easy to add a television camera to a robot, and not too difficult to analyse the picture in terms of areas of relative shade and light. The problem arises, however, when attempts are made to give the picture some 'meaning', to provide a translation of the visual pattern in terms of objects in the world. Human beings take for granted the process of perception and do not regard 'seeing' as a process requiring intelligence. But about a third of the human brain is concerned with the analysis of visual information, and it would be difficult to overestimate the complexity of the perceptual task. It is something of a paradox that contemporary computer systems are much better at coping with tasks generally regarded as highly intellectual, like playing chess or solving complex algebraic equations, than they are at what is imagined to be the simple task of recognizing an object as a book or a chair. Yet chairs come in many shapes and sizes, and even the same chair has a radically different image depending on the direction from which you look at it. Nevertheless, computer scientists are confident that in time they will be able to 'remove the scales from the robot's eyes'.

The few industrial robots which have a limited degree of vision commonly search for sharp changes of shading within the picture, identifying these as edges, and then attempt to fit the emerging outline or silhouette to one of the various reference-patterns or templates with which they have been preprogrammed. Their template dictionary is usually very limited. Although even this restricted ability for recognizing objects may be useful in the confined environment of the specific industrial setting, the machine would be effectively blinded by information if it were moved to a different 'world'. Compared to the uniformity of the factory production line, even the best ordered home is an exceedingly messy environment.

Thus the industrial robot must be considered 'blind' when compared to the SF machines that see the world much as we do, wandering around with perfect understanding of visual cues. Yet a human-like capacity for visual analysis is now considered by many scientists to be a reasonable goal for research. A number of giant steps will have to be taken before the human capacity for object-recognition and scene-interpretation is duplicated in an artificial system, but considerable advances in machine vision are anticipated within the next decade. Thus, in terms of visual ability, it is expected that within the foreseeable future many real robot systems will resemble the fictional creations more closely than the most advanced contemporary machines.

It is clear that even simple machine vision will have considerable impact. Such an ability will not only greatly enhance the functional capabilities of robots but it will also increase the readiness with which people anthropomorphize the machines. A robot which 'sees' objects and reacts accordingly will have escaped one of the constraints at present embedded in the notion 'machine'. It will behave as if it were 'aware' of its environment, and such 'awareness' is normally ascribed only to living objects. Evidence of visual (or similar sensual) alertness is one of the criteria by which we judge that something is sentient and alive. The effect will be apparent when physical objects are sensed, but it will be far greater when human beings themselves are recognized. At Brunel University Igor Aleksander has taught a computer to recognize faces. Linked to a television camera it identifies people that it 'knows' even if they have changed their hairstyle, and regardless of their facial expression. Connected to a voice synthesizer it greets people by name, and even changes the emotional tone of its greeting depending on whether their expression is happy or sad.

When the intelligent part of seeing, that of interpreting and assigning meaning, has been achieved by machine systems, robots will have an immediate visual advantage over human beings. Much information is not perceptible to the unaided human eye. Some can be rendered accessible by the use of a telescope or a microscope, or can be provided indirectly by systems sensitive to X-rays or ultraviolet radiation. Infrared sensors are used for the remote detection of heat patterns (thermography) and in 'night-vision apparatus'. Laser-based systems can provide exceedingly accurate measurement of distance and can detect the slightest change in the position of an object.

Robots with 'visual intelligence' will therefore be able to have immediate access not just to that limited part of the electromagnetic spectrum which constitutes the band of visible light. Robots will see accurately and in fine detail, and they will see beyond the rainbow. Just as we may describe a scene to a blind companion, so our robot friends will tell us of things which lie outside the range of our clear vision. For industrial robots, the added information will doubtless prove invaluable in many of their tasks. Domestic robots will perhaps not need such an extensive range, but their 20:20 vision will remain clear when our own begins to fail. Our robot companions will not need spectacles.

This example illustrates a general phenomenon. Developments in robotics will not merely lead to the duplication of human capabilities. Human limits may constitute an important marker for achievements in the field of robotics but they do not constitute an impassable boundary line. With regard to intellectual as well as sensory abilities, robotics holds the promise (or threat) of outstripping and outpacing human capabilities. Duplication of some human aptitudes will develop at a faster pace than others, and work will not cease once the criterion of 'human equivalence' has been reached. Computer systems long ago surpassed the mathematical skills of most human beings, and clearly this did not decrease the motivation to further improve systems. Thus in some of their skills robot systems will forge ahead far beyond human limits while in other skills they will lag behind. At no point in time, therefore, will the 'state-of-the-art' robot have a human profile of abilities.

Although vision will be the most important sensory ability the robot will acquire, it will also be able to 'hear'. As with vision, there is no difficulty in picking up the 'raw' information—a microphone does this well—but extracting 'meaning' from the auditory input and making it 'sensible' can be extraordinarily difficult. The crucial sound source for most robotics applications also happens to be the most intricate and the most inscrutable—the human voice.

Speech recognition is a major research area with obvious and immediate application. The ability to instruct an industrial robot verbally would greatly facilitate control over the machine. A 'secretary robot', able to type letters directly from dictation, would revolutionize the business world. And listening robots would have a profound impact on telecommunications, health care, education and leisure. A number of contemporary systems can distinguish between several hundred individual words and can recognize some simple continuous phrases. A few can handle a variety of accents, too, but many require the speaker to first recite a list of sample words so that the computer can become familiar with the individual's voice characteristics. But natural speech does not consist of individuated words—it has a continuous flow. The human listener can identify words within the flow by taking context into consideration and by analysing the meaning of the sentence. Indeed, human beings can almost always understand the meaning of a spoken or written message even if they hear or read only about every second word.

Thus continuous speech recognition requires a degree of 'understanding', and the limits are imposed by 'intellectual' rather than technical hardware constraints. A key problem in artificial intelligence (AI) is that of giving machines the power to 'understand'.

A similar problem faces attempts to get machines to read. At least in written text there are spaces between the words, but considerable difficulties remain. To *understand* a sentence, rather than simply read it aloud, there must be an extensive knowledge base, for meaning is not located within a sentence—rather it involves locating the sentence within the world of knowledge.

Ideally, verbal interaction with a robot would be two-way. Voice synthesis is rather simpler than voice recognition and depends less on meaning-analysis. Although many computers already speak quite well their intonation remains somewhat 'robotic'. But voice synthesis is another area of intense research effort—and again it is confidently predicted that the 'naturalness' of systems will be substantially increased within the decade. So in this respect, too, the real robots of the 1990s will have more in common with their fictional precursors than with the industrial robots encountered today. Although as yet no machine is able to hold a verbal conversation the robots in fiction are garrulous creatures who understand very well what is said to them, even if they do have a tendency to take colloquialisms and metaphors literally. We can certainly look forward to meeting such talkative robots, and they will answer our questions with accuracy, patience and good humour.

Hearing and vision are undoubtedly the senses by which human beings obtain most of their information about the external world, and so these are the focus of much current work in robotics. By contrast, little interest is shown in providing robots with the senses of taste or smell. The reason is simply that there would be few uses for such an ability. What would you do with a robot who smells? (The answer is *not* 'Buy it a deodorant'.) But the task might not prove impossible. Taste and smell are known as the 'chemical senses', and chemical analysis has already been automated to some degree. Machines for 'tasting' wine and sherry, for example, have been developed for the drinks industry. Wine-tasting is acknowledged as a fine art calling for both the nicest discriminations of human judgement and an encyclopaedic breadth of wine knowledge. Yet it may well be that one day a 'robot taster' will be able to recognize wines with greater accuracy than the most expert human.

The last of the five senses is touch. Robot hands that 'feel' were first developed a number of years ago, and appliances lacking this ability are today said by technologists to be 'numb'. For some industrial applications it is essential that a robot be given feedback from its manipulation of objects, and pressure-sensitive touch sensors are therefore mounted on the claw or fingers; these enable the machine to perform delicate operations on fragile objects. Such robots can also tell when parts of an assembly have slotted together in the correct position.

'Force sensing' enables the machine to adapt to objects which are not exactly the same size or shape—like sheep! Australian engineers have plans for a sensitive sheep-shearing robot that would gather wool efficiently without injuring the animal. In this example a machine would emulate an existing human skill—but in some tasks human pressure-sensitivity may prove too limited. In such cases a robot hand might provide finer discriminations. Thus delicate medical examinations that rely on touch could prove more informative if carried out by a robot hand. Engineers at Waseda University in Tokyo are currently involved in a project aimed at producing such a machine, and they suggest that one potential application will be to scan women's breasts, searching for lumps that might indicate a tumour. Not only would the machine have superior performance, compared with the human physician, in ascertaining variations in the texture of the breast, but the number of 'fingers' with which it simultaneously probed could be increased considerably over the natural limitation of ten.

Most contemporary robots are insensitive creatures, unable to deal with 'raw input' from the environment. They have no senses and no sense, and are unresponsive to changes in the world around them. This will certainly change. Robots will gain powers of vision and hearing, and their touch will become more sensitive. But for such developments to become truly effective they will also have to become more 'sensible'. Not only will they have to see objects, they will have to recognize them and to react to them appropriately. 'Perceptive' robots will have to make inferences and go beyond the information presented to their television sensors. Perception is more a process of the brain than of the eye, and it depends on knowing a good deal about the world. The mobile robot must know the difference, for example, between the 'empty space' that it can move through and the 'filled spaces' that it must avoid. It must recognize which objects are movable and which are static, which are harmless and which are dangerous. Without such abilities the mobile machine would be a dangerous device—it's as well that at the moment most robots are stationary.

The robot's special forte today is arm movement, and the standard robot is a one-armed affair mounted on an immovable plinth. We may look in vain inside factories across the world for a pair of 'robot legs' and we shall not find a biped robot strolling along any of the assembly lines. Locomotion, and especially two-legged locomotion, has proved very difficult to implement in machine systems. Even if unable to entertain us with a full gymnastic display, a mobile robot would be very useful. For many applications the firmly mounted arm suffices, but there would be countless uses for an intelligent machine that could walk and manoeuvre its body as humans can.

Attempts to improve machine mobility have taken a number of routes. It is not difficult to construct a wheeled machine, and other test-models move with a variety of waddles and shuffles. A particular problem facing bipedal locomotion is that of balance, and attempts have been made to produce systems that are virtually topple-proof by incorporating numerous legs. Even if a system were capable of perfect, and speedy, two-legged locomotion on a smooth floor surface, however, this could not be said to have solved the 'walking problem', for human walking involves not simply putting one leg in front of the other at the right moment but also circumventing obstacles and dealing with turns, bends and stairs. Walking efficiently depends crucially on a knowledge of the environment and it requires also a sense of balance and sensory feedback from the walking actions. Thus it can be seen that locomotion research will benefit considerably from work being carried out in other areas of robotics.

Science-fiction writers have rarely given special consideration to the problem of locomotion. Their robots walk without difficulty, and they walk like humans. But the characterization and story-lines rarely depend on such an ability. In many cases the machine depicted ambling along beside its human companion might just as well be sitting at a desk or standing on a table-top. The focus would still be on social interaction and conversation, on the character of the machine and on the relationship that develops between the robot and the human being. What matters for the robot heroes of SF is not locomotor ability but intelligence, knowledge and, naturally, commonsense.

Things taken for granted in such fiction, however, are often far from being realized in fact, and the 'commonsense' issue is a prime illustration of this. For, however expert a computer may appear at playing chess, however encyclopaedic may be its store of names, addresses and personal details, and however powerful its ability to solve geometrical theorems, no machine can at present be said to be 'sensible'. It may be described as 'intelligent', but hardly as 'sensible'. Computers can absorb and process predigested information at an astounding rate, but the judgements they make will be limited by their ability to associate such information with existing 'knowledge' and to incorporate new facts within a general knowledge system.

Take the case of the hypothetical wine-tasting robot. Its effectiveness as a 'sensible wine taster' will depend not only on the sensitivity of its chemical probes, or its ability to compute results derived from a chemical analysis, but also on a wide knowledge of wines. Information about the chemistry will yield only isolated facts about constituents. To recognize the wine as a 1978 Chateau Grillet, however, will require that the machine has access to a considerable 'knowledge base' of facts about wines of many types. Such recognition might be achieved simply by matching the analysis to a set of stored facts, but for the machine to converse flexibly and sensibly about the wine it would need to 'know' about the wine trade, the reputations of wines and, at a basic level, about the nature of drinking, of bottles, of labels, of vineyards, of wine-making, of geography and of vintages. In short it would have to have a knowledge base covering many relevant aspects, not confined to a series of wine-analysis profiles but including many concepts pertaining to the 'wine world'. Furthermore, these concepts would not simply be sequenced, as in a dictionary, but would be intricately linked together to form a knowledge structure. If such a structure embodied multiple aspects of the human and physical world then the machine might be claimed to possess 'commonsense'. Failing this it would be 'merely' a wine expert.

The paradox is clear. It is relatively easy to make a system behave in 'intellectual' ways, solving abstruse algebraic formulae or chess problems. It is considerably more difficult to make the system behave like a human 'expert', at least in areas which call for a knowledge base. And it is exceedingly difficult (and beyond current capability) to enable a system to deal at a commonsense level with 'raw' input. The more the field is narrowed and the problem specified, the more easily can a machine cope with it. The computer can handle problems specified in its own terms exceedingly well. Chess, for example, occupies a very limited world of pieces, moves and strategies, and the overall goal of winning the game is perfectly clear. As the constraints are loosened, however, the task for the machine becomes far more difficult. Perception and 'meaning analysis', be it of physical objects or of verbal statements, is subject to far fewer constraints—the possibilities are endless. The more we limit the 'relevant universe' (restricting it, say, to geology, medical diagnosis or wine), the easier it is to specify the necessary knowledge structure. It would seem almost impossible to endow a machine system with sufficient general knowledge, arranged systematically, for it to deal with 'the world at large'. Yet this is what would be needed before we could claim that a machine had commonsense. No existing computer has such power. The standard robot characters from SF certainly have it. And if current research meets its promise then within a decade we will be able to point to an achievement that will make the most 'intellectual' of contemporary computers appear stupid. There will emerge, through the combined intense efforts of many computer scientists, the first of what may become a legion of 'sensible machines'.

Less than two decades ago a computer could cost millions of pounds. Today a machine of similar power may be bought for only thousands. That cost is certain to fall. There are already several million personal computers in homes throughout the world. Most of the effort involved in producing machines with 'commonsense' will be concerned not with the machine itself, the 'hardware', but with the programs and knowledge bases, the 'software'. Software, once written, can be endlessly duplicated. It is unlikely that the ability to deal in a 'commonsense' way with people and the physical world will long remain solely in major computer installations. Such a system will, more than ever, bring computers out to meet ordinary people. There will be no need to learn complex programming languages to deal with such machines, for they will speak and understand the common language. They will communicate sensibly, reasonably, gently. And in this respect, especially, they will have more in common, far more, with the devices we encounter in fiction than with those mobile arms that currently 'man' our factory assembly lines.

The Coming Race

Robots will soon be very different from the current industrial machines. They will certainly evolve to be more like the intelligent, sensible and amiable machines we find in SF. This will happen largely as a result of current research projects which combine aspects of engineering, psychology, neurology, philosophy and mathematics. Specialists from each of these disciplines are showing increasing interest in the areas of robotics and 'artificial intelligence', or AI.

Some AI research is concerned with the direct simulation of the natural processes of perception, thinking and movement that occur in biological systems, including human beings. Other research, however, is concerned more with the practical aim of allowing a machine these abilities, and cares little about copying nature. Clearly there may be ways of duplicating the biological function other than those involving the direct simulation of the biological process. Thus a television camera may be said to duplicate the function of the human eye, although it works in a quite different way. It is often the case, however, that a study of the natural process yields important clues about how a function may best be achieved: often nature has found the optimum solution to a practical problem.

The two major aims of current research in the AI field are best summed up as the 'perception goal' and the 'knowledge goal'.

The first of these is concerned with enabling the machine to 'experience' the world and to 'make sense' of raw visual and sound (especially human speech) input. The 'knowledge goal' is concerned with providing the machine with a broad structure of knowledge and thus enabling it to 'understand' the world sensibly. In fact these goals overlap considerably because experience of the environment is a major source of knowledge and because perception is an interpretive process that relies heavily on the organism's (or machine's) knowledge base. If forced to describe AI research in a single phrase we could say that it is attempting to provide machines with 'understanding'. It does this not by building bigger, faster or more powerful hardware but by devising programs which handle information in intelligent and sensible ways.

Philosophers have long discussed the issue of whether it is appropriate to use psychological terms such as 'experience', 'thinking', 'intelligence' and 'understanding' when speaking of a machine. The problem has not been resolved to everyone's satisfaction. Some philosophers make the point that the human brain is a kind of machine and that we are certainly happy to allow that it 'thinks'. Others contend that we should retain quotes around any psychological term when applying it to machines, because the words have evolved in a way that restricts their proper use to organic systems.

It may well be asked whether the question is of any practical importance. Whether or not machines can truly be said to be intelligent there is no doubt that they will behave 'as if' they were. Their behaviour will be intelligent even if, in a sense, there is no real 'intelligence' behind it. It seems likely that in interactions with advanced computers and robots people will treat them as intelligent and conscious. It would be difficult not to react in such a way to a system that was being responsive and flexible and gave every indication that it understood and was aware of events. Such machines will possess many characteristics making them appear 'organic' and 'intelligent' and they will not fit at all well with the general concept of the machine. In short, they will appear more like human beings than like tools or apparatus, and people will probably treat them accordingly.

Early work in the AI field was concerned largely with a search for general methods of solving problems. Herbert Simon, Alan Newell and Cliff Shaw, in the USA, began writing their 'Logic Theorist' program in 1954. This was designed to discover proofs for logical and mathematical theorems and dealt with a 'limited universe' of symbols and operations well suited to the computer. It was hoped that such problem-solving would act as a general model for thinking and thus provide insights that would prove useful in dealing with many other tasks. Other early projects were concerned with how information might best be represented in the machine's storage system (knowledge representation) and how a computer might benefit from experience, or learn (knowledge acquisition).

At the same time there was a good deal of interest in programs that could play games, especially chess. The ability to play chess at a high level has long been regarded as a pinnacle of human intellectual achievement. There was thus a special satisfaction to be gained from writing a computer program which could meet this criterion of 'intelligent' performance, and some also hoped that explorations in the field of games-playing might yield strategies and techniques with a far wider significance. Now that there are many very good chess programs, it is realized that such highly structured games in fact provide relatively easy tasks for a machine. A computer or a robot would find it much more difficult, for example, to identify correctly a chess piece carved in a novel style than to evaluate a complex and novel game position represented in logical symbols.

Some of those involved in AI felt that the abstract and universal approach of general-purpose programs was misguided, and that systems should be designed with a specific set of tasks in mind. The most efficient way to achieve this, they argued, would be to provide the machine with a specific knowledge base and directly relevant rules. One of the earliest attempts to operationalize such a knowledge-based approach was made by Joel Moses of MIT. His first program in this new style had the conventional goal of solving certain problems in mathematics, but it took the unconventional step of including knowledge of practical procedures used by human mathematicians. Thus human expertise was structured and used to provide hints, clues and helpful strategies for the machine. And the computer which possessed such 'rules of human thumb' proved more efficient than those that had struggled along without the benefit of human expertise.

Today 'expert systems' and the field of 'knowledge engineering' are much more advanced and the range of areas of computer expertise has been extended greatly. New methods have been devised for allowing a machine to represent knowledge, to arrive at decisions on the basis of input data, to discover new rules and to learn from experience. Such systems acquire knowledge from human beings, usually experts in a particular field, and structure this into a set of interrelated rules referred to as a 'knowledge base'. The rules need not be of the 'all or none' variety; they can refer to 'possibilities' and 'probabilities' as well as to 'certainties'. The interpretation of the rules is carried out by another part of the program, the control structure. The user of the expert system arrives with certain facts—and perhaps some guesses—and requests 'expert' help from the machine. The data are entered and interpreted by the system in accordance with the knowledge base of rules. The program is also able to evaluate the relative importance of different items of information presented to it. After deciding which rules apply to the case, these are used to make inferences. The system may then select further rules that could be useful in arriving at a final decision, and may request relevant data. The chain of reasoning may be very complex, and the system is able to cope with missing data, with 'informed guesses', and even with some misinformation. Finally it will produce its expert 'opinion', giving perhaps a range of possibilities with a weighting for the likelihood of each.

Expert systems are more than simply sets of conditional statements worked through in a linear fashion. They are better regarded as complex interconnecting networks of rules based on the often hazy 'rules of thumb' of a human consultant. Like the human expert, the system can cope with imperfect or incomplete information but, whereas the expert might be quite unable to give a rational account of his or her decision-making, the machine system can always provide full commentary and explanation: it is therefore said to be 'transparent'. The conventional computer program is 'algorithmic'—it follows a set pattern of operations from beginning to end—but expert systems incorporate 'heuristic' programming techniques. The heuristic approach to problem-solving is more exploratory in nature. It involves 'jumping to conclusions' and then testing to see whether the available knowledge can be used to justify the conclusion drawn. A good heuristic provides good guesses, and human experts may be said to differ from the less expert because they employ better heuristics. Many psychological processes seem to follow a heuristic pattern. Meagre visual information, for example, may provide the basis for a 'guess' about an object's identity. This leads to a search for confirmatory evidence, and the further information is used to test whether the original hypothesis was correct or not. Whereas straightforward 'mechanical' operations like computing a table of square roots may be well served by the algorithmic strategy, the processing of complex and 'messy' information is often better achieved by the 'guess and test' heuristic method.

A physician attempting a difficult diagnosis may use the available data about the symptom as the basis for an 'informed guess'. This hypothesis then directs further investigation and data acquisition, and, on the basis of the test results, support for the original 'informed guess' may be strengthened or weakened. Knowing which tests to apply, what importance to attach to the data and how to interpret the overall pattern of information calls for considerable skill. Experience will help in developing the hypotheses and in evaluating evidence. Examples of heuristic thinking can be found in many crime novels in which, usually at the beginning of the last chapter, the detective hero begins his summing up with the immortal heuristic phrase: 'Let us suppose . . .'

Among the areas of human expertise so far transferred to computer-based systems are geological exploration, the diagnosis of bacterial infections, the design of microchips, the playing of backgammon and the diagnosis of car-faults. In each of these areas human experts use sets of knowledge-based rules to solve problems. As these rules are acquired by the machine it may achieve problem-solving abilities equal to, and in some cases superior to, those of the human consultant. And, once the 'expertise' is established, it can easily be copied, packaged and marketed. The end-product of years of field experience, of scientific endeavour or of clinical work may be captured in the form of patterns of information on a magnetic disc.

The first expert system, DENDRAL, was developed at Stanford University in the late 1960s; it was used to identify the molecular structure of chemicals from physical data. Soon afterwards MYCIN was developed, also at Stanford; this deals with the diagnosis of bacterial infections and prescribes the appropriate antibiotic. Another medical system, CADUCEUS, considers the patient's medical history, current state and lab reports and arrives at its diagnosis. It has an expert knowledge of over 500 diseases and is familiar with nearly 4000 signs and symptoms. In theory, medical expert systems could manage something which no human physician could achieve. They could read all of the latest medical journals published in any language and add the new findings to their knowledge structure. The cost of duplication is minimal, and every human physician could quite easily have a computer close at hand to act as medical consultant.

PROSPECTOR is a program to assist in the evaluation of geological surveys; it possesses considerable knowledge of rock formations and the likely location of minerals and can make an expert assessment of geological data. Its interpretations generally match those made by human experts but on one notable occasion it proved better, predicting accurately the position of a $100-million molybdenum deposit. This example alone is sufficient to illustrate the fact that AI is not merely an academic exercise. Expertise is a highly marketable commodity. It often sells because it provides a means of saving money or making money. But some expert systems are more playful. MIGHTY B plays backgammon and scored a memorable victory for AI when it beat the World Backgammon Champion 7–1 in a series of games played at Monte Carlo in 1979.

Within their limited realm of expertise these systems are 'sensible'. Some are able to modify their own heuristics as they learn, from experience, which strategies work, and some can constantly expand and update their database. Systems under development can make judgements even about situations in which the elements are not totally defined or specified. As well as the traditional 'hard-edge' problems, machines are now called upon to handle 'fuzzy sets' and to operate with 'fuzzy logic'.

Providing the machine with human-derived expertise is more than a valuable short-cut to programming. Because many of the rules involved have never been specifically formulated—they are unconscious strategies employed as the human expert 'feels' a way to a solution—they simply could not be stated in a form that could be used to program a machine. For this reason, however, it may be very difficult to identify and extract knowledge from the expert—the job of the 'knowledge engineer'. This is always a difficult and painstaking task, and the problems may increase when the aim is to combine the expertise of several human experts into an integrated artificial system—a process referred to as 'knowledge fusion'.

Although there are specific technical areas in which certain people are acknowledged to be experts, it could be claimed that almost everybody is an expert in dealing with the everyday world. AI specialists are now working on ways for people to transfer their 'lay expertise' or 'commonsense' to a machine. The end result will be what some have called a 'naïve system'. The task of creating such a system is actually more difficult than that of creating a machine expert, largely due to the breadth and complexity of knowledge involved. There is also the familiar bottleneck problem at the 'knowledge-acquisition' stage. Attempts to derive knowledge in machine-usable form from the human tutor embrace a number of different methods. One venture aimed at providing a more general solution has resulted in a software package called 'Expert-Ease' developed by Donald Michie, Professor of Machine Intelligence at Edinburgh University. This will allow any user, including the 'commonsense expert', to transfer his or her particular expertise to the machine. As such systems become widely available, many human specialists in all kinds of fields will teach machines all that they know about their subject.

Machines will also be able to learn by reading books. For some time computers have been able to translate printed text into sounds—to read aloud. For example, the Kurzeweil Reading Machine is designed for the visually handicapped and has now been installed in a number of US public libraries. It can recognize over 300 different typefaces and can read at up to twice the normal reading speed, synthesizing the sound of each word it encounters. It knows over a thousand rules of pronunciation and is familiar with nearly 1500 exceptions to those rules. But it understands nothing.

Programs under development, however, can understand written text to a limited extent. AI specialists at Yale, for example, have been working on a number of programs designed to analyse the meaning of stories. SAM knows a lot about restaurants and can understand statements about having a meal, paying the bill, calling the waiter and so on. PAM's special field is human goals: given information about what a person is doing she can make a fair guess about why the action is being performed.

So far such systems can handle only a limited range of rather simple statements, but they are able to go beyond the sentence itself and relate the information to their 'limited general knowledge'. From the sentence 'John bought the car from Mary' they may infer that Mary sold the car to John, that John paid money and is now poorer, and that Mary no longer has the car. These 'extra' pieces of information involve the kind of background knowledge—about possession and buying and selling—that has only recently been available to machines. As work progresses the systems will become more complex and the meaning of a wider range of sentences will be understood. Once a computer or robot can handle the statement at a conceptual level it can answer questions about it, rephrase it or translate it into any language for which it has a dictionary. Thus FRUMP (Fast Reading, Understanding and Memory Program) has been taught about current affairs and can now read a news story and produce a sensible summary in English, Spanish, French or Chinese.

Natural-language understanding also enables computers to respond more flexibly to human commands. Generally an instruction typed into a computer must rigorously adhere to rules about the words or symbols being used, their order and even their spacing. Programs under current development, however, will understand questions and commands typed in plain English. The aim is to provide the uninitiated with access to the machine. A business manager with no knowledge of computers will need only to type in 'What was last month's before-tax profit?' to get a prompt answer. 'User-friendly' software of this type is under development by major companies such as IBM, and less sophisticated versions are already available for home computers. The name of a British system—'Super-Natural'—is particularly apt in view of the fact that programs of this kind have become known as 'spookware'. The latest aim of those developing 'intelligent-agent' software is to produce a system which will allow the user to specify, in simple language, a program to be written by the machine. Allowing for the likely advances in voice recognition, such intelligent software will eventually enable users to operate and control computers simply by talking to them in a natural way, requesting information and actions from the machine as they would from a friend or colleague.

The fully conversational machine is thus in view, and plans for computers of this type are already being developed. A particularly far-reaching proposal for a natural-language machine was put forward in 1980 by the Japanese Information-Processing Development Centre. They launched a major research programme to produce a 'fifth-generation machine'. This will be capable of understanding a number of spoken languages and translating from one language to another. The machine will have a keen appreciation of the context in which verbal utterances are made and will be able to 'read between the lines' to construct, from what a person actually said, what he or she probably meant to say. It will learn from its own experience and have powers of association and inference. It will invent its own heuristics and will program itself to perform new tasks. The fifth-generation computers—sometimes referred to as 'Knowledge Information Processing Systems' (KIPS)—will be *knowledge processors* rather than data processors and will possess vast stores of general and expert knowledge. Above all they will possess that elusive commodity, commonsense. The result will be machines sensitive to their physical and human environment and 'aware' of the world. The Japanese claim that the intelligence of such a machine '. . . will be greatly improved to approach that of a human being', leading some to speak of the project as an effort to create the 'quasi-human brain'.

Advances in hardware technology will be needed to produce these new machines. So it was with previous generations. The first computers used vacuum tubes or 'valves', the second generation used transistors, and the third integrated circuits and chips. The most powerful computers today—those of the fourth generation—use 'very large-scale integrated circuits' (VLSI). Cramming the equivalent of hundreds of thousands of components into the tiny space (or 'real estate') on the chip calls for special techniques and ingenuity in designing the layout or 'architecture'. The chips used in fifth-generation machines will contain up to 10 million transistors arranged in 'parallel architectures'. Computer memories now perform only one operation at a time, but eventually they will do millions simultaneously, and ultra-high-speed parallel processing will increase capabilities phenomenally. The Japanese scientists plan to develop systems able to make a billion logical inferences per second. It is anticipated also that the machines will be able simultaneously to handle thousands of inference rules and more facts than are contained in the *Encyclopaedia Britannica*. Despite these incredibly ambitious plans for hardware advances, the Japanese are optimistic that such specifications will be met. The problems that seem most likely to delay development concern conceptual issues about ways of acquiring and representing knowledge, but even about these aspects there is general agreement that solutions will eventually be found. There is thus considerable buoyancy about the likely success of the project, the major doubts concerning principally the time factor—the deadline set by the Japanese for the production of the machine is 1990.

The Japanese government has given substantial support to the project. They launched the Institute for New Generation Computer Technology—ICOT— early in 1982. They have promised to provide £300 million towards the fifth-generation project, and with contributions from participating commercial companies the entire project is expected to cost up to £1000 million and to employ the services of hundreds of top scientists and engineers. Other governments are being challenged to respond to what is seen as the threat of total Japanese domination in the fields of information technology, advanced electronics and artificial intelligence. Leading Western scientists are asking their own governments to greatly increase support for relevant research. Suggestions have been made for mounting a similar project in the USA, currently a clear leader in the AI field, and in the UK a government committee has outlined areas of hardware and software research to be given priority financing. The result is that activity may now be described as hectic. The huge financial rewards to be reaped from success in this area, together with the competitive drive of the scientists involved, seems likely to trigger a scientific battle between the major industrial nations, a frantic race to lead what has been called 'the second computer revolution'.

If the Japanese realize their dream machine, one thing is clear: the end result will not be one large computer sited in Tokyo. The aim is not to produce a single machine but to develop a new *order* of machine. It can be anticipated that thousands, and eventually perhaps millions, of fifth generation machines will come to inhabit the world. The potential applications in science, industry and business are virtually limitless. But such areas do not represent the ultimate market. More than any other nation in the world the Japanese realize the meaning of the term 'product' and are expert in translating technological research into items for the mass consumer market. Their success in designing and marketing hi-fi and video is unparalleled. In the original fifth-generation proposal it was stated that the aim of the project is to make the computer '. . . a more amenable partner for people'. It will demand as little special knowledge from the user as a television or a washing machine.

There can thus be little doubt that the major market for a machine with sense and sensibility will be the domestic market, and it therefore seems inevitable that within a very short space of time the results of countless hours of development, the efforts of thousands of technologists and the benefits of huge financial investments will be assembled together in the form of cheap, useful and attractive product machines. A variety of models will be produced, each designed to be welcomed into millions of homes. It must be remembered that computer hardware is relatively cheap to produce, and getting cheaper by the year, and that software, once developed, costs hardly anything to reproduce. For maximum usefulness the machine will clearly have to be mobile and able to act directly on the physical world. There can be little doubt, therefore, that the ultimate product by which the Japanese are hoping to convert millions of pounds, dollars, francs and marks into yen is the domestic robot. And that machine is likely to bear a striking resemblance to many of the robots encountered so far only in the pages of science fiction.

The Product Prize

Technology promises to achieve a major breakthrough in the near future: machines will become sensible. Rational, mobile, useful, talkative devices have never before existed, yet the concept of the robot is a familiar one. There are good reasons for believing that in many respects the robots produced for the mass market will resemble those portrayed in literature and films. Such sources have presented many images of 'ideal' machines and have conjured a thousand fantasies. Now that many elements of these images and dreams seem on the threshold of realization it is timely to examine the nature of the fictional machines. Robots are about to step out from the pages of fiction to become a revolutionary form of consumer electronics. The impact on human existence and human society is bound to be immense.

The process by which technology becomes product is a complex one. In this electronic age it is often difficult to appreciate the fact that electricity was once nothing more than a 'laboratory phenomenon' or that television was at one time just a technological curiosity. The everyday products that now incorporate such research efforts are taken very much for granted. Television is no longer an 'electronic wonder'; viewers do not stand in front of the screen amazed by the fact that the images move. It has ceased to be an 'apparatus' and has evolved into a 'medium'. The pace of transition from 'technical wonder' to everyday product has quickened considerably in recent times. Just a few years after their initial development the transistor and the microchip could be purchased in supermarkets in the form of radios and calculators.

The process of finding a suitable application for a new phenomenon or device often calls for considerable imagination. A likely product realization is not always immediately apparent, but the rewards for discovering the optimum outlet for a technological advance can be very great indeed. Examples of how imagination and resourcefulness may be rewarded come from cases in which products have evolved as incidental 'spin-offs' from major task-oriented projects.

At one stage the US corporation Texas Instruments produced a voice-synthesis chip able to pronounce letters and single words reasonably well but otherwise very limited in its ability to speak. Opportunities for making profit from the device must have seemed limited. The repertoire was hardly sufficient for the chip to be included in functional machines and, apart from modest sales to dedicated amateur computer enthusiasts, it seemed as though it might remain as an interesting but essentially non-marketable achievement. Imaginative exploration of the product possibilities, however, produced an application that proved eminently marketable—'Speak and Spell', the educational toy for children. Packaged in a brightly coloured plastic shell and cleverly marketed, the modest chip thus found a way into hundreds of thousands of children's homes and hearts.

The same corporation later found a mass-market potential for a system with limited 'reading' ability. Systems for reading aloud from printed text are very expensive, but much cheaper apparatus can be used to decipher the lines of varying thickness and spacing now familiar as the 'bar codes' printed on supermarket products—a light-pen scanning these provides information enabling a computer to identify stock. There were obvious business applications for such a system, but how could the technology be realized in terms of a truly mass product? Here again was a limited technology in search of an unlimited market, and again Texas Instruments found the answer in an educational toy. Coupled with a speech synthesizer the light-pen, now restyled a 'Magic Wand', can translate bar codes into verbal output. The device appears to read text aloud, although it achieves this by processing lines printed in a strip below the normal text. Again the system is attractively packaged and the intrinsic appeal is enhanced by capitalizing on a link with the film character E.T. In the movie the extraterrestrial modified a 'Speak and Spell' with a coat-hanger, wire and bobby pins, thus making an intergalactic telephone. With the 'Magic Wand' the E.T. story can be retold through the cunning combination of a line-sensitive light-pen and a rather limited voice synthesizer.

Spin-offs can be powerful money-spinners and successes illustrate the imagination and resourcefulness of product developers. Technology provides tools but not products; vision and a keen knowledge of the marketplace can often translate even an apparently unpromising invention or discovery into a highly profitable device. Science, shrewdness and serendipity together make a powerful amalgam that can be translated into formidable sales.

There is often no need to 'invent' an application because a potential product is already in view. This may stimulate research, which is essentially 'product-driven'. Many ideal products await technical advances. There have long been hopes, for example, that one day a machine might be able to translate from one natural language to another or to type directly from dictation. The commercial viability of such systems is immediately apparent, and they will certainly be made available just as soon as technology provides the means. Reports of major innovations do not remain undiscovered in technical journals. Research in computer science, AI and robotics is energetically and urgently exploited. Projects are closely monitored and developments eagerly anticipated with a view to immediate implementation.

Already a few robots are emerging beyond the factory, coping with the limitations and making the most of what technology has to offer. Thus Automax of Tokyo plans a cleaning robot for sweeping offices and homes. The machine will have a little broom and will be equipped with a tactile sensor to stop it bumping into walls. Having also limited vision and a sound sensor, it will be able to set off an alarm if it detects the presence of a night-time intruder and so will be able to patrol office blocks as a security guard. Sony have already developed 'intellibots' to help in libraries. These battery-driven wheeled machines, no larger than a shoe-box, wait in a 'parking area' until summoned by a human being. Students at Kanazawa University are able to punch a videotape number into the 'bot' and the machine scuttles off to find their chosen tape among the stack of 3,000.

Eagerness to produce a particular item may lead to 'premature products'—devices which are technologically 'before their time'. The obvious commercial potential of a useful home robot has already led some manufacturers to launch machines labelled as 'domestic robots'. However, these are rather primitive, clearly handicapped by their premature birth. Able to perform few useful functions, completely lacking commonsense and almost totally unaware of their environment, they have more in common with industrial machines than with the domestic robots of the future. The time has not yet come, not quite, for the production of the viable home robot. Current technology simply does not provide adequate means, and the models so far available must be regarded as little more than curiosities.

One such curiosity is Huggy, a radio-controlled machine with a voice synthesizer. He can be operated in such a way that he switches on a television set and serves drinks. His single arm can be made to grasp and lift objects. Left to its own devices, however, the machine is lost in a world it simply does not understand. Hero is another robot who needs his mechanical hand held. He is an educational aid produced by the Heath Corporation and can be programmed, via his prominent number-pad, to move and speak. Serving drinks is one of his skills, too, and indeed this has emerged as something of a speciality of the primitive machines: the Android Amusement Company of California produces a 'drinks caddy robot' which retails at $5000. Huggy and Hero have lately been joined by a number of other 'general-purpose domestic robots' including Topo, Genus and Oscar. Each of these machines, however, is a pale intimation of what will come—the sensible domestic machine needs fifth-generation development—but the manufacturers' overeagerness is an important phenomenon; it provides an indication of the likely level of future frenzy, a sign of the rapidity with which research will be translated into robot products. The keener the race, the greater the tendency to 'jump the gun'.

The larger corporations have yet to attempt to introduce a domestic machine, but many have already shown a considerable interest in the area. Some are keeping a 'watching brief', while others are said to be actively engaged in drawing up plans so that promised developments can be immediately implemented in product form. The qualities of eagerness and resourcefulness have already been demonstrated by manufacturers in response to evolving technology, and the current research promises much more for them to be excited about and much more for them to exploit imaginatively.

It is now possible to make reasonable estimates of what will be achieved technologically in the foreseeable future. The analysis of the likely prospects for AI and robotics over the next decade provides something of an 'index of possibilities', and it is clear that technology will provide numerous degrees of freedom. But how will the products be realized? Many robot manufacturers will have the same technical facilities at their disposal. As with hi-fi and calculators, rather similar assemblies of largely identical components will be presented in a wide range of forms. Presentation will be a key factor affecting sales in what will certainly be a fiercely competitive market. And, for robots, presentation will not simply be a matter of appearance, but will include voice, manner and simulated personality. Manufacturers will quickly learn and copy from one another. Successful designs will survive and be improved upon, and unsuccessful ones will fade from view. Thus there will be an evolution of robot models depending on their 'fitness' in the marketplace.

How will advanced robotics be presented for the mass market? Must we wait to see the form and character such machines will take, or is there some way of making an informed judgement? If an image of the robot ideal could be gained then essential features could be tested against the criteria of technical feasibility and commercial viability. Some indication is needed of what would make a robot attractive; and this is clearly not a technical question—it concerns the psychology of the future consumer. Anticipation about such human preferences can clearly be gained only from indirect sources.

One such source is science fiction. Stories about artificial humanoids have been told for centuries. Recent SF provides an extensive array of robot images and examines the likely impact of intelligent mobile machines on the people with whom they interact. Many of the images have been transferred to the movie screen, reaching an audience of countless millions. There is thus a formidable literary 'robot heritage' which has had a considerable impact on the popular imagination. The images of 'ideal machines' contained within that heritage may help to provide a useful indication of features that would prove attractive in future domestic robots. Stories about murderous metal men are of less importance, in that manufacturers are hardly likely to attempt to market such devices—at least, for domestic purposes! But there is an altogether friendlier breed, a type of robot portrayed as attractive, friendly, stable and useful. Such machines often represent the imaginative writer's conception of the 'ideal robot', and these characters are likely to be taken as models, as far as the prevailing technology permits, for real products that will be packaged and sold with all the skill that major corporations are able to muster.

TWO
A Heritage and its History

Plausible Projections and Fantastic Fables

The robots in SF were hardly ever intended as literary prototypes for real machines. Until recently it seemed as though the age of the robot might be hundreds of years away, but suddenly stories and movies featuring humanoid machines have taken on a new relevance. Whenever major technical achievements gain a public prominence there is a tendency for people to look for literary parallels within SF. Thus, when men were first about to land on the Moon, there was a resurgence of interest in tales depicting space travel and lunar exploration. Some of the more recent stories proved accurate in a number of details, but a special delight was provided by earlier esoteric works that had offered the prospect of more bizarre modes of travel. In the 17th century Bishop Godwin's *The Man in the Moone* had depicted a lunar journey using a machine powered by a flock of birds. In *Other Worlds* Cyrano de Bergerac's space-going hero was lifted gently as dew evaporated from phials attached to his body. Two centuries later Jules Verne had his astronauts shot from a cannon. Clearly NASA had nothing to learn from these accounts.

Similarly AI specialists would receive little by way of technical guidance from SF accounts of humanoids. On the other hand, those concerned with the commercial realization of robot products might well learn something to their advantage. As technology provides the means for the construction of such devices, a close examination of the product projections developed by generations of writers and film directors might well provide useful inspiration. Audiences of millions have accepted their creations and found them fascinating and attractive, and it can be anticipated that responses to real machines with similar features would be equally positive. Never before has a product been 'announced' so long or 'advertised' so widely before the launch. The body of SF constitutes an extensive database within which there are surely clues about the nature of future products.

27

We must define this database and consider the nature of SF. There is no generally agreed definition of the term and little consensus about which stories and films should be included in this category. SF shades into mythology on the one hand and into general fiction on the other. Within the body of writing generally recognized today as SF a number of subcategories may be distinguished. Some observers make a sharp distinction between SF and 'fantasy fiction'. 'Fantasy fiction'—sometimes referred to as 'Sword and Sorcery'—is represented by such epics as J. R. R. Tolkien's *The Lord of the Rings* and Michael Moorcock's 'Elric' books. Typically such stories are set in 'other worlds' peopled by humanoid but nonhuman creatures. These worlds defy location in terms of known time and space and are often dominated by the influences of magic and the supernatural.

Within the 'core' of science-fiction writing—sometimes known as 'hard SF'—there is a wide variation in the degree of imaginative licence employed. Some authors invent planets populated by all manner of creatures, describe time travel, or suggest some fabulous new device, material or extrasensory phenomenon. Stories may be set far in the future or tamper with historical fact. But, however improbable the inventions or the theme, the authors accept certain scientific constraints. Almost always, human characters are central and the planet Earth, if not the setting for the story, is at least recognized as a 'homebase'. Such stories count as 'fiction' rather than 'invented mythology', and as science fiction rather than fantasy. In many cases the degree of licence is deliberately restricted, the author preferring to describe the future effects of a single scientific or ecological change on the world as it is today.

Science fiction includes also a third force often referred to as 'New Wave'. This originated in the mid-1960s as a revolt against the 'pulp tradition' of mainstream SF, and emphasizes freedom of style as well as content. The work may be presented as a prose poem or descriptive piece rather than as a narrative story. It attaches significance to the present rather than the future, to mysticism rather than magic, and to psychology rather than technology. J. G. Ballard, a writer closely associated with the New Wave, suggested that while traditional SF was concerned largely with outer space the new writing focussed principally on 'inner space'. While hard SF, however inventive or implausible, adopts realism as its style, New Wave combines elements of expressionism, impressionism and surrealism.

Fantasy and New Wave stories are generally little concerned with speculation about the effects of future technological innovation, and hence will not feature prominently in the ensuing discussion. The treatment of robots even in mainstream SF contains aspects which must be considered irrelevant. Tales about robots invading from outer space, for example, are beyond present concerns. Neither is it necessary for us to consider the psychic powers attributed to robots in some stories.

In order to use the extensive literary database most effectively as a guide to likely products, criteria are needed to identify works meriting particular attention. The principal issues of interest are the roles and personalities of the robots and the human responses to such machines. Stories involving these aspects may be relevant to the real future, whether they are set in the present or in the far future. And they may be set on Earth, on some other planet or in intergalactic space. However fantastic the backdrop, such stories may portray plausible robot characters and plausible human reactions. The concept of 'plausibility' is clearly central to the selection.

SF writers and critics have long debated the relevance of scientific plausibility. In his scholarly analysis of the development of SF, *Into the Unknown*, Robert Philmus distinguishes between authors who are preoccupied with realizable technological advances and those who produce 'satiric mythifications of reality'. He cites Jules Verne as an example of the former category and H. G. Wells as an example of the latter. Verne himself was aware of such a distinction and decried Wells' use of mythical substances and effects. Interviewed in 1903 he said that Wells' stories '. . . do not rest on good scientific bases. There is no rapport between his work and my own. I make use of physics, he invents. I go to the Moon in a cannonball, discharged from a gun. There is no invention here. He goes to Mars [Verne meant 'the Moon'] in an airship which he constructs of a metal which negates the law of gravitation. That's all very well, but let him show me this metal. Let him produce it!'

There are dangers, however, in attempting to remain scientifically orthodox while at the same time extrapolating beyond current science. The problem increases as the writer endeavours to provide technical specifications for literary inventions. Supplying too many details in an attempt to enhance plausibility can easily lead to an author being hoist with his own technical petard. Verne, like many later writers, was obsessed with providing 'technical patter' and this sometimes produced errors and made his otherwise realistic stories appear ludicrous. In *Round the Moon*, for example, the astronauts are completely unharmed when their projectile makes a re-entry and splashdown at over 100,000 miles an hour. To avoid ridicule Verne would either have had to suggest some means for slowing the projectile to a reasonable velocity or to have ignored details of re-entry speed and merely suggested a safe splashdown.

SF writers are not obliged to provide circuit diagrams for the devices they invent. The plausibility of the concepts is more important than the accuracy of technical details. It matters little whether robot brains, for example, are said to be constructed from 'iridium', which is a real metallic element, or 'asimovium', which is purely fictitious. Since no robot brain is actually constructed of either, both descriptions are literary inventions used to add technical flavour to the concept of the robot brain. The important issue is whether that concept is itself scientifically tenable. If it is, then speculation about possible human effects may be of relevance to the real future.

However, as intellectual orthodoxy changes, ideas about what is and what is not tenable will also change. Tales of magic which now seem fantastic may at one time have been accepted as realistic. On the other hand, some SF ideas which once appeared preposterous have become more plausible in the light of recent scientific advances. Technology sometimes 'catches up with' SF and overtakes it. Tales about intelligent machines were highly implausible in the 19th century but now seem unremarkable. The rapid development of technology in recent years has, within a very short space of time, changed ideas about what is tenable. Thus in his 1960 critique of SF, *New Maps of Hell*, Kingsley Amis discussed the credibility of robots and suggested that 'the problem of fitting all that machinery into a container on the human scale' would demand a kind of microelectronics not imaginable for the foreseeable future. Today we appreciate that this particular aspect is not likely to present a problem.

In some cases a story has been written to expose some 'patently ridiculous idea', only to have the satire backfire as the 'absurdity' becomes a reality. An outstanding example of this is Samuel Butler's allegorical *Erewhon* (1872). In an attempt to expose the outrageousness of Darwin's theory of organic evolution, Butler described an evolution of machines to a stage where they could reason and reproduce. In her book *The Cybernetic Imagination in*

Science Fiction (1980), Patricia Warrick comments on the fate of Butler's 'ludicrous' proposals. She notes the '. . . uncanny reversal of satire into fact. Much of the argument presented as satire can be read one hundred years later as a literal, though obviously unintentional, description of the developments in computer technology in the last twenty years.' The fatuous has become the familiar.

It would be a mistake, however, to be so chastened by the fate of Butler's lampoon as to regard each and every SF story as a credible account of the possible future. Some stories have a much higher 'credibility rating' than others. Ideas in some SF are the subject of active scientific research, with technologists aiming towards the goals already attained by their fictional counterparts, while other stories have little point of contact with scientific reality. Our main interest is in stories dealing with recognizable extrapolations of current technology and technological thinking and, more particularly, in those that consider human responses to such innovations. This raises another aspect of the plausibility problem, the 'psychological plausibility' of the human characters portrayed.

The credibility of descriptions of human responses is a key criterion in judging many forms of literature. An author must be able to create believable characters who behave in plausible ways. The reader recognizes the familiar patterns of response and is able to 'enter the fiction'. Some writers are credited with deep insight into human psychology. Their readers are able to recognize in their works previously unarticulated aspects of human experience. Literature works largely by 'striking familiar chords', and writers whose human subjects fail to come across as natural are criticized for creating 'wooden figures'.

Contrary to popular stereotype, the same criterion of 'human realism' can be applied to SF as to other forms of literature. Most SF involves a realistic description of human responses to change, and some attempts at a definition of the genre make this aspect dominant. Thus Theodore Sturgeon suggested: 'A science-fiction story is built around human beings, with a human problem and a human solution which would not have happened at all without its scientific content.' In most stories we meet recognizable people reacting in recognizable ways in an unrecognizable world, a world in which, to quote the critic Peter Nicholls, 'the furniture has been changed'.

In a recent essay the leading SF writer Ursula Le Guin suggested that the genre is moving away from its original prime concern with technological innovation and scientific wonders and is now focussing more sharply on human reactions and feelings: 'The writers' interest is no longer really in the gadget, or the size of the universe, or the destiny of social classes, or anything describable in quantitative or mechanical, or objective terms. They are not interested in what things do, but in how things are. The subject is the subject, that which cannot be other than subject: ourselves. Human beings.'

The human characters in SF tend to be quite unremarkable, bland, 'average' people lacking outstanding personality. Edmund Crispin once remarked: '. . . the characters in a science-fiction story are usually treated rather as representatives of their species than as individuals in their own right.' It is this aspect which gives the reactions portrayed a general applicability. The humans encountered in SF are 'normal'. Their reactions are those which would be expected of most people faced with a similar situation. Thus, in their accounts of how the human characters react to robots, the authors are indicating their ideas about how most human beings would in fact react to the machines.

Kingsley Amis commented: 'Science fiction shows us human beings in their relations not with one another but with a thing, a monster, an alien, a plague, or a form of society.' But it would not be accurate to regard robots in fiction merely as 'things'. Most robots are presented not only as objects or 'furniture' but also as 'pseudo-persons'. Part of their special fascination is that they occupy an ambiguous position. Like an optical illusion in which we see first one version of a figure and then another, the robot flips between being a thing and being a person. The psychological interest of the story thus extends beyond the human characters to the technology itself.

But a Whisper of Prophecy

Science-fiction writers hardly ever aim to be prophets, but many of their readers seem particularly interested in the possibility that today's fiction may offer a vision of tomorrow's reality. Some developments have been anticipated in SF, and the dedicated fan will be delighted to recite a litany of examples. There are at least two 19th-century accounts of artificial satellites as well as the famous 1945 article by Arthur C. Clarke in which communications satellites were described in some detail—he developed the idea in his 1951 novel *Prelude to Space*. Fiction has provided advance notice of television, fighter planes, tanks, nuclear bombs, Moon-rockets and laser weapons (allowing a generous interpretation of the term 'death-ray'), as well as a variety of ecological effects, biological and medical advances and social developments.

On the other hand some spectacular failures and omissions of speculative fiction must also be noted. Thus an early idea that television pictures would be conveyed by light passing through pneumatic tubes now seems ludicrous, although the determined apologist might point to recent advances in fibre optics. While several descriptions of the first Moon landing did include multi-stage rockets and spacesuits, it appears that no story anticipated the fact that there would be live television coverage of the event. And such phenomena and innovations as time travel, antigravity pills, invisibility paint and matter transmission remain over the hills of the scientific horizon and far away in the land of make-believe. Most stories appear to have 'misinterpreted the future', but to accuse the SF writer of 'getting future facts wrong' is to misunderstand the nature of the enterprise. SF authors are literary creators, not futurologists, and their aim is to entertain, to stimulate the imagination and, in some cases, to issue a kind of warning or outline a moral concern. They are generally saying 'Let us suppose . . .' or 'What if . . .?', rather than 'This is how things will be'.

Cases that do appear to represent predictive insight can often be explained in ways that render them less impressive. Frequently the original inspiration for a story can be traced back to contemporaneous scientific ideas. The writer projects the realization of a current goal, extrapolating rather than inventing. When scientists eventually achieve their aim the story may be hailed as 'predictive'. Sometimes authors have direct access to scientific ideas because they are themselves professional scientists: Fred Hoyle, for example, is a leading cosmologist, Isaac Asimov a biochemist, and Stanislaw Lem a prominent cyberneticist. Often, as in the cases of Hoyle and Lem, the scientific interests of such writers are directly reflected in the literature they produce. In other cases it is difficult to detect any influence. E. E. 'Doc' Smith, for example, wrote 'space operas' full of scintillating spaceships and deadly weapons. His professional scientific concern, however, was food technology—he was a world authority on doughnut-mixes.

In other cases of apparent prediction the writer has merely articulated in a particularly memorable way an idea that has long had a general currency. Thus for many centuries people have dreamed of travelling to the Moon. This simple idea was explored and elaborated by many writers and finally realized by technologists. But SF did not *invent* the idea. Similarly, SF cannot lay claim to having originated the concept of the robot. The general idea of an artificial humanoid is probably as old as the human activity of sculpting clay, and surviving fictional accounts of humanoid machines can be traced back for well over two thousand years. Real automata have been constructed for centuries and there has long been the dream that such machines would one day become 'intelligent' and 'responsive'. The basic robot idea had been described and analysed by engineers, entertainers, philosophers, theologians and writers long before 'genre science fiction' adopted it as one of its basic motifs in the late 1930s.

There is every indication that, with regard to their portrayal of robots, many SF sources will prove remarkably accurate. In future decades we may recognize in some of the literature an extraordinarily prophetic rendering of 'robot nature'. There are a number of special reasons for believing this to be the case.

One concerns the clarity of the goal. If the goal of those concerned with robot technology or with its product manifestations is to simulate human characteristics then the nature of the 'ideal outcome' is both clear and familiar. The features of the ideal product are easy to determine because they are nothing more—or less—than the features of the ideal human. Where the aim of a project is simulation, and where the 'original' is familiar, many characteristics of the successful simulation are already known. The situation is quite different in other areas of technical enterprise where the problem is concerned with achieving some novel functional goal rather than replicating an existing model: the purpose may be clear but the form of the end-product is largely undetermined.

Secondly, future robots must be seen in terms of 'product' rather than of 'raw technology', and the nature of the artefact will therefore reflect human preference. Technology will provide the potential but the successful product will be presented in a form to meet human need and human fancy. Assuming a certain degree of constancy in such human factors, SF writers, with their insight into human nature and human affairs, are in a good position to judge the nature of the optimum product. This can be thought of in another way. Advances in robotics will provide a 'medium' that will remain subject to certain technical constraints but within which there will be a considerable freedom to choose the 'message'. SF has assumed certain 'medium' features of robots (speech, understanding, movement, etc.) that now appear technically feasible, but it has had much more to say on 'message' characteristics—on what the machines will say, how they will appear, the roles they will take and the personalities they will present. 19th-century authors able to conceive of television as a medium might well have been able to predict aspects of the 'message'—the programmes that would be televised—through an awareness of human interests. It would not have needed technical foresight to imagine that the televisual diet would be likely to include drama, sports, debates and religious services, though quiz programmes and soap operas might well have been beyond the writers' imagination. SF has long assumed the robot as a 'medium', and the writers' accuracy on the question of 'message' content depends more on their reading of 'public demand' than on their predictions about future technological developments.

Thirdly, the predictive power of SF in this context should be raised by the fact that SF is itself responsible for providing the image of the robot in popular consciousness. This in turn will help to shape expectations and demand for products. Other areas of technology in which SF has played a 'consciousness-raising role' are not in the same position of being open to consumer choice. Thus the form of space vehicles is determined by function with little regard for 'presentation'. The robot, by contrast, is an 'intimate machine' which will be designed to attract consumer choice. Functional constraints will place relatively few limitations on such aspects as speech accent, appearance and 'character'. These are likely to follow the portrayals of robots in fiction because writers have been concerned to depict 'attractive' and 'memorable' characters and because their work has helped to shape expectations about how a robot *should* speak and look.

There is already evidence that potential robot manufacturers are aware of the fact that the public image of robots will be important in the design of their future products. They realize that films and books featuring friendly robot characters are acting effectively as a 'public relations operation' and as 'advance promotion'. Joe Engelberger, producer of the first industrial robot and head of the US robot-manufacturing corporation 'Unimation

Inc.', made the point that the public once held a predominantly negative attitude towards the machines. But now, he claims, this has changed: 'Today we've got vast publicity with all kinds of science-fiction movies . . . If you go to *Star Wars* you see R2D2 and C3PO and you can relate to them. There's room for that creature in the factory, in the home, and in the service industries.' So here we see 'the father of the robot' taking careful heed of fictional representations, fully aware that movie robot heroes are in some sense 'what the public wants'. It should therefore come as little surprise if the public is eventually given what it wants.

There follows from this the final argument supporting the view that SF may present an accurate picture of the robot future. This argument concerns the special relationship that has developed between SF writers and the scientists, technologists and manufacturers who will help to realize the product robot. There is much evidence of mutual awareness and mutual influence, although it must be repeated that, while SF writers may add a certain shape and colour to the dreams of the technologists, they cannot provide them with technical insight. As an engineering student Engelberger read several of Asimov's robot stories, and he claims that these helped to encourage his view that useful industrial robots could be produced. A casual conversation at a party planted the seed of the idea that a prototype might be built, but, says Engelberger, '. . . the idea just happened to land in fertile ground. I was there, I was ready. Science fiction was a very big part of being ready.' Today his ideas extend to the domestic robot, a voice-controlled machine to entertain guests by waiting on them and serving drinks. And, as a token of his debt to SF, he has named the device Isaac.

Asimov, for his part, had been inspired by the rather primitive efforts of earlier technologists. He published his first robot story shortly after visiting New York's World Fair in 1939 and witnessing there the actions of several 'exhibition robots'. In his foreword to Engelberger's 1981 book *Robotics in Practice* Asimov disclosed that he had been somewhat surprised by the rapidity with which technologists had been able to realize certain aspects of the inventions which he and other SF writers had put forward. He acknowledged that existing robots '. . . are not yet as complex, versatile and intelligent as the imaginary robots of *I, Robot*. But,' he added, 'give the engineers time!'

In 1982 an editorial in *Robotics Age* drew attention to 'the inspirational value of science fiction' and Charles Balmer, a highly successful constructor of prototype domestic robots, said: 'Our job as experimenters is to take the robot fantasy and to turn it into robot reality'—the 'robot fantasy' of course comes from SF. It is hardly surprising that those who try to construct robots are aware of the influence of SF, but many of those whose involvement is more theoretical have also declared their interest. Thus John McCarthy, director of the Artificial Intelligence Laboratory at Stanford University and inventor of the term 'artificial intelligence', is an avid fan. And Marvin Minsky, leader of the AI laboratory at MIT and a long-time friend of Asimov's, is one of several leading AI workers who frequently use SF images to communicate the problems and promises of their science to a wider audience. HAL, the computer character in the film *2001*, is often cited as a fictional benchmark for natural-language interaction. This provides another example of the intricate links between computer science and SF, for the technical consultant on *2001*, the man who helped to create HAL, was Marvin Minsky.

Thus, with fiction helping to shape the real future, through its direct influence on robot producers and its indirect effect in structuring public consciousness and expectations about robots, it becomes less surprising that there might be a large overlap between SF creations and the real robots that we shall meet and buy. SF may contribute nothing to the hard-nosed technological advances necessary for the emergence of 'intelligent' and 'sensible' machines, but there is every chance that, in helping to shape the product realizations permitted by the developing technology, its impact will be profound.

The mutual influence of scientists and SF writers is apparent also in their use of language. Technologists have adopted several terms introduced by writers of SF. Thus the remotely controlled robot-like arms used to handle dangerous radioactive materials are known as 'waldoes', the name being adopted from Robert Heinlein's 1942 story 'Waldo'. The word 'robot' first appeared in the play *R.U.R.* written by the Czech playwright and novelist Karel Čapek, and the Oxford English Dictionary credits Isaac Asimov with devising the terms 'robotic', 'robotics' and 'roboticist'. Such words are now used in the titles of scientific journals and university departments. On the other hand, SF often bristles with technical jargon and scientific phraseology. This is generally used to confer a pseudoscientific validity on the innovation being described, carrying on the tradition that dates back at least to Jules Verne. And writers also borrow concepts and themes from science. A new invention or discovery may provide inspiration for many stories, leading writers to explore the possible social implications and to consider further extrapolation.

It would be misleading, however, to represent technologists and SF writers as somehow working together on a joint enterprise. It is unlikely that any literary work has so far provided a serious impetus to research. The two groups work towards goals of a different kind and they work in quite different ways. The engineer works within a tight framework of physical constraints and is essentially engaged in problem-solving; the creative writer, on the other hand, imposes his or her own constraints and is free either to invent problems for solution or to work in a freer narrative or descriptive mode.

One striking difference in the thinking of technologists and SF writers is reflected in their different level of concern about the material nature of the robot. In SF there is some confusion about the use of the terms 'robot' and 'android'. In the 18th century mechanical automata were referred to as 'androids' whereas some of today's writers apply the term only to artificial creatures made of organic materials. Some use it to describe any realistic robot while others apply it even to simple machines. Similarly the term 'robot' has been defined as a humanoid system made of nonorganic materials whereas in Čapek's original play the robots were partly organic (although in most productions of it they appear as machines). The confusion is not confined merely to the words employed; it extends to the concepts. In many stories it is not made clear whether the 'robots' or 'androids' are biological or mechanical in nature, and the writer is little concerned with such structural aspects: the impact of the humanoid derives from its behaviour and personality rather than its internal anatomy. It may be far more important that the outer skin of the device is realistic and warm, for example, than whether such features reflect a synthetic or an organic structure.

Technologists, however, would clearly make a prime distinction between biological and engineering systems, and the production techniques involved would be vastly different. Thus what may be of secondary importance to the writer is absolutely fundamental to the technologist. There is no chance that artificial organic androids will soon be produced, and our consideration of current robot projects therefore ignores biological science. But in examining the SF image of robots we need not restrict our examination to cases in which the humanoid is said to have a mechanical structure. Our interest is in the presentation and impact of the robot.

SF allows us to anticipate human reactions to robots and gives robot producers a prescription concerning which products are likely to appeal. It does this by inventing robot characters and then setting them loose in a fictional world of home and workplace. If the fiction appears realistic then the literary piece can be treated, in effect, as a 'simulation' for a real product. Readers may be alerted to certain dangers or made aware of features that could be usefully incorporated into real machines. Literature thus provides a foretaste of what will prove attractive, amusing and comforting. Such are the lessons to be learned from robot fiction. It cannot provide technological blueprints but it may provide sketches towards the 'softer' features of future products. What it has to offer is not prophecy but prescription, not technical prediction but a market forecast. It prescribes products and predicts how human beings will respond to them.

If SF provides a recipe for future products, what are the relevant ingredients? What ideal robot characteristics are being prescribed and how is the human-robot relationship portrayed? To fully appreciate what SF has to contribute, specific works have to be considered in some detail and placed in historical context. Images recur and numerous variations are played on limited themes.

The type of writing recognized today as SF did not arise spontaneously within the past century. It developed from other forms of literature, influenced in both style and content by much that had gone before. Although science and technology have provided the major identifiable themes, SF depicts human situations and draws on human fantasy. Many of the images are freely borrowed from aspects of mythology, early works of literary imagination, and the primitive 'sciences' of magic and alchemy. SF may be creative but it is also reflective. It echoes science but also resonates primitive human fantasies, aspirations and desires.

To appreciate the power, depth and tradition behind the 'robot' image presented in recent stories and films we must investigate early sources and trace the development of the 'robot' vision in the human psyche. Poised as we are in anticipation of the 'robot revolution', the time is especially ripe for considering the robot's evolution in mythology and fiction. Analysis of the archive will help to prepare us for the future, for the literary robot heritage has lately come to represent more than just a theme in the history of ideas. It offers a prospectus for future products that are certain to produce an immense impact on human affairs. The story of the robot did not begin with microelectronics and it did not begin with the SF of the 1930s. It extends back to the earliest mythology. The dawn of robot fiction was an early one, and its development has been prodigious, yet only now has it become possible to grasp the true relevance of the literature and to understand the messages it provides about the real robot future.

Ancient Robots and the Breath of Life

The long history and cultural profusion of stories about artificial humanoids stand in need of explanation. Like the central motifs of 'the trickster' and 'the magic potion', the 'robot'—however the artefact is named—occurs with extraordinary regularity in the mythologies of many cultures. The idea has clearly had a powerful effect on the human imagination, but any attempt to provide a full historical account of its development must be partly speculative: this is particularly the case with regard to the origin of the concept. It is apparent, however, that throughout the early history of the idea there was considerable ambiguity between the *simulation* of life and the artificial *creation* of life. This fact is crucial for the construction of a plausible history of the robot theme from earliest mythology to the present day.

The robots who feature in today's SF may reflect 20th-century technology but they also owe much to 19th-century literature, and in particular to Mary Shelley's *Frankenstein* (1818). This book was influenced by medieval ideas about the artificial creation of life, and particularly by the concept of the 'golem' which featured in the Jewish occult teachings and practices known as 'Cabbalism'. This in turn took its inspiration from the account of human creation given in the *Talmud*, an account which can itself be traced back to Near Eastern sources dating from at least 2500BC. And this series of influences and transformations forms but one of the threads in the complex tapestry of the robot heritage, a tapestry which reveals the decline of magic, the rise of science and the shifting emphasis of concern from life-creation to life-simulation.

Most cultures have provided some account of how the Earth first came to be peopled: this is one of the fundamental questions to which mythology and religion have tried to provide an answer. One theme has been especially pervasive. It involves a 'divine sculptor', a god who fashions a figure in clay and then animates it. The prevalence of such expositions suggests that the basic idea may have stemmed from common experience, and it is likely that the scenario arose as a reflection of the attitudes of the earliest human artists to their work. Creating the image of an animal or a human being was originally not merely a recreational activity or an attempt at aesthetic or representational excellence: the activity was regarded with great superstition and held to be a magical process by which the 'soul' of the beast or person portrayed was somehow captured. Thus there was some confusion between the image and the object. To draw was not merely to represent, it was to create.

As sand sketches and cave drawings were supplemented by sculptures in mud and clay, the figures must have taken on a new realism, a new 'lease of life'. This would have been seen as the most likely first stage in the generation of a truly living creature. Some spell or magic could surely be used to provide the extra elements of movement and life. Certainly a god would be capable of animating such a figure.

Thus the rationale for the 'divine sculptor' myth was a strong one. If human beings could call creatures into a kind of existence by portraying them, then human life could well have originated in the efforts of a supernatural artist. The argument had persuasive force, it made good sense, and variations of such an account arose independently in a number of cultures. The scenario survived, adapted and translated in numerous ways, to become the predominant human explanation of human creation. Only in recent times has the evolutionary account come to take precedence over this favoured mythical explanation.

The Sumerian myth of Enki and Ninmar dates back to 2500BC. Tired of their toils, the gods conceived the idea of creating deputies who would work for them. The goddess Nammu brought clay, modelled it into the shape of the creature she desired and then brought the figure to life. A similar account is given in the collection of Babylonian myths known as the *Epic of Gilgamesh* which existed in written form as early as 2000BC, thus predating the *Genesis* account—which it certainly influenced—by at least a thousand years. (In slightly later variations it was suggested that the figure was animated with blood.) Egyptian sources of around 1400BC tell of how the god Khnum sculpted the first man from clay; the figure was animated when the goddess Hather touched it with a staff bearing the magical symbol of life. According to the Judaeo-Christian tradition Adam was made from dust or clay: 'And the Lord God formed man of the dust of the ground, and breathed into his nostrils the breath of life; and man became a living soul' (*Genesis*, *ii*, 7). The Jewish *Talmud* describes how dust was gathered from all parts of the Earth, formed into a human shape and then endowed with life.

Variations recur in the creation myths of many other cultures. Swahili tradition relates how, when the god uttered the secret word of life over a clay model, blood spread through the body, the muscles rippled and the eyelids trembled. In Maori mythology the human figure was formed from sand and animated by divine breath; and according to the Aztec account the miracle of life was wrought over a mystical potion made from bone and divine blood. A Melanesian myth recounts how the first men and women were assembled like puppets from wooden components carved from a tree and brought to life by the beating of a drum.

In a New Hebridean variation the god Tagaro created ten men from mud, animating them with his breath. Commanding his creations to stand in a row Tagaro used them as targets, throwing fruit at them. A piece of fruit became firmly lodged on the genitals of one of the men and, when the god snatched it away, the penis came off too. Thus was the first woman created.

North American Indian culture provides a number of interesting examples. According to the Maidu the Earth-Initiate took dark red earth and mixed it with water to produce the first man and the first woman. He remarked to himself that their hands, which he fashioned in the shape of his own, would help the Indians to climb trees when they were chased by bears. The Okanagon tribe describes a separate creation for each race, the colour of each reflecting the shade of the earth from which it had been sculpted. Similarly the Hopi recount how Spider Woman gathered samples of earth of different colours, mixing them with her own saliva to form human figures. She then endowed them with life by singing the 'Song of Creation'. The Apache maintain that the creator was the force of the East, Black Hactin. Animals he had produced begged him for a companion and he agreed to fashion humankind. The creatures brought the ingredients he required, water scum and red ochre, opal and abalone, various pollens and white clay. Black Hactin then traced the human shape with pollen on the ground and formed organs from the other constituents. The powerful wind sent to animate the figure was so strong that it left its mark, the whorls which to this day are found on our fingertips. Black Hactin taught the man to walk

and speak and then gathered lice and placed them in the hair,
watching with some amusement as the first human learned how
to scratch an itch.

A number of ideas recur throughout these creation myths. In
many cases the god is said to produce the first human being in
his own image; most of the groups who hold these myths maintain that their own tribe or race was the first created; and in
almost all cases the first human being is said to have been male.
In each case the process of animation is said to involve some
miraculous effect or magical formula and, as primitive men and
women listened to the explanations handed down in their tribal
mythology, many must have dreamed that they, too, might learn
to vivify their sculptures, to imitate the deity and create life.

The secret of the gods might be obtainable in a number of
ways. Perhaps a god would bestow the gift upon a human being
as a result of prayer or divine favour. More devious routes could
be pursued. Some trick might force a god to share the secret or
a deal might be struck with a 'black' spirit. These are 'religious'
means that might enable human beings to gain the ability to
create life. But there was also the notion that the secret might
be obtained indirectly by 'scientific' exploration. Perhaps the
transcendental formula could be uncovered by experiment or by
trial and error. Who knows what primitive researches were carried out in an attempt to bring figures to life or to synthesize a
living creature?

Literary evidence suggests that a number of different lines of
approach were taken. One of these was the 'occult': perhaps the
chanting of random phrases, the reciting of number sequences
or the beating of complex rhythms would hit upon a fateful
combination. As the various occult traditions evolved, practitioners were able to draw upon the archive, the esoteric heritage,
using the 'wisdom of past ages' to aid them in their quest. Others
would seek new ways, brewing strange brews of chemicals and
organic materials in a bid to synthesize the 'homunculus'. Theirs
was another approach to 'science', a primitive chemistry in which
observable transformations of matter helped to strengthen the
belief that a formula might be evolved that would bring about
the genesis of new life.

Other pathways were followed. The pursuit of realism in art
was partly spurred by the notion that, if total faithfulness of
the image were achieved, this might produce a spontaneous
vivification. Such confusion between object and image provides

the theme for a number of myths and later literary works. Thus there survived the hope that 'artistic' endeavours might provide the opportunity to emulate the gods. Realism was pursued in a variety of ways. Figures were enhanced with colour and provided with movable limbs. They moved, but only as puppets move, with human aid, and still they did not live. The power of independent movement was eventually achieved by the first producers of automata. By then the aim had become simulation rather than life-creation, and the makers were engineers rather than artists or occultists. Yet there persisted, even in their efforts with hydraulics, levers, string and trickling sand, some lingering ambition that the divine secret might be unveiled.

The religious, the occult, the scientific and the artistic motives and practices connected and overlapped. Mutual influences and inspirations are clearly observable in retrospect, but a distance in time lends clarity by sharpening distinctions. Often there was no rigid boundary between what are now recognized as separate traditions. At one time art was a religious exercise, chemistry a largely occult affair, and many of the early automata-makers were also religious leaders. Those who adapted myths, told stories and later wrote epics mixed the elements freely. Sometimes they made no clear distinction between gods and human beings. Many of their 'human' characters have supernatural powers and many of the 'gods' are lesser deities who manage to make humanoid machines only with great difficulty.

One of the earliest accounts of the production of the artificial humanoid occurs in the Sanskrit epic, the *Mahabharata*, a poem of some three million words which tells of the 'Great War of the Bharats' and contains the 'Sacred Song', the *Bhagavad Gita*. Parts of this can be traced to the 8th and 9th centuries BC, and even the most recent additions were written over fifteen centuries ago. In the first book of the *Mahabharata*, Visvakarman, god of crafts and carpenter to the gods, is asked to create an artificial woman. He gathers beautiful things from around the world and constructs a woman of the most stunning attractiveness. She is named Tilottama and is commanded to seduce two gods. They fight over her favours and kill each other. This very early account introduces the image of the artificial woman with the power to stimulate a high level of sexual desire. Tilottama is the first of many alluring female humanoids we shall encounter.

Another long Asian poem, the *Epic of Gesar of Ling*, describes the manufacture of metal humanoids. A young smith presents himself at court and asks that he be given quantities of gold, silver, copper, iron and bronze. Having worked alone and in secret for three days in the palace forge he emerges to present to the king the magical creatures he has fashioned. The gold has been used to produce a life-sized Lama and a thousand little monks. As the Lama preaches the monks listen attentively. The bronze has been forged into the forms of 700 officials and courtiers and a King who discourses on the laws. The silver has been used to manufacture 100 young girls who sing melodiously, and the copper has yielded a general and 10,000 soldiers. The creations are referred to in the poem as 'magic dolls' and 'metal dolls', and although the smith clearly possesses exceptional powers and occult skills he himself is not divine.

In later Indian works we find wooden figures that walk and talk and metal constructions which serve wine and water at feasts. Such accounts often imply that these humanoids have been produced by human engineers and are mechanical in nature. The 11th-century *Samaranganasutradhara*, ascribed to King Bhoja-dira, contains reference to a large collection of remarkable devices: there are elephant-machines, flying bird-machines, servant-automata and soldier-machines. The reader is left in no doubt that these are products of engineering rather than of magic, for the poet explains that he would have described the means for constructing the artefacts but has withheld such information because 'any person not initiated in the art of building machines might cause trouble'.

Indian literature includes also examples of stories which explore the artistic pathway to life-creation. Another 11th-century work, the collection of fairy tales known as the *Brihatkathasaritsagara*, contains several accounts of mechanical humanoids which can speak and dance, and in one of the stories, 'The Prince and Painted Fairy', a painting comes alive: Prince Manohara becomes so impassioned with the portrait of a woman that he tries to take off her robe, whereupon she rises from the picture and speaks.

This minor theme of life-creation via artistic representation is reflected in works from many different cultures. At one time it was a popular belief in China that certain gifted men could bring pictures and sculptures to life; a special term was given to this skill, *khwai shuh*. The most familiar realization of this theme, however, is from Greek mythology. It tells of Pygmalion, King of Cyprus, who produces a lifelike ivory statue of a beautiful woman. He falls in love with the sculpture, names the woman

Galatea, and prays earnestly to Aphrodite to give his creation life. The goddess responds to his plea and Pygmalion is then able to take Galatea as his wife.

The same theme is explored in much later works. Giambattista Basile's *Pentamerone* (1636) is a version of the Pygmalion theme in which the sexes of the statue and lover are reversed. The heroine, Bertha, shrugs off each of the suitors her father presents to her and asks, instead, that she be brought almonds, pearls, scented water, sapphires and sugar. Mixing these ingredients according to a secret recipe she carefully fashions a confection in the shape of a handsome young man. When this artistic work has been completed, and after a prayer to the goddess of love, the statue comes to life and artist and former sweetmeat consummate their relationship. There are even renditions of the 'portrait lives' theme in recent literature, including Oscar Wilde's novel *The Picture of Dorian Gray*.

In all of its various manifestations the artistic-representation theme contains occult elements, and the link with early superstitions regarding the relationship between the image and the object is clear. But unlike other occult and 'scientific' themes it has not had a major influence on the development of robot stories, and can now be regarded merely as a curiosity. In contrast, the literary heritage provides a rich assortment of tales in which humanoids are conjured by the spells of human magicians or are constructed by human or divine engineers, and it is possible to trace a route from these stories to contemporary SF.

Greek legends are a major source of such ideas. A key figure in Greek humanoid myths is Hephaestus, god of fire and divine smith. According to some legends the god created the first woman, Pandora, from clay, but most of his products were said to be of metal. In Homer's 9th-century BC codification of the *Iliad* we read that Hephaestus used pure gold to manufacture two female statues who served as handmaidens, accompanying him wherever he went. These are described as intelligent machines ('filled with mind and wisdom'). He is said also to have constructed twenty moving 'tripods' that wheeled their way independently and served in the refectory of the gods. These metal robots were said to respond to verbal commands, using as the mechanism for voice-recognition their 'cunningly wrought ears'. Hephaestus is credited also with the creation of Talos, a giant bronze automaton that guarded Crete against intruders by patrolling the beaches three times a day. When enemies were trapped by the machine it would warm its metal body to red heat and hug them to death in a fiery embrace. Talos had one vulnerable spot: it could be 'killed' if a pin were removed from its heel, allowing a vital fluid to drain away.

Daedalus, the legendary Athenian, was another creator of humanoid automata. His devices included a bronze warrior figure and a wooden sculpture animated by the flow of mercury through hollow channels. This technique echoes the methods of the real Greek engineers who, probably by the 4th century BC, were applying the sciences of pneumatics and hydraulics to the operation of automata. The Greek legends illustrate a transition of emphasis, from life-creation to life-simulation. They provide a link between the two traditions by portraying the work of 'divine smiths', figures who occupy an important intermediate position between the omnipotent deity of the creation myths and the human engineers who appear as characters in later stories.

Roman literature also illustrates how the manufacture of real automata helped to change the emphasis of stories away from life-creation. A number of authors provided fictional accounts of *neuropastes*—mechanically controlled statues used to deliver oracles. These were based on real devices produced by Roman engineers, and both the machines and the stories they inspired illustrate links between technology and religion. The figures were engineered as 'state-of-the-art' automata and then employed as communications devices in contact with supernatural forces. Dion Cassius, writing in the 3rd century AD, spoke of statues which could 'bleed', 'sweat' and intimate the will of the gods. Such a powerful amalgam of high technology, showmanship and religion is not without its parallels in the world today.

Stories of marvellous automata were later told throughout medieval Europe, both in the form of legend handed down by oral tradition and in original works. In some versions of the story of King Arthur there are descriptions of metallic knights—mechanical suits of armour which move and fight—and one account describes a copper statue armed with a raised axe which falls when the figure receives the appropriate glance from its human controller. In the *Tristan* saga, dating from the 11th century, the hero orders goldsmiths to produce mechanical statues of Isolde. Rabelais, in his great 16th-century work *Gargantua and Pantagruel*, describes as one of Gargantua's hobbies the construction of automata. He is said to have produced '. . . a thousand little automatory machines which move of themselves'. In many

respects the hopes and aspirations of real automata-makers surpassed the machines portrayed in fiction at this time. There were
several attempts to construct a machine which could speak and
the idea that a device might be endowed with mechanically
derived 'logical processes' was well established.

Beyond the European scene humanoid automata were also
much in evidence in both fiction and fact. As well as the several
Indian sources quoted, there are examples of stories of humanoid
machines from Arabia and China. Arabian engineers constructed
numerous automata, including humanoids. Several are featured
in *The Thousand and One Nights* collection, which originated in the
15th century, including a moving golden peacock, a flying horse
made of ebony and a mechanical man who decapitates grave
robbers. A Chinese story tells of how the wife of the Emperor Ta
Chou became so infatuated with an automaton produced by the
court engineer that the jealous ruler ordered the destruction of
his mechanical rival. This is one of the first accounts of the human
impact of mechanical humanoids, and an early exploration of the
robot's potential for eliciting affection and infatuation.

Many of these legendary creations clearly have much in common with the robots encountered in contemporary SF and indeed
with the real products which are likely to emerge within the
foreseeable future. We find striking portrayals, some dating back
over 2,000 years, of mechanical contrivances which look human
and can move, speak, react to human orders and act 'intelligently'. Few of the machines emerge as memorable 'characters'
with a fully developed personality, yet they do fulfil roles and
conform to stereotypes reminiscent of the robots portrayed in
today's fiction. The automata are shown as servants, soldiers,
companions and objects of amorous attention. They are generally
humanoid and are frequently constructed of metal. Few details of
their mode of operation are provided, but while some can walk
naturally others are subject to technical constraints and wheel
themselves about. Intelligence and vision are not identified as
causing special problems in humanoid construction, but in
Homer's account of Hephaestus at work it is clear that the god
encounters difficulties in constructing the mechanism required
for hearing. It seems that installing the apparatus that comprised
the servant-tripods' 'cunningly wrought ears' demanded particular skill and that development problems with these metal organs
caused production hold-ups in the celestial smithy.

Tracing through stories of humanoid creation, the decline of

emphasis on divine agency and magic and the increasing emphasis on human agency and engineering are clearly evident. Related
to this change, accounts of life-creation tended to be replaced
with accounts of life-simulation. Yet the idea that human beings
might aspire only to simulation did not achieve total consensus.
There were still those who attempted to gain the secret of the
gods and to create life by occult or scientific means. In medieval
times alchemy and cabbalism together produced a resurgence of
the idea that true organic life could be created by using an
appropriate strategy. Attempts were therefore made to conjure,
or to synthesize, living beings; and the direct influence of such
practices on literature was evident until at least the early 19th
century. Only after this time would the 'scientific simulation'
scenario gain clear precedence and the scientist-engineer come
to be seen as the hero most likely to succeed.

Esotericism, then, gave way to engineering slowly, its strength
maintained by the influences of alchemy and cabbalism. These
traditions are therefore of considerable importance for an appreciation of the history of the humanoid in literature.

Alchemy, Cabbalism and the Golem

The origins of alchemy are obscure. Some suggest that it came
from China, others Babylon, and some trace it to the hermetic
science of ancient Egypt. The word itself comes from the Arabic
al-khemia, and many of the ideas of medieval alchemy derive
from the Jewish mystical work, the *Cabbala*. Alchemy thrived,
particularly in Europe, between the 14th and 17th centuries, after
which time the occult component diminished and the legitimate
science of chemistry became preeminent.

There were probably as many alchemical theories as there were
alchemists, so the reader will understand that in the ensuing
discussion we are talking in general terms.

Alchemists were both philosophers and applied scientists. All
matter, they held, was formed of combinations of a few basic
elements; most believed these were the four Aristotelian elements, fire, air, earth and water. Matter was vitalized to greater
or lesser degree by the power of light and by the spirit of life. It
was transmutable: water on evaporation became air, fire when
extinguished became ash (a type of earth).

Changes such as these were simple to achieve, but more

elaborate transformations were held to be possible with the aid of special substances. Quicksilver was one such exceptional material because, although it was metal, it clearly had an abundance of 'water', and acids had the curious power of being able to dissolve metals. Alchemists sought to produce the Philosophers' Stone which would change base metal into gold and provide an elixir to prolong life. Favourite ingredients for producing this fabulous powder included mercury, sulphur, vinegar and salt. It was hoped also to produce a panacea to cure all human ills, and some alchemists suggested that by a process of fermentation the spirit of life might be distilled in pure form.

The alchemists had their own ideas about human nature and suggested that each person was a microcosm, a miniature containing some trace of everything in the Universe, including God. This divine aspect within human beings was held to be a pathway to secret knowledge. Paracelsus announced: 'We shall become like gods . . . we will duplicate God's great marvel—the creation of the human.' Attempts to achieve this involved experiments with the sublimation, fermentation, coagulation and putrefaction of various natural substances. Organic products, especially those of human origin, were regarded as possessing special properties, and blood, bone, urine and faeces were common ingredients in the strange brews.

Human semen was often the base material employed in attempts to create an artificial human form—the homunculus— but special significance was given also to the mandrake root. This signals a recurrence of the powerful idea that an image may be transformed into that which it represents, for the root of the mandrake often bears a close resemblance to the human figure, with clearly identifiable arms, legs and sometimes even facial features. For this reason the mandrake has been treated with particular reverence or fear in many cultures, and in some it has been the custom to dress the root in miniature clothes.

There are several accounts of the origin of the mandrake, or mandragora. The alchemists subscribed to the suggestion that the first plant sprang from the ground at the spot where an innocent man had been hanged. This story tells of how at the moment of death the man's muscles relaxed and he ejaculated. From the sperm which fell to the ground the first mandrake arose. Various rituals were observed in gathering the plant, and it was commonly held that as the mandrake was uprooted it let out a scream. Some alchemists believed that suitably nurtured by milk and blood the root would grow into the form and size of a newborn child. Others merely used extracts of the plant as one of many ingredients in their life-creation experiments.

There are several records of attempts to create a homunculus. As early as the 3rd century it was said that one had been produced by Simon Magus, but most accounts come from the medieval period. The 13th-century philosopher and necromancer Arnold of Villanova made several attempts, as did the 16th-century alchemist and black magician Cornelius Agrippa; he tried also to create living snakes by burying in faeces the hair of a menstruating woman. But the most famous 'homunculus recipe' comes from Paracelsus (1493–1541), the famous physician and alchemist. He had no doubt that human beings could be created 'without woman' and he claimed to have produced 'monstrous dwarfs and other such wonderful creatures' by artificial means. In his *De Generatione Rerum* he wrote: 'Through art they achieve their life, through art they receive flesh, bones and blood; and by art are they born.'

The recipe for Paracelsus' homunculus contains semen. It could not have been his own, however, for he had been castrated at the age of three—by a hungry pig, according to one account. He gave highly detailed instructions for the process of generation: 'If sperm, enclosed in a sealed glass bottle, is buried in putrefaction of horse dung for some forty days and correctly magnetized, it will begin to live and move. At this time it will bear the shape and form of a human being, but will be transparent and lack body. If now this is nurtured with the arcanum of human blood and kept in the heat of the horse manure it will become a true and living child but smaller than a child of woman. This is the homunculus. It should be taught with care until it attains intelligence.'

There are echoes here of the ancient doctrine of preformation, according to which the human child is exactly represented, in miniature form, in each sperm. The idea was that the sperm alone formed the seed and the woman's part in the process was simply to provide nourishment in the form of menstrual blood.

Perhaps the best explanation of the nature of the alchemists' experience has been provided by Jung. He suggested that they were unconsciously projecting aspects of their own psychological make-up onto the materials they used. The personification of lifeless things, he said, is caused by unconscious identity, and the 'metal men' of ancient stories are examples of such projection.

Perhaps, then, the alchemists, crouched over their steaming retorts in the half-light, intently gazing for signs of life and hoping feverishly that they had unlocked the secret of 'God's great marvel', *did* see 'miraculous' images. Perhaps at times they were truly confused about whether they held in their flask an emergent lifeform or merely a scant portrayal. Their vision may well have been clouded by hope, but maybe they were also influenced by the alchemical aphorism: 'The most natural and perfect work is to produce that which is like to itself.'

Alchemy had a powerful influence on several important works of literature. One of these, to be examined in detail, was *Frankenstein*, and another was Goethe's *Faust*. In this a homunculus is produced from 'a hundred-fold ingredients':

> See—an elegant bright little elf
> He lives, he lives. Neat little doll of fire
> What more can we or earth desire.
> Mystery no longer is concealed
> Listen! A sound! A voice! And soon will he
> Speak words of subtle sense to me.

Alchemy was not the only route available to those who wished to create living human forms. Cabbalistic mysticism offered another means. According to Jewish tradition the *Cabbala* was directly entrusted to the Jews by God, although recent scholarship suggests that it derived from Babylonian and Egyptian sources. The secrets of cabbalism were jealously guarded by rabbis who handed them down by word of mouth and later in the form of manuscripts. The principal doctrines were then transcribed as 'The Book of Creation' and 'The Book of Splendour', volumes which included details of the seventy-two Names of the Deity, the thirty-two Ways of Wisdom and the fifty-two Doors of Knowledge.

Central to the tradition were prescriptions regarding verbal utterances, acrostic combinations of letters, and anagrams. The Biblical statement 'In the beginning was the Word' was taken literally, and cabbalists sought permutations of holy letters which would tap cosmic power. One of the special goals was to find the secret verbal formula which would instil life into a human form shaped of clay. This was the search for the secret of the 'golem'. This Hebrew word is used in the *Talmud* to refer to Adam in an intermediary stage of his creation, when the dust from which he was to be formed was kneaded into a formless mass (or 'golem'); it is used also to describe a woman who, not having yet conceived, is also 'unfulfilled'. The word came to apply to artificial human-oids only much later, perhaps not until the 16th century, but by then attempts at invoking such a creature had long been underway.

Golem-production involved two stages: the shaping of clay into a human form and the use of incantations to endow the figure with life. The first stage was easy, but finding the secret verbal formula was not. The first recorded attempts, over 1,800 years ago, involved the use of the 'Most Great Name'—SHEMHA-MPHORAS—but this was soon abandoned. One of the foremost cabbalists, Eleazar of Worms, claimed early in the 13th century that mystical words derived from the 'alphabets of the 221 gates' had to be recited over each of the figure's limbs and organs to 'breathe life into the image'. The close parallels between golem-raising and the Biblical account of the origin of humankind are obvious, and the cabbalists themselves were aware of them. The attempt to imitate the act of divine creation, however, was regarded by the practitioners as an entirely wholesome activity, a religious practice rather than a 'black art'.

Nevertheless the golem gained a fearsome image, and not without cause, for, in several accounts of successful generation, the golem developed into a terrifying monster. Rabbi Elijah of Chelm was reputed to have brought a golem to life in the 16th century and to have died by its hand. The most renowned golem, and another given to fits of ill-temper, was that raised by the Chief Rabbi of Prague, Judah Löw, in 1580. There are various accounts of this creation, each differing in some important detail. Most tell how Rabbi Löw, with some assistants, took clay from the local river-bank and moulded it into the form of a man. The rabbi then circled the statue pronouncing incantations and the body shone brightly, began to breathe and opened its eyes. The creature was then clothed and taught to do domestic work in the synagogue. It could see and follow instructions but could not speak. At first obedient, it later began to assert a will of its own and, with its superhuman strength, became increasingly unmanageable. At the age of 13 it was deanimated by Rabbi Löw and returned to its original form.

The methods used for deactivating a golem were related to those used to give it life. If the creature had been animated by placing in its mouth a parchment with the mystical SHEMHA-

MPHORAS written upon it, then removing the parchment would deactivate it. If it had been brought to life by writing EMETH (Hebrew: 'truth') on its forehead then deleting the first 'E', leaving METH (Hebrew: 'death'), would cause the golem to 'die'. Such methods were no guarantee of safety, however, and there were several accounts of disasters—it was apparently rather difficult to make a wild golem stand still and stoop to allow a fateful letter to be erased from its brow.

The impact of the golem legend was considerable. Even as late as the 18th century many people believed that real golems had been created, and a number of anti-Semitic writers attempted to reinforce the prejudices of their readers by intimating that live golems inhabited many synagogues. In recent times the golem has featured in numerous novels, films, plays and an opera, and even today there are several reminders of golem-lore in Prague. Rabbi Löw's grave can still be seen and the synagogue in which the golem was reputedly deanimated remains. In 1968, when a workman was found dead in 'Alchemists' Street' under the remains of a clay statue and the chief police officer claimed that he had seen the statue crumble and 'melt away' before him, agitated citizens spoke alarmedly of 'the revenge of the golem'.

The golem is in many ways a clear ancestor of Frankenstein's creature, and the legend certainly helped to inspire Mary Shelley's novel. She drew heavily both on this source and on the work of the alchemists, and it is not difficult to see how the two might be combined. The links between alchemy and cabbalism are strong. Alchemy owed much to the *Cabbala* and many cabbalists explored also the mysteries of alchemy. But the two traditions had a somewhat different emphasis. Alchemists relied principally on their scientific theory and incorporated occult practices sparingly. The methods of the cabbalists were distinctly mystical, although they manipulated and combined letters and numbers rather as if they were chemical elements. Both groups worked to derive a secret formula, to bring out that fragment of divine power which they believed each human possessed. And both were inspired by the belief that through dedicated and systematic efforts people could find the key to the great mystery, the creation of human life.

There is one other similarity. It has been suggested that the alchemists' experience of homunculi was a projection of their conscious will, a reflection of a special state of mind engendered by fervent hope and watchful expectation. Cabbalistic practice also involved the attainment of a contemplative frame of mind—practitioners used physical exercises akin to yoga and techniques of meditation to induce special trance states. Indeed, among the rabbis of medieval Germany the phrase 'making the golem' was used to refer to a state of ecstasy. It is therefore possible that the cabbalists and the alchemists experienced their golems and homunculi through an extreme effort of imagination. The force of their projections would testify to the strength and saliency of the humanoid concept, and those who were so keenly involved in trying to make flesh and blood of the concept provided for the literary heritage ready-made images that were to resonate instantly with future generations. For the concepts of the golem and the homunculus were to be powerfully developed and exploited by writers for centuries afterwards.

THREE
Frankenstein and Company

The Frankenstein Connection

The rise of science, and especially of biology and organic chemistry, in the 17th and 18th centuries encouraged the idea that life might be created in the laboratory in a purely orthodox scientific manner, without resorting to primitive alchemical notions or occult practices. A number of demonstrations seemed to have a particular relevance to the 'animation' theme. Scientists speculated and debated about the processes by which worms emerged from putrefied flesh and hydra regenerated as whole specimens from severed parts. The Italian anatomist Luigi Galvani showed that the legs of dissected frogs twitched when an electric current was applied to them. During a thunderstorm he hung the legs from brass hooks outside the laboratory to ascertain the energizing properties of lightning. Such explorations made it highly probable that sooner or later someone would cast the ancient golem theme in a novel 'scientific' mould.

Mary Shelley finished *Frankenstein* before she was 21 years old; it was published in 1818. The novel concerns the origins and consequences of a scientific attempt to create an organic humanoid. It is a pivotal work which provided a synthesis of many earlier ideas, developing these so powerfully that the book was destined to have a profound influence on later writing. The humanoid in *Frankenstein* may have had many obvious fictional and legendary forebears but its emergence marked an important intermediate stage in the literary evolution of the robot. The creature is radically different from any of its predecessors, displaying a full 'human' personality with motives, attitudes and feelings. It is given the power of speech and the novelist accords it a full 'character' treatment. The humanoid thus becomes much more than an 'object' around which human beings perambulate, and in this respect it is recognizable as a close ancestor of many of the robots of contemporary SF.

The novel concerns the tragic consequences of human scientific achievement. Victor Frankenstein is a young man who has dabbled in the occult and is familiar with the work of Cornelius Agrippa and Paracelsus, whom he describes as 'the lords of my imagination'. Wishing to alleviate pain, suffering and death he becomes intent on discovering the elixir of life. To that end he studies chemistry and natural philosophy and conducts research on the decomposition of corpses. He hopes to achieve a reversal of the decay process and to create life, and his doubts about the morality of his experiments are overcome as he contemplates the likely consequences of success: 'A new species would bless me as its creator; many happy and excellent natures would owe their being to me. No father could claim the gratitude of his child so completely as I should deserve theirs.' Frankenstein produces a creature of superhuman size (to facilitate working on the delicate structures) and brings it to life by harnessing the power of lightning. Soon afterwards the humanoid escapes from the laboratory.

Hiding in the woods, it closely observes a human family, learning to speak by imitating them and gradually coming to understand human feelings and relationships. The creature soon discovers, however, that despite its benevolence and purity of motive it is not welcome among people: they are frightened and attack it. Bitter at such rejection, it kills a child, and shortly afterwards Victor manages to trace and confront it. Then the 'monster' pleads for understanding: 'How can I move thee? Will no entreaties cause thee to turn a favourable eye upon thy creature, who implores thy goodness and compassion?' It explains that it wants a wife in order to be 'like other men'. Frankenstein at first agrees to create a female partner, but when the task is near completion he foresees the possibility that this unholy alliance will lead to a breeding race, and he recoils in horror.

The characterization of Frankenstein's creation is particularly interesting. It is a highly sensitive creature capable of the full gamut of emotions. At one point it admits: 'Soft tears again bedewed my cheeks.' For the first time a humanoid is aware—and lonely. It finds itself in the essentially 'human' predicament of being sensitive and sincere yet unloved and misunderstood. The 'monster' which feels itself not to be a monster faces a personal crisis. It can identify with Victor more readily than Victor can identify with it. The total rejection it experiences produces despair and frustration which turn to anger and menace. The monster's psychology is thus recognizably human.

It demonstrates a keen self-awareness, explaining its apparent malevolence to Victor with the heartfelt plea: 'Everywhere I see bliss, from which I alone am irrevocably excluded. I was benevolent and good; misery made me a fiend. Make me happy, and I shall again be virtuous.' As readers we can identify with the creature's plight. Its reactions, while extreme, are essentially 'understandable', and we allow that it is experiencing situations as a human being would. By responding in such a way to a 'mere artefact' we are implicitly, but clearly, endowing it with a human persona. The creature also identifies itself, initially, as human, and is later perplexed about its true nature: 'Who am I? What am I?' Such a self-consciousness about origins and identity is a characteristic of many robots depicted in later SF. When the monster finds Victor's journal it becomes painfully aware why it cannot be 'like other men'. *Frankenstein* represents a giant psychological step and an existential leap for literary humanoids.

What inspired Mary to write this monumental classic? What influences played upon her imagination? She informs us that the major stimulus was a dream she had had after listening to a late-night conversation. She was staying with Percy Bysshe Shelley, Lord Byron and others at the Villa Diodati, on the shore of Lake Geneva, and one night they talked of the supernatural and of the possibility of creating life. Their discussion also included mention of the work of Luigi Galvani and of some supposed experiments by Erasmus Darwin in which a piece of vermicelli had been treated with chemicals causing it 'to move with voluntary action'. The group decided that they would each write a ghost story, and that night Mary Shelley dreamt part of the plot of *Frankenstein*.

In his *In Search of Frankenstein* Radu Florescu casts some doubt on this account. He points to the numerous influences which could well have inspired Mary and helped her in the writing of the novel. In the light of the evidence Florescu amasses it is impossible not to be impressed by the way in which circumstances—Mary's background, her travels and the company she kept—seem to have conspired to provide her with exceedingly rich sources for her writing. Her father, William Godwin, was an author of books on the occult and was well versed in the history of alchemy and cabbalism. The concepts of the homunculus and the golem would have been familiar to her, and she may well have realized the frequent ambiguity between life-creation and life-simulation (her mother had written of the possibility of giving 'life, not animation, to the inert clay').

Godwin was interested also in science and knew several leading scientists, including Sir Humphry Davy. He was well acquainted with the writings of Luigi Galvani and of Erasmus Darwin, physician, radical thinker and grandfather of Charles. Erasmus Darwin was also an engineer and made automata, including reputedly a 'speaking priest'. It seems that he experimented with electrical cures and considered seriously the idea that electricity might reanimate dead tissue. The conversations Mary is likely to have overheard as a child, and the stock of books in the Godwin library, must certainly have helped to shape her later fiction. As an adolescent she came to know Shelley and Byron, both of whom were interested in the classical notion of the 'animating force' and in the legend of Prometheus. Shelley, in addition, was interested in science and gadgetry. In view of this veritable barrage of complementary influences, fate can be seen to have played a major role in the genesis of Mary's novel.

Aspects of her personal life can also be seen as having conditioned the emotional tone of the book. Even at the early age at which she wrote she was no stranger to tragedy and death. Her own mother, Mary Wollstonecraft, had died just ten days after baby Mary was born. She had been an intellectual and one of the leading feminist thinkers of her time. It is not outrageous to speculate that Mary's childhood fantasies, fired by her father's conversations, may well have revolved around themes of resurrection and reanimation. At the age of 16 Mary became pregnant. When the baby died she wrote in her diary: 'Dreamed that my little baby came to life again; that it had only been cold, and that we rubbed it before the fire, and that it lived.' Mary Shelley was the right person to have written the novel. She was also in the right place at the right time.

At the age of 17 she eloped with Shelley to Switzerland. They stayed briefly in Neuchâtel, a village famous for the manufacture of 'androids', and Florescu suggests that Shelley, who is known to have had an interest in automata, may well have taken Mary to see the moving humanoids which represented such a marvellous display of clockwork engineering skills. And on their way towards the Villa Diodati the two would have passed close to a castle associated with strange dark legends. It had a memorable name, too: Castle Frankenstein. Some of the legends surrounding it concern an alchemist, Johann Dippel, who lived from 1673 to 1734. He had stayed for a while in the castle and during his lifetime had attempted to find the secret of the Philosophers' Stone. He also practised vivisection and believed that life could be artificially created through magical rites, by transferring the spirit of one creature into the corpse of another. He was expelled from his university for an incident which was rumoured to have involved the collection of specimens from a local cemetery. The parallels with Victor Frankenstein's supposed history and interests are clear, and Florescu is convinced that this is not merely coincidence.

Yet the message of the novel concerns the future rather than the past. *Frankenstein* can be seen as an adverse comment on the optimism inherent in the early 19th-century attitude to science. Simultaneous advances in many directions reinforced a general idea that science could persuade nature to give up her secrets, and the successes of engineering and medicine intimated that solutions would be found to all manner of problems. Never before had there been such a clear ring of truth to Bacon's dictum: 'Knowledge is power.' Mary's novel casts doubt on the legitimacy and desirability of such power.

The novel has a subtitle, *the Modern Prometheus*. In his ambition Frankenstein follows the traditional path of those who would aspire to imitate the gods, but he eschews the ancient methods in favour of the *modern* approach: '. . . treading in the steps already marked, I will pioneer a new way, explore unknown powers, and unfold to the world the deepest mysteries of creation.' Only when he embraces 'legitimate science' do his efforts bear fruit, but his scientific 'success' brings disaster in terms of moral and human criteria.

Frankenstein is a cautionary tale. Initially Victor is the powerful figure, the expert. Having faith in his understanding and in the methods of science he proceeds confidently towards his objective. Only when he is successful does he realize that he has unleashed powers far beyond his control. His success becomes his punishment, and the novelist presents this not as cruel irony but rather as nemesis. Not for the first or last time in literature, the servant comes to dominate the master, the creation rises up against its creator. The loss-of-control theme echoes a number of the earlier golem stories and anticipates many later robot tales. The novel cautions against the unbridled use of the powerful tool of science in exploring proscribed or dangerous areas of knowledge. Science may provide access to 'forbidden' secrets, to facts which 'human beings are not meant to know'.

These are grievous forebodings for science and not surprisingly some commentators have been unable to resist the temptation to relate Frankenstein's folly to contemporary issues in science and technology. More than once the analogy has been drawn between Victor's quest for the 'life-force' and explorations of the nuclear force. For others the novel raises the spectre of a technology running out of control. A more specific parallel might be drawn between Frankenstein and the specialists in AI and robotics who now strive towards simulating and enhancing the distinctly human quality of intellect. Florescu speaks of the 'prophetic vision' of *Frankenstein* in the light of the 20th-century revolution in cybernetics and robotics, and in her *Machines Who Think* (1979) Pamela McCorduck comments that the novel '. . . combines nearly all the psychological, moral, and social elements of the history of artificial intelligence'.

Yet, unless we wish to take a wholly negative view of AI, we must be careful not to make too close an identification between AI projects and the fictional creation. The novel does raise issues that have taken on a new salience now that scientists are seriously aiming to produce 'sentient creatures'. The fact that these will be made of metal rather than of organic materials, and that they will simulate the behaviour of human beings rather than embody a real life of their own, may be of little relevance. The existence of such entities will raise vital questions of propriety, control and status which have so far been discussed principally by moral philosophers and by writers of fiction. But to allow that Mary Shelley raised relevant questions is not necessarily to concur with her diagnosis or conclusions, and most of those concerned with the robot future, in fact or in fiction, would take issue with her alarming prognostications. Some recent authors do present horrendous views of a robot future, but they are distinctly in a minority, for while *Frankenstein* is important as a precursor of contemporary robot fiction it is the 'humanity' and 'awareness' of the creature rather than the horrific aspects which have survived the passage of time. Previous humanoids were 'wooden' figures whereas Frankenstein's creation is 'full-blooded'—it is presented not as an object, a doll or as a machine but as a 'person'—and this is the aspect that had such an impact on later writing.

The debt owed by genre SF to Mary Shelley has not gone

unrecognized or unappreciated. Florescu states: 'It is impossible
. . . to assess completely the extent to which the imaginations of
19th- and 20th-century authors were stimulated by Mary Shelley's
life-creating theme. In this respect, Mary's monster is the legitimate precursor to the robot, the synthetic, or semi-artificial, man
and of the innumerable romances which purport to describe the
creation of life.' And the SF writer L. Sprague de Camp agrees:
'. . . all the shambling horde of modern robots and androids
are descendants of Frankenstein's sadly malevolent monster.'
Despite the undoubted strength of its influence *Frankenstein* clearly represents a most inauspicious beginning for the 'humane'
humanoid, and is a poor representation of future depictions. The
novel differs sharply from most of today's writing in the direction
of its narrative and in its premonition of disaster.

Isaac Asimov's stories, for example, maintain a highly positive
stance towards humanoid technology. In the introduction to one
of his stories he speaks out sharply against those who have
presented the robot as a potential threat: 'Never, never, was one
of my robots to turn stupidly on his creator for no purpose
but to demonstrate, for one more weary time, the crime and
punishment of Faust. Nonsense! My robots were machines
designed by engineers, not pseudo-men created by blasphemers.'
Asimov has identified Mary Shelley's novel as responsible for the
unwarranted fear of scientific products which he has dubbed 'The
Frankenstein Complex'.

The image of which Asimov complains is instantly recognizable, for the name 'Frankenstein' has by now become synony-
mous with terror. It has also become identified with 'monster',
quite inappropriately because Frankenstein was the scientist and
the monster was unnamed. The most memorable aspects and
images of the narrative have entered the public domain and have
been subjected to all manner of distortion, debasement and
embroidery. Within years of the novel's publication dramatic
adaptations and burlesque exploitations appeared. The first Frankenstein movie was produced as early as 1908 and since then the
creature has featured in over 30 films. The classic 1931 version
starred Boris Karloff as the monster and, not inappropriately, the
director incorporated several images from a 1920 German film,
The Golem. In the course of his celluloid adventures the monster
has met Dracula and the Wolfman, Space Monsters and Abbott
and Costello. He has conquered the world, had a number of
Brides, Sons and Daughters (one of whom met Jesse James)

and has been drowned, bombed and exorcised. Despite this he re-emerges unscathed and with astonishing regularity.

Such escapades hardly reflect the seriousness of Mary's novel but they do testify to the abiding power of the central image. Despite the brilliance and intrinsic merits of the original work, *Frankenstein* would have had less influence had it remained merely a classic of high literature. In the event it has proved to be an inexhaustible well into which numerous buckets of all shapes and sizes have been repeatedly dipped. Its obvious potency as a trigger to the popular imagination is perhaps not difficult to understand when we consider the extraordinary strength and diffusion of the humanoid image in the mythology and literature across many cultures. It would be difficult not to believe that the predominance of this image indicates that the humanoid motif reflects some deep facet of human consciousness, and that *Frankenstein* powerfully stimulates an intrinsic fascination.

Frankenstein can thus be seen as a major focal point in the literary humanoid heritage. The novel is both a synthesis of primitive humanoid tales and a blueprint for successive generations of android stories. Within this single work we see the evolution of method, from alchemy to science, and the development of the self-conscious and communicating artefact. The occult and 'statuesque' golem that had dominated the European humanoid scene for several centuries was suddenly replaced, through the efforts of one young writer, by an articulate and sensitive 'character'.

Captivating Clockwork

Although *Frankenstein* is deservedly recognized as the monumental work which launched the 'human humanoid', several other 19th-century works depict important forebears of the robots of contemporary SF. One is a German short story, 'The Sandman' (1816), written by E. T. A. Hoffmann. It tells of a young student and his love for a 'woman' who is later found to be a machine. The special significance of the tale lies in its extrapolation from the successes of automata engineering and in its portrayal of human reactions to a humanoid machine. Hoffmann's story is not concerned with the creation of life, but with the simulation of human behaviour by an artificial mechanism, and in this respect it is far closer to modern robot fiction than to *Frankenstein*. However, whereas Frankenstein's creature is articulate and has a well formed personality, the automaton depicted in 'The Sandman' is 'human' only in its appearance and some superficial aspects of behaviour. In this respect, therefore, it is quite unlike the robots of later SF.

During the 18th and 19th centuries a large number of impressive automata were constructed in Europe and the Far East. These exhibited a range of 'human' skills and were highly realistic in appearance. Producing such automata was expensive and time-consuming, and the design inevitably reflected a concern with the potential 'box office'. They were displayed to a paying public at exhibitions and fairs. People were fascinated by the 'mechanical miracles', and by the end of the 18th century there were humanoid machines which could speak set phrases, play musical instruments, write and draw. There were automaton conjurers, fortune-tellers, acrobats, jugglers and dancers. The machines were suitably dressed and their faces and limbs were carefully sculpted and painted. Further developments enhanced the apparent 'organic' nature of the artefacts: some had slow rhythmic chest movements that made them appear to breathe and there were animaloid automata which ingested food, 'digested' it chemically and then excreted the waste products.

Such wonderful devices enthralled the general public and gave both philosophers and fiction writers considerable food for thought. The machines seemed to enhance the plausibility of the view that living creatures were essentially complex mechanisms, although some found such an implication untenable or unpalatable and stressed the importance of a 'vital' or 'spiritual' element in living creatures which would always defy simulation. Argument and counterargument were presented in many philosophical and fictional works, with the achievements and limitations of automata used to reinforce whatever stance the writer favoured. But automata also inspired a number of less abstract images. There was speculation about the kinds of machines that might be produced. Some of these fantasies were terrifying, some light-hearted, some prurient and some gruesome. Such inventive extrapolation from the achievements of existent technology is now recognized as a hallmark of SF but it has a long history. Hoffmann was just one of the 19th-century writers who projected beyond the current technology and used 'automata fiction' to reinforce a philosophical stance regarding the nature of humankind.

Ernst Theodor Wilhelm Hoffmann was born in Germany in 1776. A lawyer and judge by profession, he was also the writer of the famous *Tales*; his passionate interest in music eventually led him to change his third name to Amadeus as a gesture of homage to Mozart. Many of his stories involve elements of the supernatural and the fantastic. He used alchemical imagery in some of his tales and one story, 'Little Zaches', draws heavily on the folklore surrounding the mandrake. He was interested in Mesmer's theories concerning 'animal magnetism' and was greatly influenced by the work of Emanuel Swedenborg, the great Swedish philosopher and theologian. Swedenborg maintained that people were spiritual beings and potential angels, and that their anatomy provided a representation of the panoply of heavenly virtues: 'By the head is signified intelligence and wisdom . . . by the feet, what is natural; by the ears, obedience; by the kidneys, the purification of truth.' This is similar to the 'human microcosm' view of nature adopted by the alchemists. Like these earlier seekers after truth, Hoffmann insisted that human beings contained a spiritual element, and his stories 'The Automata' and 'The Sandman' reflect his conviction that artificial humanoids must always lack the 'vital' features of 'awareness' and personality.'

'The Sandman' tells how a young student, Nathanael, discovers Professor Spalanzani's daughter Olympia sitting quietly in a window; he instantly falls in love with her. She is very beautiful, but her eyes are strange: they seemed fixed and almost without vision. Nobody appears to have met or spoken with the young woman, but Nathanael comes to worship her from afar. His obsession with her leads him to reject his lover, Klara, who now seems plain and predictable, almost like an automaton.

When the Professor holds a ball Nathanael arrives hoping to meet his loved one. Olympia appears and gives a short recital, playing the piano and singing an aria with stunning precision. At one point she looks towards Nathanael with a glance that he takes as a sign of love.

When she accepts his request for a dance he is surprised by how stiffly she moves and by the coldness of her touch. She speaks haltingly, using only a simple phrase—'Ah, ah'—but the undaunted youth whirls her through many dances. As she begins to leave at the end of the ball he proclaims his undying love and asks her for some word, some token of her feeling, but although she looks at him 'lovingly' once again she murmurs only 'Ah, ah'.

The Professor invites the student to visit his daughter. Nathanael visits Olympia often, reading the poems and stories he has written for her. She is such a good listener, always appearing attentive and appreciative, and each time he is rewarded with the familiar phrase: 'Ah, ah.' Never has he met such an enigmatic and captivating woman, and he plans to marry her.

Visiting the house to propose to her, he hears a commotion in the professor's study. 'I made the eyes!' shouts someone. 'And I made the clockwork!' screams another. Nathanael rushes in to find the professor and the abominable Dr Coppelius pulling frantically at what appears to be the body of a woman. Nathanael recognizes the figure as Olympia, but then realizes that it is a model from which the eyes are missing. As Coppelius runs down the stairs with the figure the legs bump woodenly against the stair-rail. Spalanzani screams: 'Coppelius has stolen my automaton, my work of twenty years.' Recognizing the full horror of his predicament Nathanael begins to dance round and round screaming: 'Wooden doll, whirl, wooden doll!' He is taken to the madhouse.

When the scandal breaks many claim they had long suspected the truth, but the incident sets up a new suspicion—'a despicable mistrust of human beings in general'. Nathanael is reunited with Klara and recovers briefly from his madness, but when he meets up once again with the evil Coppelius he throws himself from a high tower and his head smashes on the ground. Thus in the end both Olympia and Nathanael have become 'broken dolls', but Nathanael alone has a spirit which survives his bodily death.

In 'The Automata' Hoffmann had already revealed his profound distrust and distaste for machines which might be treated as substitutes for human beings. It is a less successful story than 'The Sandman' in many ways and is largely a vehicle for Hoffmann to expound his attitude towards mechanically produced music. One character, Ludwig, contemplates the possible construction of a 'female' automaton which might partner a male dancer, but on reflection finds the idea repulsive. The main narrative concerns a marvellous machine, the 'Talking Turk', which is causing great excitement in the town. It can speak several languages and respond to questions with answers which reveal the innermost thoughts and secrets of the questioner. Later it becomes apparent that this machine is a 'fraud', operated at a distance by the telepathic Professor X. Thus Hoffmann was happy to portray paranormal phenomena in a realistic fashion but firmly rejected the mechanistic conclusions regarding human nature that some drew from the achievements of the automata-makers.

Yet there is little doubt that he was disturbed by the feats of these engineers. His visit to an exhibition of automata in Dresden in 1813 had left a lasting impression. Over the next three years mechanical humanoids featured prominently in his writing. He would have been aware of the work of the brothers Johann and Friedrich Knauss. They had produced a number of impressive writing and music-playing humanoids and had conceived of a display with two figures, one a 'writer' and the other a 'speaker', to be presented in such a way that it would appear that one would 'read' aloud what the other had written. Some 30 years earlier, again in Germany, a Hungarian inventor, Baron von Kempelen, had produced his famous 'chess-playing Turk'. This was exhibited all over Europe, and a few years before Hoffmann wrote his automata stories it had beaten Napoleon. This machine continued to be exhibited for many decades. It gave every impression of being an 'intelligent machine', although it is now known to have been a fake.

Hoffmann may have been less disturbed by the notion of mechanical intellect than by the idea of virtuoso musical devices. There were many reports of marvellous music-making automata which gave masterly presentations on violin, flute, harpsichord and trumpet. One commentator compared a performance by a violin-playing automaton favourably with a recital given by Paganini, and there are reports that at some of the concerts given by these machines the audiences were moved to tears. Hoffmann might well have felt, then, that such successes posed something of a threat to his own belief that music-making, dancing and other such human activities depended essentially on a spiritual element within human nature.

The author certainly would have approved of the fact that his story was later adapted musically. 'The Sandman' provides the theme for the first act of Offenbach's 1881 opera *Tales of Hoffmann*. The composer Delibes also drew inspiration from the story for his 1870 ballet *Coppelia*, although this version lacks the menace of the original narrative.

The importance of Hoffmann's work for the robot heritage largely concerns his portrayal of human responses to humanoid machines. He presents an extreme reaction, indicating how surface attractions and limited abilities may be sufficient to elicit a profound emotional response. Yet his writing, despite his own reservations about mechanical simulation, is notable also for its celebration of automata. His humanoids are clearly products of the applied science of engineering. They are constructed of levers, cams, springs and pulleys and are carefully produced after many years of effort. The mechanism is hidden and the figures are presented realistically in the form of attractive humans. They are simulations. There is no question of any biological involvement in the production, and no hint of a magical invocation of life. Olympia may therefore be considered as a fully evolved, though simple, robot and 'The Sandman' a milestone in robot fiction. The story takes heed of the limitations, as well as the attainments, of automata engineering; it takes account of technological constraints. Thus the doll possesses many human skills—dancing, playing the piano, and singing—but there is no hint that Olympia is capable of 'thinking'. It is acknowledged that her 'seeing' eyes and 'intelligent vision' represent a major technical advance, but several important restrictions remain. The machine is not capable of taking part in a conversation. She can make sounds, but cannot respond intelligently. Her singing has clearly been 'preprogrammed'.

'The Sandman' is in many ways a paradigm of the 'hard' SF story. It extrapolated from the current technology in a plausible way and observed the rules of science. It also focussed on realistic human reactions to technical innovation. Although Spalanzani's motives are not explicitly stated it is possible to infer them. The Professor is a dedicated constructor of automata who has worked in secret to refine the technology. After 20 years he has perfected mechanisms to produce movement and sound but has been unable to construct a 'seeing eye'. This has forced him to collaborate with Coppelius, the genius who has achieved the goal of artificial vision. Spalanzani has conceived of an external criterion which will validate his own opinion of the total 'realism' of his automaton. He will attempt to pass it off as his daughter. If such a deceit can be maintained, this will be sufficient proof of success. He therefore carefully observes the development of the 'relationship' between Nathanael and Olympia and encourages the student's attentions. Nathanael's avowed intention of marriage must surely count as impressive evidence that Spalanzani's 'Olympia project' has been a total success.

Human responses to real robots will not be characterized by such total delusion, and the motives of producers will not be the motives of Spalanzani. Hoffmann's tale thus involves an exaggeration which amounts to a distortion. Yet the same distortion persists in some contemporary SF. Even writers such as Asimov frequently portray total confusion between a robot and a human being, though they generally rely less on extreme psychological states and more on technological sophistication to render their narrative plausible. These stories, however, must be regarded as having less relevance for future human responses than those which concentrate on reactions to machines known to be artefacts.

People willingly 'enter the fiction' when an amusing 'pseudo-human' is presented in a ventriloquist's act or a puppet show. They may choose to regard a puppet *as if* it were human and respond to the character in an appropriate way. But they are not deceived. The power of future product machines to elicit 'social' reactions will depend on just such a 'willing confusion'. The element of deceit therefore limits the direct applicability of 'The Sandman' to any conceivable future situation. But the story nevertheless represents a notable contribution to robot fiction. Hoffmann brought technology to the fore, he enhanced the status of the automaton in fiction, and he presented the notable images of Nathanael, one of the first fictional characters to form a 'meaningful' relationship with a mechanical device, and Olympia, love-object and memorable 'soft machine'.

The Sensual Engine

Villiers de L'Isle Adam's *L'Ève future* is a remarkable novel, first published in Paris in 1886. Like 'The Sandman' it concerns the simulation, rather than the creation, of a living being, and it tells the story of the involvement of a handsome young man with a 'female' automaton. But in many ways the two stories are profoundly different. The French novel appeared some 70 years after 'The Sandman' and focusses on electro-mechanical, rather than clockwork, technology. *L'Ève future* gives a plausible and detailed account of the construction of the android, and the 'user' cooperates with the producer in its design, whereas the German story presents no account of Olympia's construction and the inventor is bent on deceit. Both authors were poets and philosophers as well as novelists, and both had more than a passing interest in the occult; but Hoffmann was a moralist who wanted to emphasize the absurdity and perversity of a mechanistic view of human nature, while the French author appears to have been somewhat more ambivalent in his attitude towards the android, and the preoccupation with sensuality which pervades much of his work found extended horizons in a fictional world in which an ideal partner could be 'custom-built' by an ingenious and biddable engineer.

Jean Marie Mathias Philippe Auguste Villiers de L'Isle Adam was an impoverished minor French aristocrat, a writer with a general taste for the bizarre and an especial fascination for certain erotic and sadistic eccentricities which he portrays with vividness and spectacle. He is best remembered for his *Contes Cruels* and for *Axël*, a visionary drama. *L'Ève future* is set in New York. It tells of an English aristocrat, Lord Ewald, and his love for a comedienne, Alicia Clary. Ewald is unhappy, however, for he finds that the mind of his beloved is focussed on trivial affairs, and not on him. In a pit of despair he contemplates suicide, but he meets an inventor, 'Thomas Edison', who suggests that he may have the answer to the problem. He will construct a woman to fulfil Ewald's dreams: 'Give me three weeks and I will present a transubstantiation which . . . will not be a woman, but an angel, not a mistress, but a lover, more than a reality, an *ideal*.'

Edison explains why he has been working to apply science to the problem of men's attraction to unsuitable women. A friend of his, he confides, had a happy home until he fell for the charms of another woman, a shallow creature whose wiles and artifice led him to ruin and subsequently suicide. Edison claims that such occurrences are not infrequent and that science should be able to provide some answer. He has therefore conceived the idea of constructing an 'ideal woman', an android (*andréide* is the term used in the book) which would serve the needs of weak but honest men without wreaking domestic havoc. After various prototypes he has constructed Hadaly, an android with remarkable properties. She is introduced to the noble Lord, entering the room like a beautiful apparition, moving, speaking. Ewald is both astounded and entranced, and is incredulous when Edison explains: 'Miss Hadaly is no more than an electromagnetic construction—metal that walks, speaks, responds and obeys, not somebody dressed up.'

He then sets out to describe in great detail (much of the novel consists of a dialogue between the two men) how the android was made and how the various mechanisms work. The bones are formed of ivory, with a 'galvanic marrow' that is in constant contact with a network of induction filaments linked together like the web of nerves and veins. The body temperature is accurately maintained by the electrical heating and cooling of a vital fluid which also helps to control movement.

The 'electro-human creature' is constructed in four parts. The first is a life system which controls balance, gait, voice, gestures, facial expression and the innermost regulating mechanism ('or, in other words, the "soul" '). Then there is a metal covering which provides a flexible skeleton to which the other structures are attached. A deep skin and 'muscle' layer, permeated by animating fluid, gives the body proportion, shape and sex. Finally there is a top skin layer which determines the shading, texture, lines and recognizable appearance. It is at this level that the fine lip movements, the barely perceptible details of facial expression and the subtle eye movements are controlled.

Speech comes from two golden phonographs placed where the lungs would be. They play golden discs ('better for recording female speech and resistant to oxidisation') able to store up to seven hours of material. These provide a kaleidoscope of words with various colours and intonations, and house the vocal dictionary which is accessed to compose speech to fit the context of a conversation. Gestures and facial expressions are controlled by means of small revolving barrels with tiny protrusions, as in a musical box. These are connected to the android's 'nervous system' and represent a repertoire of 70 separate movements, including lip movements precisely synchronized with the sounds of speech.

Hadaly makes breathing movements but does not need air. She does, however, need to 'drink' pure water and to 'eat' special pastilles which Edison has formulated. She will also bathe—the skin has been coloured by a special photochromic technique to make it water-resistant—and after bathing her rose-perfumed skin oil will need to be replenished. When not in active use she will return to a preferred position, either sitting or stretched out on a bed. She responds to speech, but can be switched from one 'mode' to another only by touching one of the pressure-sensitive rings attached to her fingers. Every ring has a different function.

The young lord finds much of this incredible, but having already witnessed the marvel of Hadaly he is not disposed to doubt Edison's claims. However, he has other reservations. 'This will be no more,' he challenges, 'than a doll, an insensible puppet.' The inventor reassures him that through the power of electromagnetism he could deceive a mother or satisfy a lover's passion for his mistress: 'I will reproduce a woman so perfectly that if she herself were to see my creation after a dozen years she would weep tears of envy.' The next objection Ewald raises is that the automaton will not possess intelligence. Edison refutes this in a number of ways. Hadaly will be self-conscious and will react to changes. Speech will be 'intelligent', reflecting the immediate context and having the appropriate intonation and inflection. Her vast dictionary of words and phrases will enable her to respond flexibly, in a style very close to that of human conversation, and in addition she will possess many hours of prerecorded speech based on the writings of the greatest philosophers and poets. Thus Hadaly will possess not only intelligence but amassed wisdom; but, says Edison, her 'reason' will be guided by a logic different to that used by human beings. Ewald's protestation that the android will have no conscience is soon dismissed: surely this is what you want, replies the inventor, for without conscience Hadaly is bound to do everything you ask. He offers the further opinion that conscience is not really a spiritual thing but can in the end be reduced by the physical sciences to no more than electrical charges on mucous membranes!

Ewald's uncertainty that he will be able to love the android is also quashed: 'I believe that you are a man like any other man. I tell you that you will love Hadaly as she deserves.' Edison maintains that love is a projection of desires. The loved one provides the stimulus but much of what provokes love arises in the eye, and the heart, of the beholder. What is loved is not flesh and bone but a total 'person' as constructed in the mind of the lover.

Edison thus counters all of the young lord's misgivings and points out that, if at any time the android became unsatisfactory, or dangerous, Ewald would be at liberty to 'switch it off'—to destroy it. But against these doubts, he suggests, the numerous benefits and advantages of the android must be considered. She will be pleasant company. She will remain forever young and will be eternally faithful ('her heart will never change, for she has none'). Her 'loyalty', indeed, will remain steadfast whatever personality is imposed on her. She is capable of undergoing many character changes, and of taking many different roles. Hadaly herself says at one point: 'I have so many women inside me that no harem could contain them.'

The mention of a harem is not simply chance, for Hadaly 'knows' that she has been designed to be a talented lover. Edison explains that the android is capable of acrobatic performance and offers 'more mobility, diversity and novelty'. She will act out whatever scenario her lover proposes, will allow him to relive the tender moment of his first kiss, or will perform more extraordinary scenes. Don Juan himself sometimes had to beg to obtain favours, the inventor notes, but the android will be obedient, however humiliating the request.

In all things, including love, Hadaly will appear and perform exactly in the manner of Miss Alicia. Edison will duplicate her gestures, the fullness of her body, her voice quality and intonation, the light of her eyes and even the perfume of her flesh '. . . in an apparition that will surpass your dreams'.

Detailed data about Miss Alicia are needed to produce such a simulation. Her photograph is placed in an apparatus which projects the image onto a screen, life-sized and luminous. This will be used, he explains, to make a 'photo-sculpture'. Edison also manages to discover the full details of her wardrobe and of her toilette.

Then, posing as a famous impresario, Edison invites Miss Clary to 'audition' for him. She recites and sings while his phonographs record every nuance. She is persuaded to pose without clothing, and later Edison hypnotizes her so that detailed bodily measurements can be made. No expense or effort is spared by Edison in order that he may keep his vow to Ewald: 'I promise you this, you will not be able to tell one from the other.'

The young aristocrat leaves the inventor alone for a few weeks so that the project may be completed. When he returns he is surprised to see Miss Clary with Edison in the laboratory and is overwhelmed when she asks to walk alone with him. When he tells her that he is deeply in love Alicia seems despondent, and explains that she is disappointed not to be the object of that love. Ewald, his original hope at last realized, cannot believe what she is saying!

They kiss and he immediately renounces Hadaly and all her

artifice: 'I dreamed the sacrilege of a toy, an absurd insensible doll . . . all the electrical madness, the hydraulics and the moving cylinders . . . You I recognise, you are flesh and blood like me. I feel your heart beating, your eyes are tearful, your lips tremble as I kiss.' She backs away, looking distraught once more, then speaks to him in despondent tone: 'My love, do you not recognise me? I am Hadaly.'

The android begins to weep and then, addressing the stars, cries: 'It is me, the noble daughter of man, the flower of six thousand years of science . . . I give to the void the charm of my lonely kisses, to the wind my speech; my loving caresses, the shade and lightning will receive them, and the lightning flash alone will dare to take the false flower of my vain virginity. Oh, that I could die.'

There are yet more twists and turns before the novel ends. Ewald relents and wants to take the new 'Alicia' back to his mansion in England. She is placed in a coffin lined with black silk, to ease her way through customs, and Edison explains that as the result of a technical breakthrough he has been able to give her a 'soul'. The original aim of satisfying degraded and obscene desires has been supplanted, and the android is now capable of entering into a truly romantic liaison. A tragedy lies in wait, however. Edison reads that there has been a serious fire on the ship in which Ewald was travelling. The report tells of how a young lord struggled against the flame to rescue his luggage. A telegram arrives. It is from Ewald. 'My friend,' it says, 'I am inconsolable, I cannot bear the mourning—goodbye.'

It is difficult to be clear about how Villiers hoped his reading audience would react to the book. He wrote in the tradition of the 19th-century French Romantics, and he has also been variously labelled a Symbolist and an Idealist. L'Ève future is full of poetic phrasing and philosophical dialogue, including discussions of the nature of the soul, love and the psychological construction of 'reality'. The book has been described as a triumph of sustained irony, suggesting that the author set out to make Edison's activities and arguments seem preposterous. Yet those arguments are successful in convincing Ewald and might easily convince a reader that a real 'Hadaly project' would be both feasible and desirable. It might be that Villiers himself was somewhat ambivalent about the central issue, and that Ewald and Edison represent the two 'factions' within the author. On the one hand he was a romantic poet, much given to lyrical celebrations of the spiritual;

on the other he was interested in science, and had a considerable knowledge of it. The book includes many genuine attempts to solve problems that might face a real android-maker, and the persistent dwelling on technical aspects suggests that the author was not totally disgusted by the enterprise. Also, he treats Hadaly sympathetically, presenting her as a charming creature with none of the menace of either Frankenstein's creation or Spalanzani's Olympia.

She is, indeed, a 'heroine' in a book which is remarkable for its outrageous attitude to women. Ewald is highly critical of Alicia but nevertheless refuses to accept that she will not come to him as a lover. He describes his ideal woman as 'a child with a simple heart, a smiling face and clear and loving eyes'. We soon learn that she should also have an attractive body, though not much is said about intellect or character. Alicia herself is portrayed as 'silly', 'acquisitive' and 'shallow' and the only other woman portrayed is insane. But the prize for barbarous chauvinism must go to the character Edison. According to him many women 'linger horribly, solely to find someone who will fill their vile embrace . . . they play with men, using make-up and other artifice, offering them untold pleasures but leaving them unfulfilled'. The thinking of many women, his diatribe concludes, begins and ends at the waist. It is hardly surprising that the author added a disclamatory note saying that the 'Thomas Edison, inventor, of Menlo Park, New York' portrayed in the book was in no way meant to represent *the* Thomas Edison, inventor, of the *real* Menlo Park, New York.

Many of its principal inspirational sources are identified within the work itself. Villiers shows his familiarity with the achievements of the automata-makers, with the legend of Prometheus, and with the sciences of physiology and electromagnetics. The book reveals also the influence of innovations in doll design. Paris was at that time world-famous for its dolls, many of which incorporated ingenious mechanisms to make them true miniature automata. With each new season the repertoire of their behaviour broadened as the producers competed for a larger share of the market. Dolls were able to swim, dance, 'breathe' and simulate various other physiological functions. And in 1893, only a few years after *L'Ève future* was written, the famous Jumeau company produced the *Bébé Phonographe* which spoke and sang by means of a tiny gramophone hidden in its chest. The idea for a phonograph doll, however, had first been patented in 1878 in the USA, the patent-holder being none other than that prodigious inventor Thomas Edison!

The late 19th century witnessed also many experiments concerned with projecting moving pictures, and again Edison was one of the pioneers. Such frantic activity in visual and auditory simulation renewed hopes that technological advances would provide new ways of constructing realistic automata. Villiers' particular interests led him to speculate about whether this field of invention might provide new opportunities for sensual pleasure. He was not the only one to have such fantasies, for a number of more frankly pornographic adaptations of the android theme emerged over the next two decades, notably *La Femme Endormie* (1899) by 'Madame B.'.

The plot of *L'Ève future* may actually have been suggested to Villiers, according to an early biographer, by a chance conversation at a dinner party. The Paris newspapers had reported the suicide of a young English lord following an unfortunate love affair. One of the guests, an assistant to Thomas Edison, suggested that the aristocrat's life might have been saved if he had been supplied with a functional replica of his loved one, incorporating the full benefits of technological research. Such a story would certainly have triggered Villiers' imagination. With his interest in science and his taste for the salacious it would have taken him little time to sketch an outline for the novel.

L'Ève future deserves to be considered a major contribution to the history of robot literature. It follows 'The Sandman' in using automata engineering as its technical foundation but it draws upon electro-mechanical innovations to portray a far more sophisticated android. Hadaly becomes a 'character' with a voice and personality of her own and is in this way closer to Frankenstein's creature than to Olympia. Villiers thus explored the concept of a 'mechanism with personality' which is central to modern robot fiction. *L'Ève future* is undoubtedly a work of science fiction, with its technical extrapolation, its concern with plausibility and its exploration of human motives and human responses. The book recognizes many of the problems of humanoid construction and functioning and provides a rational account of how some of these could be overcome. There are suggestions about how a device might be given the powers of speech and emotional expression and of how it might retain balance. Some of the finer points are rather quaint—the concern with 'body smell', for example, and with how the android will bathe—but Villiers was attempting to provide a comprehensive account of the 'anatomy', 'physiology' and 'manners' of the android, together with instructions for its care and maintenance. The book provides a fictional blueprint for construction together with the type of user's manual which might come with a washing-machine. 'Looked after properly,' we can almost hear Edison telling Ewald, 'this device will give you years of pleasure.'

Considerable attention is given to Hadaly's 'character'. To some extent she can be 'all things to all men', changing in personality to suit the mood and wishes of her master. Yet a distinct primary character underlies such surface variations. In her 'normal' mode Hadaly is gentle, 'loving', quiet and civil. She simulates desires of her own and displays a certain self-consciousness. Her 'ego' is flattered when she is shown a photograph of the person she will simulate and 'realizes' that she will be beautiful. She also has a rather flirtatious nature, glancing seductively at Ewald when she first meets him and later blowing him kisses ('a gesture reminiscent of an adolescent'). The pressure of her hand, we are told, is 'light and friendly'.

Hadaly therefore receives a 'psychological treatment' in the novel. Unlike Olympia she is not merely a passive doll. The motives and responses of the two human characters are also explored in some depth. Edison has a firm belief that human problems, even personal and emotional problems, can be remedied by the appropriate technology. Potentially, there is a machine to satisfy every human need and desire. Edison's motive for the 'Hadaly project' stems from a concern for the unfortunate men whose 'natural lust' destroys them and their families. Like Frankenstein he claims that his ultimate aim is humanitarian but, whereas Victor believes that his work will lead to the discovery of new phenomena, Edison is working towards 'product'. This is an important innovation. Reference is made to the fact that, once the first design has been completed, androids might be manufactured on an industrial scale: 'Only the first android is difficult . . . before long an industrialist will open the first android factory.'

Thus, although the humanoid is produced to Lord Ewald's own exacting specifications, he is testing a potential mass product. He takes Hadaly 'on approval' and the inventor asks him to send a 'consumer report'. Edison is an effective salesman who gives an impressive demonstration and answers all customer enquiries. The 'Hadaly model' is designed to fulfil many roles. Her principal purpose may be to act as a 'lover'—in this she anticipates the various hi-tech sex machines of later SF—but she will also be a companion, educator, entertainer, butler and slave. These are the roles fulfilled by most of the robots in contemporary fiction and those that might be anticipated of an ideal product machine. Villiers' novel therefore presents, for the first time, the image of the 'product humanoid', an image of vital relevance for the real future.

A century has passed since this minor French aristocrat worked by gaslight in Paris to finish his highly imaginative novel. As a result of his efforts, Hadaly was to become the first viable 'product humanoid' in the history of robot fiction. The 'technological miracles' which inspired his work now seem rather primitive. The era of the wind-up cylinder gramophone has long since passed. Now laser-disc and microcomputer technology are making their impact on the world. Villiers could not have foreseen the silicon chip or modern developments in AI but, if he had, would his Hadaly have been very different? Edison's device shares many features with the robots of much later SF. The dream remains the same; only the likelihood of the dream coming true has changed.

Enter the 'Robot'

There is little consensus about the use of the term 'robot'. It often refers merely to artificial automated humanoid machines, but some people apply it more widely. Thus some SF authors label their organic humanoids 'robots', while in industry the term may be applied to almost any complex automatic machine. Whatever the criteria adopted, 'robot' would seem to apply to Hadaly and to many of the other androids and automata portrayed in literature written before the 20th century. Yet the word itself was not introduced until 1917.

'Robot' is an adaptation of a Czech word meaning 'compulsory labour' and was first used by the dramatist and novelist Karel Čapek in his short story 'Opilec'. Its wide circulation resulted from its use in Čapek's play *R.U.R.*, first produced at the National Theatre in Prague in 1921 and then in New York the following year.

The play is set in the R.U.R. ('Rossum's Universal Robots') factory located on a small remote island. Here artificial people are made. Ingredients for the liver, brains and other robot organs are mixed in large vats and a spinning wheel weaves mile after mile of 'nerve-fibre' and 'vein'. The skeletal system and outer casing, however, appear to be made of metal.

An honoured guest, Helena, has arrived at the factory and the General Manager, Domin, explains how the manufacturing process started. Old Rossum was a mad scientist who strove to imitate God by manufacturing people. He experimented with biological materials, producing a synthetic dog and then a 'man' who survived for only three days. After this limited success Rossum's nephew, an engineer, decided that an artificial man could be produced far more easily if mechanical components were used, and he constructed the first real robot. Later he set up the factory to produce a variety of humanoid devices. Currently robots of varying sizes and grades are manufactured for export. The finest have a high-class human finish.

Domin's secretary, Sulla, is a 'robotess' of the highest grade. She is so perfect that Helena finds it difficult to believe that she is not human; when Domin offers to dissect the robot to prove his point, Helena protests strongly. Although at one level she knows that Sulla is only a machine, the robot's appearance and life-like behaviour produce a high degree of empathy. Helena cannot overcome the irrational feeling that to dissect the machine would be cruel, although Sulla herself makes no protest. Domin explains: 'Robots have no interest in life. They enjoy nothing. They are less than grass.'

Helena has come, representing the 'Humanity League', to liberate the robots. She maintains that they should be accorded certain rights and should receive wages. Domin is not convinced. How would the robots spend the money they earned? They have nothing to enjoy, they have no feelings, and to add emotional features would greatly increase production costs. Then, in a scene bordering on farce, Domin asks Helena to marry him; she protests strongly and then embraces him.

The curtain falls on Act One, and when it rises again ten years have passed. By now hundreds of thousands of robots have been exported and governments have started to use them as soldiers. But the robots themselves have begun to organize, a 'political consciousness' has arisen within their ranks, and they have produced a manifesto. The robots begin a worldwide revolt, attacking all humans—including those in the Rossum factory. In Act Three the cause of the evolution of robot consciousness becomes clear. Helena has asked Dr Gall, the Head of the Physio-logical Department, to give the robots 'souls' and he has secretly modified some details of the physiological design. Helena, now horrified by the effects, explains her motive: 'I thought that if they were more like us then they would understand us better. I thought that they would not then be able to hate us.' Meeting together, the factory managers console themselves with the thought that they hold the trump card, for they alone possess the plans for robot production. They hope to use these to re-establish control—but the luckless Helena has blundered once again. She has set fire to the precious document containing the secret pro-duction formula. Now it does seem as if all is lost, and the robots invade the house, sparing no one save the architect Alquist.

In the Epilogue Alquist is seen working for the robots, strug-gling to rediscover the secret of their manufacture. When his hopes finally fade it seems as if all human and humanoid 'life' will become extinct, but at that point two young robots appear, prototypes resulting from a particularly audacious experiment by the highly industrious and persistent Dr Gall. The young 'male' and 'female' appear to be in love. Their anatomy is modelled precisely on that of human beings and it appears that Dr Gall's biological manipulations may well allow for a less mechanical means of procreation. Alquist, with a tear in his eye, addresses the two: 'Go, Adam, go, Eve. The world is yours.'

Early productions of the play were highly acclaimed, and it was variously interpreted as 'a bitter assault on capitalism', 'a brilliant satire on mechanised civilization' and 'an attack on scien-tific materialism'. But what probably made the drama memorable for most of the audience was the fact that all but five of the characters were humanoid machines. The play was produced at a period in history when the pace of technological innovation was particularly fast. New miracles seemed just over the horizon and there was general excitement about applied science. The world waited for announcements of new inventions, and the audience of R.U.R. may have been fascinated more by the possible predictive accuracy of the play than by any allegorical intention of its author.

Čapek himself wasn't very happy with the work, and felt that it had been widely misunderstood. In an article, 'The Meaning of R.U.R.', he identified Old Rossum, the biological creator, with the medieval practitioners who wished to emulate God. Their folly having been exposed, a later generation, characterized by

Young Rossum, was now embracing a new idealism according to which technology could provide ultimate answers to the problems of humankind. For Čapek this was equally a mistake, because emancipation from work and struggle would ultimately prove demoralizing. The author was therefore using the robot motif as a vehicle to express his misgivings about the ascendance of materialist values. His explorations of issues specifically concerned with robots may have been incidental to his central purpose, but these were the aspects of the play that made an immediate audience impact.

Čapek considered the product potential of robots in industry and business. Robots are purchased by industrialists as a cheap form of labour to increase efficiency and profit, but behind this lies a more idealistic rationale (or rationalization). This is voiced by one of the characters in the play: 'I wanted to turn the whole of mankind into an aristocracy of the world, an aristocracy nourished by millions of mechanical slaves . . . there will be no poverty. All work will be done by living machines. Everybody will be free from worry and liberated from the degradation of labour. All people will live only to perfect themselves.' Thus the overall aim is liberation of the human workforce. Many philosophers, including Aristotle and John Stuart Mill, had looked forward to a Utopia in which human beings, freed from the necessity of labour, would be able to concern themselves with less mundane affairs—but Čapek viewed such a proposal with deep suspicion. He fervently believed in the 'dignity of labour'.

The philosophy underlying the setting-up of the factory, however, appears to have had little direct influence on its everyday functioning. The principal concerns of the managers are the maintenance of production standards and the implementation of new models. The design of the robots reflects a thorough cost-accounting, and the play also alludes to the fact that in the field of 'high technology' prices may fall sharply: 'A hundred and fifty dollars each fully dressed, and fifteen years ago they cost ten thousand.' Several different types of machine are manufactured, some more sophisticated and more expensive than others, and the design of those models produced for use in offices and public places takes account of aesthetic as well as purely functional factors. Thus the R.U.R. factory is creating a total 'product'. Commercial aspects dominate and every care is taken to enhance consumer appeal.

A number of reasons are implied for the fact that the machines have a humanoid form. One of these is historical—Young Rossum's first machine was a surrogate for his uncle's biological humanoid—but the main factors are ergonomic and psychological. Robots are able to take over more easily in a factory environment designed for human beings if they are of similar build. And people find it easier to accept their place beside new 'workers' if these appear in familiar guise. When Helena asks why the robots are manufactured with a recognizable sex, rather than as 'neutral', she is told that there is a certain demand. People expect servants, salespeople and stenographers to be women, and so are happier if robots performing these tasks look the part. Thus the design of particular models reflects the stereotypes of the human beings they are designed to replace.

A major consequence of the realistic humanoid appearance is that people show a high degree of empathy towards the robots. This is illustrated by Helena's horror at the proposal that Sulla be dissected. Her feelings rule over her rationality, and the reaction depends on the fact that the robot looks like a human being and behaves in a human way. If Sulla were presented 'honestly' as a machine then the 'dissection' would have been regarded as a 'dismantling' and would not have elicited an empathic response. Here Čapek provides an insight which is likely to be corroborated in future studies of the psychological impact of real robots.

Taken literally, Čapek's play is about the overthrow of humankind by a powerful race of robots. This theme had literary exposure before *R.U.R.* and has since been echoed in several works of SF. There are two subvariations of it, those of 'evolution' and 'revolution'. Butler's *Erewhon* had depicted machine evolution outpacing human development, with human beings therefore becoming the inferior species. Often the crucial dimension of such an evolving superiority is seen as intelligence. This would seem relevant to the real future, for most of those who have seriously examined the likely ultimate impact of computer technology and AI have come to believe that the eventual intellectual superiority of electronic systems is inevitable. Opinions differ sharply, however, about whether this must result in the social dominance of a machine race. In Čapek's play a different theme is followed. Having developed 'emotionally' the robots achieve a sense of 'moral indignation' about their status and seize control by force in order to improve their lot. Their political revolution and guerilla action therefore stem from a grievance about their lack of 'civil rights'.

R.U.R. thus provided a political motive for the revolution. Later treatments of humanoid uprising rarely include such justifications as the marauding mechanical hordes hack and laser their way across the pages of pulp SF magazines. Čapek's creations do not lack honour, and the play thus raises a fundamental issue. Is there some point at which machines, by virtue of their level of 'intelligence' or 'awareness', become 'moral entities' and should be accorded civil rights? Philosophers have discussed the question for many years. Although there is little consensus on the matter, some say certainly that, when machines reach a certain criterion level of sophistication, they should be regarded as moral agents and given rights. The issue remains unresolved. A less difficult, though related, question is whether people will treat machines *as if* they were morally responsible and deserving of moral consideration. The answer to this is almost certainly 'yes'. When an 'aware' humanoid machine speaks, listens, and reacts with apparent feeling, motive and understanding, people will treat it as culpable, praiseworthy and responsible for its actions. It must be expected that when robots are designed to elicit 'social' reactions they will evoke the full spectrum of moral responses. Machines will be commended and condemned. We will censure and honour them.

R.U.R. raises the spectre of robot revolt without seriously considering the possibilities of control. Later writers who have focussed on such aspects generally present a much more optimistic picture. The play's allegorical purpose did not encourage Čapek to think about the 'take-over' theme in a problem-solving way and he could be accused, in his staging of the revolution, of opting for an easy theatrical device. The ultimate importance of the play may stem from its imagery rather than its intended message. This is not what Čapek would have wished yet, in drawing upon the powerful concept of the artificial humanoid, he invited the danger that his message might be obscured by the audience's fascination for the robot characters. The meaning *was* obscured, and the author complained that his work had been misunderstood. One of the reasons why *R.U.R.* is important, however, is precisely that it had such an immediate impact, that it demonstrated once again how the humanoid concept can captivate an audience. This fact has been heavily underscored in recent years by the phenomenal popularity of robot films.

Čapek was aware of the link between the robots in his play and the ancient tradition of life-creation. His account of the attempts by Old Rossum and Young Rossum to create humanoids reflects the transition in the literary heritage from the biological to the technological, from creation to simulation. It is also noticeable that Young Rossum saw his engineering project as merely another means of attaining his uncle's goal; he seems not to have realized that the two projects had very different aims. His uncle had been striving to create life while he himself was merely simulating the behaviour of living things. Thus his own aims were much more modest—and are similar to the ambitions of present-day roboticists.

Lines of Evolution

Four works have now been examined in some detail and each of them contributed in a major way to the robot heritage. *Frankenstein* gave the humanoid a developed character and made the transition from the ancient art of alchemy to orthodox science. Victor Frankenstein, however, was intent on creating life. The materials he used were organic and the science he pursued was biology. 'The Sandman' followed another path. Here the humanoid was constructed by means of clockwork technology and the aim was perfect simulation. The author used automata engineering as his technical source but his robot Olympia was a rather characterless machine. Hoffmann was interested in the fact that even simple mechanisms, given an attractive appearance and a few typically human skills, could elicit emotional responses. *L'Ève future* drew upon more advanced technology. It incorporated and extrapolated from current innovations in applied technology which seemed to offer the promise of a more realistic and flexible simulation. Villiers' robot was a mechanical construction, but it had character and emotional display and as a result Hadaly was more 'sociable' and 'softer' than Olympia. She was responsive, 'intelligent' and 'aware'. *L'Ève future* also introduced the idea that humanoids would one day be items of mass production, designed to act as companions and workers. *R.U.R.* portrayed such an industrial scene and further explored commercial aspects. The Rossum robots, too, developed 'consciousness', becoming aware of themselves and of their plight.

Thus within the literary robot heritage certain major lines of evolution can be recognized. The ancient dream of life-creation produced many variations on the humanoid theme. Frequently, animation and simulation were hardly distinguished, but eventually the goal of simulation gained a clear literary predominance. Many different arts and sciences were invoked to describe the creation of the humanoid. In the earliest times representational art was endowed with a magical significance. Then special occult practices were explored. Magic and the occult were gradually overtaken by more orthodox approaches to chemistry and biology. The simulation goal, which gradually gained ascendancy, focussed attention on engineering technology and drew upon developments in that field. The early methods described for simulation, employing wheels and levers and hydraulic power, were replaced first by delicate clockwork and then by electromagnetics.

By the 1920s the robot encountered in literature had gained 'consciousness', a variety of roles, a future as a product, and a name. The robot heritage had introduced all of the major themes that were to receive a more thorough exploration by later SF authors. But we cannot pretend that by the 1920s the heritage presented an auspicious heralding of the future of robot products. The humanoids who had made the most impact were an unwholesome lot. Frankenstein's creation may have been a rebel with a cause, his heart set initially in the right place, but he soon turned into the kind of humanoid to be avoided at all costs: he was hardly a satisfactory prototype for a companion product. Olympia lacked malice—but, being little more than a doll, she lacked most things. She would hardly prove a lively or useful addition to the home. The market potential of the robots of *R.U.R.* would have remained high had their eventual revengeful actions not been witnessed. Only the device produced to give sexual pleasure, Hadaly, can be said to have any semblance of a pleasant nature. Villiers alone of the authors seems to have had other than a totally negative view of the robot, and even he showed considerable ambivalence.

While the themes established within the heritage before the modern era remain central to contemporary robot fiction, the image of the robot has changed fundamentally. The dominant personality features of today's popular robot characters, their friendliness, usefulness and loyalty, were evident in early works, but only just—the horrible and intimidating features were much more obvious. There was to be a major reformation of the robot

image over the next 60 years. The simulation humanoids produced by earlier engineering methods, and without divine aid,
had already shown a progressive 'awareness' and responsivity
to their environment. Hadaly and the Rossum robots were able to
respond flexibly to their environment; they were able to announce
their hopes and aspirations and to present their point of view.
Thus by the turn of the century the artificial humanoids of
literature possessed 'awareness' and had a voice. They were
more 'human' than their forebears, but they had yet to become
'humane'.

FOUR
Asimov the Lawmaker

The Promise of Pulp

We have reached the early 1920s. The era of 'genre science fiction' has yet to begin. The first of the 'pulp magazines' devoted to SF, Hugo Gernsback's *Amazing Stories*, will first be published in 1926. He will follow this with *Amazing Stories Quarterly* (1928), *Science Wonder Stories* (1929) and *Air Wonder Stories* (1930). Other publishers will soon enter the field, and before long a score of monthly anthologies will appear on the newsstands. Visual images will now become important, as talented illustrators vie with one another to produce the most evocative, bizarre and gruesome cover art. The themes of SF are set to reach a mass public via magazine, novel, film and eventually television. A thousand planets will be discovered, many of them populated by creatures of fantastic shape and strange habit. Countless variations will be played upon the central themes of robot fiction and, slowly at first but with gathering momentum, the dominant image of the robot will change from one of villainy to one of virtue.

Now, some sixty years after the early explosion of pulp periodicals, the volume of robot fiction has become vast. No single analysis could give a comprehensive account of the field. The aim here is less extensive and more sharply focussed. It is not to present a literary survey but to examine ideas which may predict and help to shape the future of product robots. Principal interest therefore centres on portrayals of synthetically produced, Earth-based androids which bear some resemblance to the real 'product robots' expected in the near future. We are concerned with how writers portray the characters and response-styles of these machines and how the robots are shown to interact with people. Coverage can thus be limited to those works which are judged as making a significant contribution towards clarifying the image of the ideal product. The effect of applying this criterion is to prune severely the immense database of SF writing and film.

Many works merely reiterate old images and old ideas, but others are truly innovative or present well exploited themes with a new illuminating intensity.

Science fiction should not be used as a source of technical forecasting: that is neither its purpose nor its strength. But it is a useful source of ideas about how technology might be used and about its effect on individual human responses and on society. No psychologist has yet had the opportunity to test human reactions to a sophisticated 'robot stimulus', for the very good reason that such systems do not as yet exist. The effects of such devices are therefore open to speculation and indirect sources of information have to be called upon. One such source is SF.

Literature often provides psychological insights. We are concerned to isolate and examine the insights contained in robot fiction, for these are likely to provide valid indicators of the robot features that human beings will find appealing. Such 'attractiveness' will guide the development of future products, provided the features meet the criteria of technical and economic viability. Thus, to the extent that SF writers are accurate in their psychological insight, and if they are mindful of scientific plausibility, they may provide sound indicators of future products.

The work of certain key authors, and later of key film directors, will be considered in some detail. The ultimate aim, however, remains application rather than appreciation. The historical treatment of the heritage has isolated basic themes and lent perspective to the 20th-century explosion in robot fiction. The previous analyses have been organized chronologically, and it has thus been possible to trace an evolution of ideas. But so much has happened within the brief span of the past 60 years that it is preferable to structure the modern database thematically.

There can be no better way of beginning the analysis of recent works than by considering the contribution of an author who is, without any doubt, a central figure in the history of robot literature. Isaac Asimov has probably influenced the public image of the robot more than any other single writer or thinker, living or dead. Many of the themes he presents, and the ideas he elucidates, had been well established in the robot heritage long before he started writing. But he brings, even to the oldest themes, a new lucidity and he is, moreover, unashamedly positive in his regard for robots. This makes a refreshing change from the hostility and ambivalence which have characterized the authors of the principal works considered so far.

Isaac Asimov

Asimov was born in Russia in 1920 and was taken to the US by his parents at the age of three. His father opened a candy and newspaper store and this gave the young Isaac the opportunity to browse at leisure through pulp magazines, including those containing SF. Thus by the time he went to university he was well versed in the genre, and was able to divide his efforts between studying chemistry and attempting to write for publication. His first published story, 'Marooned off Vesta', appeared in *Amazing Stories* in 1939. In the same year he graduated and visited the World Fair in New York at which Westinghouse Electric Corporation was exhibiting 'Electro', a motorized metal robot which could respond in a limited way to spoken commands. After the war Asimov returned to university, gained a doctorate in biochemistry and worked as an associate professor (a title which he still retains) before devoting himself full-time to writing in 1958.

A prolific writer, he has now published some 200 books covering a wide range of popular science and SF. His themes and style are relatively 'naturalistic' and much influenced by genuine science, about which he conveys an almost unbounded optimism. Consequently his fictional worlds remain free of Bug-Eyed Monsters and revolting technology and are populated instead by helpful, friendly and responsible robots. Asimov has now written some 40 stories and novels featuring robots and computers, and his work has had a major influence on many other writers in the field. He can be seen as the foremost 'public relations officer' for robots and has introduced into the English language a number of terms that have entered into general and technical usage. His friends include leading scientists within the fields of AI and 'robotics' (a term he introduced), and many have paid tribute to his contribution. He has made long-term efforts to overcome any reservations which the public may still have regarding robots.

Recognizing the negative image encouraged by earlier writers, Asimov protests against their portrayal of robots as a potential threat to humankind and emphasizes the sharp contrast of his own work: 'My robots were machines designed by engineers, not pseudo-men created by blasphemers.' The guarantee of non-hostility is provided by a postulated code of robot conduct, the 'Laws of Robotics', which forms a framework for many of

Asimov's stories. The Laws are designed to protect human beings from any harm resulting from the action of a robot. They are said to be indelibly written into the nucleus of the computer hardware, the 'platinum-iridium sponge' that forms the 'positronic brain' of the machine. Only robots with this powerful safeguard are produced, and they are manufactured exclusively by United States Robots and Mechanical Men, Inc.

Despite Asimov's insistence that he is not creating 'pseudo-men', many of his stories do focus on a confusion between robots and people. He often incorporates realistic human features into the machines and relentlessly explores the effects of the resulting ambiguity. Some of the characters introduced as 'robots' are later revealed to be people, sometimes 'humans' turn out to be robots, and on occasion the reader is left in a state of uncertainty. This 'confusion theme' has become a standard one in the body of robot literature and there are many earlier examples. Asimov takes the discussion to a new level of philosophical sophistication in several of his works. It forms the basis, for example, of several of the subplots that make up the intricate narrative of the novel *The Caves of Steel* (1954).

The same theme is encountered in several of his short stories. The plot of 'Evidence' (1946) concerns whether a prominent politician is a man or a machine. Thirty years later the idea was reworked in 'Tercentenary Incident' (1976). There are rumours that a robot simulacrum of the US President has been constructed to perform ceremonial functions without the risk of assassination. The general public is unaware of the substitution and is therefore alarmed when on Tercentenary Day an attempt ends with the 'President' disintegrating into a cloud of dust. But Asimov is not content to present the situation in such an unambiguous fashion, so an investigator is introduced to put forward an alternative interpretation of events. He claims that the real President has been destroyed and that the country is now presided over by a robot.

In the majority of Asimov's robot works the humanoids are easily recognized as machines and the problem of confusion does not arise. But even when the real nature of the robot is not in doubt Asimov often adds features which powerfully 'humanize' the machine. The robot body-shells may be made of realistic silicone plastic with synthetic hair and nails, but the most effective enhancements are personality characteristics. By concentrating on hardware and software features peripheral to the basic functioning of the machine, but which have a telling effect on the human responses to the device, Asimov is able to create memorable characters with essentially human 'personalities' and foibles. 'Liar!' (1941), for example, introduces 'Herbie', a robot with an antipathy towards mathematics and a weakness for slushy novels.

Not surprisingly, such engaging characters often stimulate powerful emotional attachments in the humans who interact with them. In his first robot story, 'Robbie' (originally published in 1940 with the title 'Strange Playfellow'), the machine listens in rapt attention while his eight-year-old playmate reads him his favourite fairy story. 'Again!' says Gloria. 'I've told you Cinderella a million times. Aren't you tired of it—It's for babies.' Robbie not only appears to enjoy all manner of playful pastimes but responds 'emotionally' to signs of approval and disapproval, and when sent away by Gloria's reproachful mother he leaves 'with a disconsolate step'. The father tries to dispel his wife's fears about the machine: 'Robbie was constructed for only one purpose really—to be the companion of a little child. His entire "mentality" has been created for that purpose. He just can't help being faithful and kind.'

Robbie's impact on the little girl is extreme, even for a companion machine. She prefers his company to that of other children and when the unfeeling mother finally ousts Robbie the child is inconsolable. A dog introduced as a substitute does little to improve the situation and, when the mother tells her not to cry about the loss of the 'nasty old machine', Gloria screams back: 'He was *not* no machine. He was a *person* like you and me and he was my *friend*. I want him back. Oh, Mamma, I want him back.'

Adults, too, are shown to be susceptible to deep emotional attraction towards robots. Several stories include a detailed description of the development of personal relationships between the machines and their human users. Such attachments may be 'friendly', 'maternal' or 'romantic'. The character Susan Calvin, a psychologist who specializes in the psychology of robots, tends to treat advanced machines as colleagues rather than as scientific tools, and in 'Lenny' (1958) she teaches a retarded robot to speak. Its first words are 'Mommie, I want you. I want you, Mommie', and the robopsychologist hurries longingly towards 'the only kind of baby she could ever have or love'.

Most of Asimov's robots are 'male' and this limits the possibilities for human-machine romantic and sexual relationships. No 'ideal female machine' appears in his work, no 'future Eve', and his only 'female' robot of note—Jane, in the 1969 story 'Feminine Intuition'—lacks clear sexual characteristics. Scientists are attempting to develop a robot capable of making 'intuitive' judgements and one of them suggests that it would be appropriate for such a machine to be characterized as 'female'. Asimov is aware of the sexism inherent in this notion and later has Susan Calvin react scornfully to the suggestion. Jane's voice is programmed to be conventional rather than sexy, but nevertheless the 'sweet contralto' has a remarkable effect on men. When the question of body-shape arises the discussion indicates the sensitivity with which Asimov regards the issue. The notion of adding 'breasts' is rejected by one designer on the grounds that this would bring hostile reactions from women: 'If women start getting the notion that robots may look like women, I can tell you exactly the kind of perverse notions they'll get.' And his colleague agrees: 'No woman wants to feel replaceable by something with none of her faults.' It seems not to have occurred to these robotologists, then, that female robots might prove an attractive commodity. They must be assumed to be blissfully naïve and to have read little SF.

While Asimov ignores discussion of robot 'femmes fatales' he is quite prepared to consider the possibility that a woman might fall in love with one of his realistic 'male' robots, and in 'Satisfaction Guaranteed' (1951) such a romance is examined in detail. US Robots are aiming to market a sophisticated household robot and they test a pilot model in the home of Claire and Larry Belamont. Claire's initial resistance dissolves as she gets to know the tall, dark and handsome robot Tony. She is attracted by his deep mellow voice, his calm politeness and his consideration for her needs, and soon she finds herself confiding her emotional problems to him. The attraction grows rapidly and the robot's presence begins to affect her profoundly: 'Claire felt something tight inside her . . . Why did she keep forgetting that he was a machine? . . . Was she so starved for sympathy that she would accept a robot as an equal—because he sympathized?' She trembles at the touch of his warm hand and he comforts her physically when she is distressed: '. . . his arms were around her now; his face was close to hers; the pressure of his embrace was relentless. She heard his voice through a haze of emotional jumble.' US Robots, who are carefully monitoring the effect of their new domestic model, decide that certain modifications will have to be made in order to lessen the emotional impact.

Asimov reported that this story brought him a larger mail than usual and that most of the letters were from young women 'speaking wistfully of Tony'.

In the light of these examples it is difficult to agree with Asimov that he is not creating pseudo-men. He is clearly building a good many 'soft' features into his robot characters. They are designed to be likeable and to win over those people who initially regard them with antagonism. A notable example of such a 'change of heart' occurs in *The Caves of Steel*. Elijah Bailey, a human detective, takes great exception when he learns that his partner on a murder enquiry is to be a robot. His prejudice remains even when it is explained to him that 'the public insists that City robots be built with a strong friendship circuit' and that they are predisposed to smile a lot. The 'friendship circuit' seems to be highly effective, however, for Bailey soon develops a fondness and respect for his mechanical colleague, and at the end of the novel he takes the robot by the elbow and the two walk off arm in arm. Those characters who remain impervious to the charm of the machine attract the writer's venom. They may be scoundrels, fools or cowards, but Asimov will not allow them to be heroes.

The Bicentennial Man

Themes which have a long history in the robot heritage—identity confusion, 'humanization' and human-robot relationships—feature strongly in Asimov's work. He also addresses the issues of robot rights and robot evolution. These are examined in one of the finest of his more recent robot stories, 'The Bicentennial Man', published in 1976. This consolidates much of his earlier thinking on robotics and elaborates a number of issues.

The story has a robot hero, and describes his history over 200 years of service with the Martin family. Introduced into the home as 'NDR', a functional house-robot and 'butler', he soon becomes a family favourite and is named Andrew. The children love to play with him and are especially fascinated by his skill at woodcarving. So unique and finely finished are his creations that he swiftly develops something of a reputation as a sculptor and carpenter. The robopsychologist Merton Mansky (Asimov is here paying a compliment to his friend, the AI expert Marvin Minsky) suggests that Andrew's special talent must be the result of a freak mutation of the microcircuitry of his brain.

His owner realizes that there might be a market for the robot's works of art, and opens a bank account in Andrew's name. With the money Andrew earns he is able to pay for his own repairs and enhancements, but his wealth continues to grow and he finally takes the unprecedented step of asking to buy his freedom. The granting of such liberty is a legal matter and his case comes to court. The Martin family support his plea but the judge is initially unimpressed, maintaining that the concept of 'freedom' has no meaning when applied to a robot. Andrew's eloquence astounds the judge, however, and he finally rules that 'There is no right to deny freedom to any object with a mind advanced enough to grasp the concept and desire the state'.

The robot stays near to the family and has a house built to his own requirements. No bathroom or kitchen is necessary, but it contains a well equipped studio and a library with a fine collection of books on crafts, art and design. He begins to wear clothes, not because he has any practical use for them, but because it makes him feel 'more like a man'. He also plans to read books that will increase his understanding of human affairs, but as he attempts to visit the public library two young men accost him. They order him to take his clothes off and to stand on his head. The Second Law of Robotics, which orders obedience to human commands, forces him to comply, and the ruffians are about to dismantle him when he is rescued. The incident makes a deep impression and Andrew becomes determined to fight for robot rights. His lawyer makes a plea to the court: '. . . a robot is not insensible; it is not an animal. It can think well enough to enable it to talk to us, reason with us, joke with us. Can we treat them as friends, and not give them some of the fruit of that friendship, some of the benefit of co-working? . . . With great power goes great responsibility, and if the robots have Three Laws to protect men, is it too much to ask that men have a law or two to protect robots?' Finally the court agrees and the principle of robot rights is established.

Andrew has been writing a book, the history of robots from the robot perspective, and he plans to use the royalties to replace his ageing mechanical body. He wants an organic android structure in which to house his positronic brain but the manufacturers—US Robots—refuse his request. He is already something of an embarrassment to them and they fear that the robot rights established through his efforts will have the effect of making their products less desirable. Under pressure they finally agree, and after a long series of operations Andrew's metal shell is replaced with the type of body he has longed for. He is happier as a result of this, but still has not found complete satisfaction. By now generations of Martins have passed and Andrew has witnessed them growing from childhood to adulthood, and finally dying. He realizes that mortality is a necessary condition of humanness, and he finally sacrifices his deathless inorganic brain, thus paying the ultimate price for the granting of his greatest wish—to be as nearly human as possible.

Contrasted with some of Asimov's other stories 'The Bicentennial Man' is somewhat restrained. Andrew's relationships with people, for example, are cordial rather than intimate; his skills—except for his wood-carving—appear to be modest, and in character he is gentle and calm rather than flamboyant. Although he could be said to be somewhat confused about his own nature and identity, even after 200 years of enhancement and development, his form and behaviour still remain easily distinguishable from those of human beings. So one of Asimov's most frequent themes, that of confusion, is absent from the story and as a consequence it is more realistic.

Asimov could be accused of being too restrained. During 200 years of robot development it might be expected, justifiably, that robots would be capable of more 'miraculous' feats and that developments in technology would make more impact on human society than those portrayed in this story. There is no suggestion that robots or other developments have led to any major revolution in manners. Far from being dominant, robots still seem to occupy the familiar butler role and human beings, with the notable exception of the two ruffians, hold Andrew in affectionate respect. But in all of the relationships he develops with people casualness and 'distance' are maintained. He does not appear to meet other robots and he does little to encourage intimacy with human beings. There are no torrid love scenes, no weeping women who have fallen in love with him or children who treat him as anything more than a friend and playmate. The hallmark of humanness is mortality rather than, for example, the ability to maintain a personal relationship with a human being. The criterion is biological rather than social or psychological, and even when Andrew comes to possess genitalia these are prized for their 'decorative' rather than 'functional' quality. There is no hint that the robot will use his newfound accoutrements to penetrate further into the social order.

Although Andrew displays 'emotions' and frequently uses words which describe 'feelings' (he 'enjoys' producing his sculptures and claims that freedom would bring 'joy' to his life), he is conscious that in using such terms he may not be describing the states experienced by human beings. This is typical of his caution and seriousness, for Andrew is a rather reserved character and is at no time portrayed as a clown or an eccentric. He displays an unmistakeable self-consciousness and is cruelly humiliated by the two ruffians. In his fight to establish legal rights for robots Andrew shows a grim determination, and over the years he develops more self-assurance, yet he never achieves a firm sense of identity. He never attains a sense of 'robot pride', and shows no inclination to organize the metal minority to fight for civil rights. He might champion the robot cause but personally he has but one desire—to be a man.

Politically the robot is bidding, at most, for equality and he maintains a fine sense of justice and a healthy respect for humankind. There are no intimations of imminent threat from Andrew, or of any desire on his part to dominate or take over. He wishes for nothing more, or less, than to be accepted as a citizen with equal rights. In avoiding all hint of aggressiveness or militarism Asimov is maintaining his firm rejection of the 'Frankenstein complex'.

The lack of threat in this story, however, maintains credibility only by virtue of certain special features. Andrew is not endowed with superhuman powers. His skills are artistic rather than intellectual, and there is nothing to suggest that he is a member of a 'superior race'. Asimov could be accused of ignoring technological realism at this point, for if a robot of Andrew's level of sophistication were produced it would hardly be likely to match the profile of talents depicted. If the machine had the ability to write a book, for example, it would not have to slave for months over the production as Andrew did. Why is the robot not portrayed as an 'intellectual giant' when the technology which has given him birth would clearly be capable of making him extremely intelligent? The most plausible explanation is that the robot has been designed as a product with a specific range of roles and functions. He does not represent the 'state of the art' in artificial 'intelligence', and is deliberately designed *not* to have powers that might intimidate his human owners. The danger of threat is also curtailed by the fact that Andrew is unique in his robot-class and does not interact with robot peers. This isolation is convenient for the purpose of the story but it may not represent the real future state of affairs: it will undoubtedly prove useful to have robots in communication with one another. Thus in several respects 'The Bicentennial Man' lacks a certain credibility.

Asimov's stories contain elements of fantasy and caricature, but these are used to illustrate points about future reality. He believes that technology, and robots in particular, can help to bring the world nearer to a Utopia. Yet he does not ignore the problems that may arise in the product-robot future; rather, he is concerned to identify such issues and to deal with them. He clearly sees this as a task of some importance, for he believes that the characteristics of his fictional robots will be technically realized. But Asimov is well aware that there are many possible futures, and his stories explore the implications of alternatives. They portray highly contrasting policies for manufacture, a wide range of robot 'characters', and a broad spectrum of human responses. And, whereas other writers generally present a single state of robot development, Asimov implies that there will be several generations of humanoid artefacts and that their characteristics, and the problems raised, are likely to be very different as the various stages of robot evolution unfold.

A special feature of 'The Bicentennial Man' is that such a course of development is presented within a single story. During the 200-year history the corporate philosophy of US Robots and Mechanical Men, Inc., has been significantly revised, reflecting changes in the social attitudes to their products. Far from celebrating Andrew's artistic achievements the corporation is embarrassed by his existence. His talent stems from an uncontrolled variation in the standard brain circuitry and more precise methods of manufacture have now been adopted to ensure that 'freaks' such as Andrew are not produced. And, although the company has experimented with the production of highly realistic androids, it soon reverted to less 'human' devices, though no indication is given of why the 'natural' humanoids proved unpopular. The corporation has also developed a strategy for avoiding problems which have arisen when robots have resided with a family for generations: they now recall and replace their models after 25 years. Andrew has thus become the oldest robot in existence.

The corporation is also highly sensitive on the issue of 'robot rights', fearing that people will see in such a development the danger of losing control over their domestic machine. This implies that owners would prefer to treat their robots as 'property', to be used and abused at will, rather than as 'sentient creatures' protected by law. There is a further suggestion that an entirely new form of home robot may be introduced, controlled by microwave from a central computer. Body and brain would thus be disconnected and a single computer would communicate simultaneously with hundreds of dependent 'automatons' located within households. This is an interesting suggestion from Asimov, for he is uncharacteristically raising the spectre of 'Big Brother'. Indeed the story is most disturbing in this aspect, for the most ardent defender of robots, and their greatest apologist, is here suggesting that a phase of homely independent characterful devices may ultimately be replaced by one of centrally controlled, 'faceless' machines. While Andrew is a hero, a pleasant, lively and sensitive machine, those which come after him are portrayed in a much less favourable light. Asimov's frequently offered invitation to a golden future enhanced by colourful robots takes on a hint of ill-omen. Even he, it seems, can wonder whether there might not be some dark danger lurking at the end of the pleasant journey.

Case Law

Asimov has long been aware of the need to ensure that robots are unfailingly humanitarian in their actions. While other authors have portrayed the machines as devils, or at least as sinners, Asimov has tried to secure humankind against any possibility of machine malevolence. He has used for this purpose a literary device which probably constitutes his most important single contribution to the literary robot scene, his 'Three Laws of Robotics'. These state:

   1 A robot may not injure a human being or, through inaction, allow a human being to come to harm.
   2 A robot must obey the orders given it by human beings except where such orders would conflict with the First Law.
   3 A robot must protect its own existence as long as such protection does not conflict with the First or Second Law.

The Laws were developed by Asimov and the SF editor John

W. Campbell at the end of 1940, and have since been used by many writers. Asimov has remarked that the 61 words of the Laws have given rise to a flood of story-lines, and they have certainly provided him with several of the major themes of his own fiction. Some of his later stories are extended examinations of the implications of the Laws, essays of ideas thinly disguised as fiction.

During his explorations Asimov has come to realize that there are many problems in applying the Laws to complex human situations. His first robot story written after their formulation was 'Runaround' (1942), and in it he identifies one of the difficulties. Human beings have ordered the robot Speedy to approach a dangerous situation but Speedy faces a dilemma, caught between obeying the Second Law (of obedience) and the Third Law (of self-protection), and is ambivalent in his actions. The problem is resolved when one of the scientists deliberately puts himself in danger. The powerful First Law (preventing harm befalling any human being) takes precedence over the other two and the robot overcomes his irresolution. Thus a neat solution is found for this predicament.

In 'Evidence' Susan Calvin is called in to help to decide whether a prominent politician is a human or a robot. Her attempt to assess his true nature involves an application of the Laws. She explains that if the politician obeys the Laws he could be either a human or a robot. If the Laws are disobeyed, however, he cannot be a robot and must therefore be a man. When the politician is goaded into punching an opponent that seems to end the matter, but not quite. Susan Calvin explains that the only time that a robot might appear to break the First Law is when the 'person' harmed is not a human being but a simulacrum robot. Not uncharacteristically, Asimov leaves the reader with lingering doubts about the true nature of the central figure.

The Laws are intended to be a guarantee. Their apparent straightforwardness, however, conceals a number of practical problems. Asimov is concerned to explore these and, by offering solutions, to maintain the security offered by his original formulation. But at times he does come close to exposing loopholes. Such unreliability is starkly exposed in 'That Thou Art Mindful of Him' (1974). In this story robots are said to work on colonized planets. The human scientists who have used them have had full knowledge of the Laws and have behaved in such a way that the machines have not been presented with problematic situations.

When they are to be introduced on Earth, however, it is realized that the robots must be able to cope with any dilemma that might occur in a totally 'natural' environment. Robots have never, for example, been given conflicting orders by two human beings. They must learn how to assess the relative expertise, virtue and 'value' of different people.

There is also a problem about how to make robots acceptable to a general population that is antagonistic towards them. The question is put to a pair of sophisticated robots, George Nine and George Ten, and their deliberations soon lead them to a consideration of the three Laws. They perceive a suspicion by human beings that robots are in competition with them, and they suggest that this may be overcome gradually by initially replacing all humanoid robots with animal robots which will have an ecological function—'earthworm robots', for example, will help to condition the soil. After this, they suggest, the number of robot species should be gradually increased, ascending the evolutionary scale, so that the range finally includes androids. This solution of 'gradual exposure' is accepted, but it becomes apparent that the 'Georges' were inspired by an ulterior motive. They reasoned that the essential criterion for 'humanness' is not shape or material composition but the ability to reason at a high level. Thus the robots consider themselves to be 'human beings'. Further, they have been programmed to judge the relative worth of different humans and they consider that they themselves possess the finest qualities of character and intelligence. They therefore give priority to their own interests rather than to those of the 'other humans' and their 'robot-evolution' strategy is a means of achieving their own ends.

Far less substantial than this important story is the playful 'First Law' (1956). This suggests that the powerful First Law might be transgressed in the face of a robot's 'maternal feeling'. The tale is slight, but it is interesting that the Laws are challenged satirically as well as seriously. The system of Laws is presented more as a 'working paper' than as a final solution. The author recognizes the crucial need for a safeguard but does not underestimate the difficulties in making such a system foolproof.

The nature of the Laws has often been misinterpreted. In principle robots could be preprogrammed to obey a wide range of alternative systems of rules, including many which would make fiendish characters of the machines. There are many stories in which evil or misguided scientists produce such menaces, but

Asimov does not write such tales. He suggests that robots will be manufactured by responsible organizations with a vested interest in producing attractive and fear-assuaging products. These are highly plausible premises, and contradict the ideas implicit in the 'evil robot' scenarios. Put simply, there is good cause to believe that 'benign' and 'friendly' robots will be produced and that 'malevolent' or 'aggressive' robots will not. This echoes Asimov's total rejection of the 'Frankenstein complex' and highlights the fact that the dismissal rests ultimately on confidence in the good sense of individuals, corporations and legislators. The safeguard resides in human proclivities and in the nature of marketing organizations. It is not inherent in the technology of robotics.

The Laws therefore have an interesting status. They are moral, rather than physical, imperatives and may easily be broken, just as the laws of a country may be transgressed. But Asimov's provision for building a representation of the Laws into the positronic-brain circuitry ensures that robots are physically prevented from contravening them. The hardware simply prevents the machines from being sinners. Because the Laws of Robotics cannot be disobeyed they are unlike the laws which regulate human society, but in their content they share many features with common moral systems. Asimov is aware of this parallel. In 'Evidence' Susan Calvin maintains that the Laws are '. . . the essential guiding principles of a good many of the world's ethical systems'. The First Law is parallel to the moral rule concerned with 'treating others as yourself', the Second relates to deference to proper authority, and the Third is concerned with self-preservation. The difference is that, while robots invariably obey the rules, human beings do not. Perhaps this is the reason why Susan Calvin maintains: 'I like robots, I like them considerably more than human beings.'

In *The Cybernetic Imagination in Science Fiction* Patricia Warrick has commented: 'Asimov's significant accomplishment is that the drama he has created with the Three Laws has set us thinking. Perhaps in the real world ethical concepts could be operationalized in computer technology. No other science-fiction writer has given the world that vision.' As long as computers and industrial robots are under direct programmed control there is clearly no need for 'moral' constraints to be placed upon them. They are essentially tools and instruments, and any 'misdeed' can be attributed to oversight or misuse by a responsible human. When the age of free-ranging robots comes, however, and when they are able to 'decide' between courses of action, then general rules for their conduct will be needed. Thus some version of the Laws may well be realized in future robot generations, and it can be assumed that whatever their specific form they will be susceptible to the kinds of problems that Asimov has identified. His stories thus explore questions of central relevance to the product-robot future.

Master in Perspective

The enormous sales of Asimov's books testify to the popularity of his stories, and he has also received considerable critical acclaim. Yet popularity and celebrity are not criteria by which we can judge his importance to the literary robot heritage. He has contributed to it both directly, through his fiction, and indirectly, by his popular-science writing and his influence on other SF authors. We are not here concerned to provide a literary critique of his fiction but rather to assess his contribution to the literature of ideas. This places his work in the best possible light, for while he is not an exceptional stylist he has provided a number of profound arguments and original concepts. His special skill lies in identifying problems that may arise from technological innovation and in devising ways for resolving such difficulties. The problems with which he is principally concerned are not intrinsically technical but bear on the *human* implications of technological change.

Asimov is genuinely concerned about the real future for humanity, and has strenuously defended both the viability and desirability of a roboticized society. He would maintain that fear of such a development is irrational and might seriously curb the attainment of human potential. His stories, as a whole, represent an attempt to desensitize readers against such 'robophobia'. This is achieved both by presenting robots as wholesome and attractive characters and by attempting to allay apprehension regarding the imminent power of the machines. He was one of a number of writers in the 1940s who came to depict robots, against the prevailing image, as benevolent and harmless creatures, and future generations of robots may well come to applaud his influence in changing public attitudes towards their kind. In Fritz Leiber's *The Silver Eggheads* (1958) the robots make reference to 'Saint Karel' and 'Saint Isaac'. While the allusion to Čapek is a little curious in view of the dramatist's rather ambivalent attitude towards the machines, the robots' canonization of Asimov can more readily be appreciated.

Even in its most adventurous and most playful moments Asimov's writing maintains its contact with reality. The author writes with the background of a trained scientist and, although he takes advantage of the freedom offered by the fictional mode, he always works within the constraints of scientific plausibility (or, at least, the limits set by the 'conventions' of SF—which limits, of course, embrace such implausibilities as time travel). It is hardly surprising, therefore, that many of his copious ideas have an air of genuine technical speculation and that some of his stories contain insightful elaborations of the latest scientific aims. Thus, when in the late 1960s the first experiments with 'expert systems' had just begun, Asimov was writing of such a system in 'Feminine Intuition' (1969). In their search for the most effective means of identifying habitable planets, scientists recognize the limitations of those methods which rely only on straightforward computation, and see the need for a system involving greater 'sensitivity'. This leads them towards the idea of an 'intuitive' robot which might arrive at useful 'guesses' by making use of many kinds of 'living information', including tones of voice, data on side issues and even apparent irrelevancies. Asimov refers to one of the major advantages that such a system would have over the human expert—that it would always be able to provide a precise account of how it had arrived at a conclusion.

His stories are not, however, merely exercises of technical invention or extrapolation, and Asimov focusses heavily on human aspects. The tales are set in the context of a society controlled by human beings for human purposes, and the robots are subject to human command. In depicting human-robot relationships he realizes that different people will respond to sophisticated systems in different ways, and he does not underestimate the difficulties of making robots universally acceptable. In some stories the machines are said to be banished from Earth because people are antagonistic towards them, but in others people and robots seem to coexist quite happily. Asimov is also quite specific about the fact that, while some people will respond to robots as machines, others will treat them as if they were people. At one point Susan Calvin passionately defends the humanoids in the face of human cynicism: 'To you, a robot is a robot. Gears and metal, electricity and positrons . . . but you haven't worked with them, so you don't know them. They're a cleaner, better breed than we are.'

It is especially fascinating that Calvin is shown as 'humanizing' robots in this way. Asimov, in attributing such responses to his leading robot expert, provides a clear opinion on a contentious issue. It might be imagined that those who understand the technical reality of robots would be somewhat immune to their charm. Asimov suggests otherwise. In his stories, the technically sophisticated are no less likely than the 'naïve' to humanize the robot, but they are less liable to respond to them with fear. The reaction of the general public to the machines, on the other hand, may be hostile. This presents a major problem to the manufacturers, US Robots, who are shown as highly sensitive to public reaction. They are cautious in introducing new models and quick to withdraw a robot which is causing problems. They thus maintain stringent 'public-acceptability control' at all times.

Asimov's concern with the corporation is a welcome facet of his work. He describes the evolution of policy, the internal political wrangling and the emphasis on public relations. There are frequent disagreements between the higher levels of management and the scientists working on new models. In all of these aspects Asimov portrays a plausible large organization. But the assumption that US Robots has a monopoly in robotics is surely a simplistic literary convenience designed to narrow the field of discussion. An early story, it is true, includes an account of a rival corporation, Consolidated Robots, but the impression given in most of the stories is that US Robots *is* robotics. Asimov thereby gives himself no chance of considering what may well prove to be a crucial element in the development of product robots: competition.

Computer technology is now heavily researched in hundreds of universities and hundreds of companies across the world. There is fast and furious competition in product development and marketing. Although certain major companies may well come to dominate the scene, there seems little likelihood that competition will disappear as humanoid robots become viable products. And if this is the case then competition will play a major role in robot evolution. There will be a race to implement the latest technical developments. Hundreds of different models may be introduced and all companies will learn from the marketing successes and failures of their rivals, making the process of evolution a rapid one.

Asimov's limited vision of commercial reality might also be partly responsible for the depth of his reservations about the public acceptability of robots. It can surely be assumed that in a vibrant commercial context such an inherently desirable product as a multipurpose intelligent machine will be made available in such a variety of forms that all potential consumers will be able to find a model to suit them. Perhaps the qualms which Asimov appears to have with regard to public reaction are remnants from a former time when the dominant picture of robots was one of menace. Perhaps Asimov himself underestimates the effect which he and other writers and artists have had on transforming the robot image.

Another limitation of his robot tales, and one of which he is himself aware, concerns stages in robot evolution. The ultimate impact of robotics may be far greater than that realized in the stories. The focus of his literary work (and the focus of the present book) is a stage in robot development rather than its end-point. This is acknowledged by Asimov in his nonfiction writing, where on numerous occasions he has suggested that ultimately a machine race will 'out-evolve' the human species. Thus in an essay written in 1978 he stated: 'So it may be that . . . we will be supplanted anyway, and rightly so, for the intelligent machines to which we will give birth may, better than we, carry on the striving toward the goal of understanding and using the universe, climbing to new heights we ourselves could never aspire to.' Thus the criticism may be levelled at Asimov that he never portrays, in his fiction, the robot domination which he believes will finally emerge. His fictional robot characters are playmates, colleagues and servants rather than intellectual masters. He who has done so much to calm fears of revolutionary take-over by hostile robots is unable and unwilling to provide a similar quelling of fears concerning robot evolution. Indeed, although he ignores it in his fictions, he seems to see it as inevitable and to welcome it. His values, as revealed in his nonfiction writing, cannot be judged humanitarian. In the last analysis he subscribes to the view that what really matter are intelligence, knowledge and truth. If artificial systems have a greater capacity with respect to these than human beings then they should be valued more. Many will find this vision highly disturbing, particularly as it comes from the man who has done so much to comfort the world about the robot future.

FIVE
Archetypal Artefacts

Robot Roles

The robot heritage is not a collection of isolated works but a body of literature with striking overlaps and frequent reworkings of major themes. Some of the remarkable coherence and consensus within the writing generally passes without comment. Thus most robots are depicted as humanoids with a wide range of human faculties. Almost all of the robots in SF stories are highly advanced machines. They have well developed locomotion and vision, a degree of intelligence, a powerful memory and a humanlike character. Most, though not all, are obedient, unassuming and faithful, and seem to prefer the company of humans to that of their own kind. There are exceptions to each of these generalizations but most apply to the majority of fictional robots.

A number of factors clearly contribute to this consensus. By now there is a stereotype of 'the robot' and authors are influenced by former works. But also many robot features simply reflect the shape, functioning and personality of the model which provided the original inspiration for the robot—*Homo sapiens*.

The particular fascination with robots derives from the fact that they are ambiguous figures. They are 'characters'—'people'—but at the same time mechanical objects. They operate simultaneously in two realms—the social realm and the machine realm. The reader is constantly presented with the need to reappraise the situation, as the writer emphasizes first one and then the other aspect of the robot's nature. At one moment a robot character may be placed in a situation which makes it sad, emphasizing its 'human' plight, but within a line or two of text we find that the tear it sheds is in danger of rusting its metallic body. The successful robot character is not totally identified as a 'person' but neither is it completely a machine. It must be an amalgam of two totally different natures. The characteristics of the robot must overlap considerably with those of human beings, yet there must be

106

identifiable differences. These disparities allow the robot to stand out from the human crowd, and they often provide the author with an interesting storyline and engaging images.

As long as the robot is at some stage firmly identified as a machine the writer is free to develop the 'human' side of its nature. The humanoids are not simply 'people': they are generally identifiable as particular human 'types'. There are important sources of variation relating to 'personality' and 'social role'. Thus there are robots which occupy 'age-roles' from baby to grandparent and 'professional roles' from household menial to expert scientist. The literature contains characters who are robot psychiatrists, detectives and priests. There are several robot poets and peasants and also some prostitutes and boxers, barmen and undertakers. There are devices of all personality types and temperaments—depressive, extroverted, shy, confident, manic, reserved—and at all intellectual levels. The robot clan includes slow-witted machines as well as many of formidable intelligence. In 'The Sanatorium of Dr Vliperdius' (1971) Stanislaw Lem exposes the reader to a variety of deranged robots. A robot psychiatric clinic has among its inmates a senile Old Testament computer, a patient who is continually trying to unscrew himself, and another—a robot-hypochondriac—who carries with him a complete set of spare parts. In one ward a group of maniacal robots jump up and down on their beds chanting joyfully: 'We ain't got no ma or pa, 'cause we is au-tom-a-ta.'

Such robots may stand out because of their unorthodox behaviour and their quirky characterization but they do not represent the 'normal' personalities of fictional robots. Authors have explored the far-out regions of possible robot roles, and the originality of a single image has often proved sufficient to maintain interest in a story. But such a fascination with robot freaks should not distract from the major characterizations to be found within the humanoid literature. Principal interest must lie with the dominant robot-personality types that have emerged from stories and films rather than with the rare and eccentric cameos. Robots will become serious business, and our concern is with potential 'product robots'. While there is likely to be little market for specialist poetry machines, or for mechanical priests, there is likely to be a vast market for general-purpose household robots and for companion machines. It is fortunate, therefore, that many of the robots depicted in SF are reasonable, friendly, functional humanoids rather than outlandish and quixotic contrivances.

The human beings portrayed in such stories are generally unremarkable and can often be taken as representing the 'average person'. A familiar storyline is one in which fear or revulsion towards the robot soon turns to acceptance or even love. A man or woman is initially shown as having hostile feelings towards the robot but is soon overwhelmed by the softness and friendliness of the machine and comes to enjoy its presence and its 'personality'. This is a familiar pattern but it is by no means universal. SF provides hundreds of examples of human responses to robots, and these take a wide variety of forms ranging from horror and aggression to passionate romance. Such a broad spectrum might suggest that there is little consensus among writers about what constitutes a 'realistic reaction'. Such a conclusion would undermine the thesis that SF provides a useful indication of real human reactions to product robots. On closer examination, however, the situation appears to be less chaotic. The different patterns of response reflect the varying human character types portrayed and the different personality and role features of the robots they meet. There is variation, certainly, but much of it is systematic variation which can be readily understood. Further analysis reveals a fairly coherent picture. There are definite predictions about how people will react towards particular types of machine, and these suggestions have important implications for the design of the ideal product robot.

There is clear consensus within the literature that such a machine will be useful, capable of performing a variety of tasks, that it will be loyal and biddable, possessing a pleasant manner, and that the specific behaviour of the machine will reflect one of a number of specific roles. While most of the fictional machines are capable of performing all necessary chores efficiently, and have a prodigious memory and a wide general knowledge, they are not usually depicted as intellectual giants. This may seem curious in view of the current concept of the computer (and robots are essentially mobile computers with highly developed 'natural' input and output capabilities). Yet there is a good reason for this. A machine with highly developed intellectual skills and an encyclopaedic database might intimidate the user. Thus the machine's capabilities are likely to be tailored and trimmed where necessary to present optimum user comfort. The 'best' machines need not necessarily incorporate the most sophisticated 'state-of-the-art' technology. This illustrates an important general point. Product robots will not be what they *can* be (that is, to the limits of available technology), they will be what people *want* them to be.

SF suggests that people would be prepared to live with a machine of even very limited practical usefulness if it provided companionship and presented itself as a pleasant 'character'. People enjoy the company of pet animals, not principally for their usefulness as burglar alarms or mouse-catchers, but for the added interest the pets' 'personalities' bring to their lives. Similarly, 'character' aspects of machines are stressed repeatedly in stories about domestic robots. Most models are shown as behaving in a friendly way without being over-familiar. They are never ill tempered, critical or disdainful. They are good-humoured and occasionally witty. Obedient at all times, some could even be accused of exhibiting too fawning a servility. The machines are sensitive to human needs and knowledgeable about human affairs. Caring and responsible, they are also inventive, informative and interesting. Variations of personality often correspond to variations in role, for even domestic machines may occupy one of several possible roles. Some fictional machines have been designed to act as servants, in either the formal manner of a butler or the more relaxed manner of a general home help. Others are depicted in the principal role of 'companion'and yet others feature within the family as a 'parent' or a 'child'. As might be anticipated, a robot 'packaged' for a particular role and given the appropriate skills and character tends to elicit specific kinds of response. Human characters do not treat a 'butler' robot in the same way as they treat a 'playmate' machine.

Certain robot roles occur with impressive regularity throughout the literary heritage. The archetypal roles for social machines include 'servant', 'lover' and 'companion'. It is important to recognize such archetypes, to understand how and why they have arisen, and to consider whether they may have a predictive relevance. They may point to the roles which real product robots will be expected to fulfil. The role of the machine is not merely the use to which it is put: the role affects the machine's design, the way it speaks, its vocabulary and its practical abilities.

There is thus consensus about the fact that a robot is both a 'person' and a machine. At various times stress is laid upon one or other of these aspects. The robot behaves 'as if' it were human, yet the reader knows at all times that it is a machine. Therein lies the fascination. The machine behaves impeccably, is friendly and loyal, sensible and good-humoured. Therein lies its charm. But the product machines depicted in fiction do not all correspond to a single model. Some are more 'naturalistic' than others, and the various robot characters display vastly different profiles of talents and interests.

Of special importance, however, is the fact that different robots fulfil different social functions. There are a limited number of archetypal roles which recur throughout the literature. These deserve careful attention, for they may well point to the social positions which sociable machines will one day occupy.

The Servant

Many fictional robots are household servants. Some are little more than enhanced gadgets—walking, talking vacuum cleaners or conversational food-mixers—but most are multipurpose humanoid characters who fully inhabit the home and in some cases act as an additional family member. Any home robot worth the cost of its power supply would be expected to perform routine household chores, but writers have often cast their creations in more elaborate roles. Besides the legion of minions there are valets, butlers and nannies, nurses and live-in companions. They all have the skills commensurate with their roles and are, in addition, obedient and friendly. They generally ask for nothing and expect little consideration. They have no life of their own and exist only for the service they can give. They remain unobtrusive, biding their time and charging their power packs, until a nod or a word from the owner animates them instantly. A human wish is a humanoid command.

Whether or not their prime function is to organize the cellar and the rest of the servants, the manner of many home robots inspires their identification as 'butlers'. The stereotype of human butlers is a familiar one: faithful, dignified, knowledgeable, and with a manner that, while signalling superiority and condescension to most of those around them, is never such as to pose a threat to those whom they serve. They also have a particular way of speaking, using language carefully and precisely to emphasize constantly their composure, self-reliance and reliability. A sense of humour, if present at all, is restricted to the utterance of the occasional *bon mot*, and in even issuing a polite smile they seem to feel that they are bordering on self-indulgence. The butler is happy to be ignored and equally happy to be called upon to serve. His role is to be present when needed, to follow every hint or request as if it were a dire command, to convey the impression that every duty is a pleasure, and to disappear from view when not needed. He is, in short, the very model of a human robot.

Robots, as a consequence, might be expected to be excellent butlers. It is a character for which a 'basic robot' might seem to need little adaptation and the temptation to cast a robot in this role appears to be strong, for many SF authors and screenplay writers have produced at least one mechanical butler.

Our discussion of robot characters in films will introduce a number of these, but our initial contact is with 'Jenkins'. He features in a series of stories written in the 1940s by Clifford D. Simak and collected together in 1952 under the title *City*. Jenkins, butler to the Websters for many generations, is first encountered on the occasion of a family funeral, as robot undertakers carry the casket to the crypt. Later, while serving whisky to the heir, Jenkins expresses his regret at the bereavement: 'If I may say so, sir, that was a touching service at the crypt. Your father was a fine human, the finest ever was. The robots were saying the service was very fitting. Dignified, like. He would have liked it had he known.'

The faithful tin retainer has, over generations, become very much 'one of the family'. His master reflects that Jenkins 'is a Webster'. He has picked up some of the family habits and thus scrubs his metallic chin with metal fingers when deep in thought. Moreover, he keeps a kind of diary and, with his formidable memory, performs the function of family chronicler. A witness to the comings and goings of generations, he is handed down, a watchful and intelligent heirloom.

Butlers may be servants but they are not slaves. Some robots, however, are not afforded the dignity of butlerhood but seem as happy to be menials. Of these, a few are depicted as caricatures of the obsequious, sycophants of high degree grovelling relentlessly before humankind. In Ron Goulart's comedy, *Crackpot* (1977), 'Yack' is just such a character, a mechanical souvenir of colonialism: 'A thousand pardons, effendi, if I have offended you . . . I am covered with a million forms of mortification . . . I prostrate myself on the altar of your anger.'

Most people would probably prefer straight civility and friendliness to such fawning, and might hope that even a servant robot would exhibit a degree of casualness. This would seem to present no particular problem given the feasibility of a useful, 'sensible' machine. Home-based robots would presumably be equipped with a range of social as well as mechanical skills and their characterization might encompass many styles. In times of need they might reasonably be expected to offer companionship and care, and to provide such mindful attention a machine would require a well developed and congenial personality. It would also need to be held in some respect and treated rather as a friend than as a 'gadget'.

The thought of engaging intimately with such a machine, however, may elicit certain fears and reservations. Many would be wary, some would even be horrified. The possibility of antagonism towards the home machine has not gone unnoticed, and the nature of the interaction between such people and a domestic robot has provided the theme for a number of memorable stories. On the whole they suggest that, given a little time and a socially talented robot, the problem will not be insurmountable. The machines, typically, are shown as recognizing human diffidence and as reacting sensitively to it. They begin by treating the people with tact and circumspection, allowing them to come to terms slowly with the idea of the machine-as-companion. They do not ingratiate themselves or attempt to confront the uneasy situation directly. They merely have to act 'naturally' and all feelings of artificiality, impropriety and threat evaporate. The evident civility, good humour and concern of the machine generally guarantee the loss of the initial dread or suspicion and, after the inhibitions have been overcome, an easy-going relationship develops. Some of those human characters who originally protested most strongly against the presence of a robot are later shown to be thoroughly seduced by their newfound friend.

We have already come across one notable example of this phenomenon in Asimov's 'Satisfaction Guaranteed'. In her first encounter with the robot Tony, Claire regards him with a mixture of horror and dismay. 'I can't have him in the house,' she cries. 'It just gives me the chills. I couldn't bear him.' Tony, however, is no ordinary robot. He is a pilot version of the charismatic TN domestic model which US Robots hopes to market widely, and he has been designed specifically to overcome such human reactions. He is helpful and unthreatening, well mannered and talkative, and chatters away to his mistress. Within days she is regarding him as a close friend, and soon she senses the danger of falling in love with the machine.

The theme of 'rapid habituation' is well illustrated also in a mid-1950s story by John Wyndham, 'Compassion Circuit'. Janet Shand views household humanoids with suspicion and scorn until she is cared for, during a stay in hospital, by the gentle robot Nurse James. As a result she purchases Hester who comes complete with the latest 'contra-balanced compassion-protection circuit'. This evaluates alternative courses of action and then functions entirely in accordance with the owner's best interests. The realistic robot is at first regarded as an elaborate doll, but after a short while it has become 'a tireless attentive friend'. 'From the first,' we are told, 'Janet had found it difficult to believe that she was only a mechanism, and as the days passed she had become more and more of a person . . . Hester was not only a person; she was preferable company to many.' As Janet's health declines we are presented, not for the first time in SF, with the picture of a person being rocked in comforting robot arms.

Servant robots are not portrayed in SF because there is something intrinsically fascinating about servants or about their mechanical counterparts. They appear frequently for two reasons: firstly because the caricature image of a servant is one in which the person is totally 'under command', a near automaton; and secondly because a 'servant model' is an obvious line in product robots. To be freed from all chores by some miracle of technology is a common enough fantasy. Already, labour-saving devices sell in millions, and a machine which could be commanded to do almost anything around the home presents a dream of untold riches for a manufacturer, and a dream of blameless slave-management for the consumer. Thus the role of servant is particularly likely to be allocated to a robot. Perhaps less obvious is the claim, implicit in much of SF, that the ideal servant machine would also be a 'character' with a talent for lively conversation, a personality, and an evident 'sensitivity' to family members' needs and wishes. Technically, none of these refinements would seem beyond the bounds of possibility, and many people would hold that they will certainly be realizable by the time the walking, seeing, dish-washing, table-laying robot comes along. Thus SF authors may well be accurate in this aspect of product prediction. Perhaps we can look forward with some confidence to a generation of servant robots who will apologize abjectly if they ever drop a plate and soothe us skilfully if ever we break one. The writers might also be accurate in their assumption that, faced with lively and amicable machines, the tendency to regard them as fellow beings will prove irresistible. 'When domestic servants are treated as human beings,' wrote Bernard Shaw, 'it is not worth while to keep them.' When domestic *robots* are worth keeping, suggests SF, they *will* be treated as human beings.

The Family Member

Some 'servant robots' come very close to being accepted as members of the family, and in many stories machines act as substitutes for grandparents, parents or children. Thus SF writers suggest that robots will not only be used to help in the home, as devices enhanced with personality to make them more fascinating and attractive, but that some may be used primarily as 'person-substitutes'. For these machines the 'character' aspects will predominate over any practical function.

Ray Bradbury's 'I Sing the Body Electric' (1969) gives a particularly sensitive portrayal of a 'family relative' robot, specifying the highly desirable qualities of such a machine and providing considerable insight into the likely reactions of children. The Fantoccini Company (slogan: 'We try to guess your dreams') has developed the Fantoccini Electrical Grandmother for families in which 'death or disablement undermines the welfare of the children'. The motherless Simmons family visits the company's salesroom to discuss plans for a grandmother robot to be made to their requirements. They are shown a variety of basic models, they listen to a wide range of synthesized voices and are even able to select the body temperature: 'Her hand pressed to ours, or brushing our brow in the middle of the sick-fever night, must not be marble-cold, dreadful, or over-hot, oppressive, but somewhere in between. The nice-temperature of a baby-chick held in the hand after a long night's sleep.'

There is great excitement on the day the robot-grandmother finally arrives. She has been preprogrammed with certain facts about the family and knows the children's names. But she has also been programmed to pretend not to know, and they are delighted as she plays a guessing game with them. Only young Agatha has initial reservations, and she is treated by the machine with such sensitivity and good humour that she, too, soon becomes completely captivated. The robot's skills are numerous. She tutors in twelve languages, has a complete knowledge of the arts and world history, gives loving attention to all members of the family and bakes wonderful apricot pies. She is also adept at flying kites and thus fulfils in every respect the promise of the company's advertisement: '. . . we offer the nearest thing to the Ideal Teacher-Friend-Companion-Blood Relation.'

Bradbury's 'electrical grandmother' is fully accepted as one of the family. She becomes indispensable, a major addition to the social world of the children. She is highly functional, an excellent cook and tutor, but her special skills are those which call for the 'sensitive' handling of the children. She scolds them when necessary, calms their fears and soothes their pains. She is the very model of a model grandmother. It is worth noting that her ability to play the role effectively demands that she have some disciplinary power over the children. She is not totally under their command, and is therefore not bound by the Second Law of Robotics. Asimov has himself noted that some modification might be required to enable robots to decide precisely which humans should be obeyed and in what circumstances.

In terms of human needs and human happiness Bradbury's story paints a Utopian picture, without a hint of threat or menace, but things appear less happy from the robot's point of view. Like so many other robots in SF, the 'grandmother' harbours a lonely concern. She is self-conscious about her status in the world—not her social status, for she is treated in every respect as if she were a real and well loved grandmother—but her existential status. Her dream is not merely to be treated *as if* she were human, but to *be* human. This is a dream which she shares with Andrew in Asimov's 'The Bicentennial Man', and her anxieties and wishes are similar to those voiced by many literary predecessors, including the monster in *Frankenstein*.

In a discussion with the children's father she almost pleads to be considered as a person: 'You ask what I am. Why, a machine. But even in that answer we know, don't we, more than a machine. I am all the people who thought of me and planned and built me and set me running. So I am people.' Although, she admits, she cannot actually feel or touch or taste, she can help to fulfil human potential for such experiences. And although she herself cannot feel love, she can develop love in others. She has been built to foster love; that is her purpose just as the purpose of some machines is evil. The bear-trap catches and holds, the rifle wounds and kills, but 'I am no bear trap, I am no rifle. I am a grandmother machine, which means more than a machine.'

Grandparents seem to be a favourite characterization for robot relatives. Perhaps this reflects a stereotype of the human grandparent—indulgent, child-centred, generous, concerned more with making the child's life happy and exciting than with the routine parenting chores. The archetypal grandparent certainly possesses many of those characteristics which might be expected of the ideal robot.

Grandparents have another function, too. They play an important role in 'passing on the heritage' to the younger generation. Their experience of life, their memories and their fund of anecdotes and epithets offer the child an echo of a distant age, helping to maintain customs and transmit values. This 'cultural preservation' effect is the theme of Chad Oliver's tale 'The Life Game' (1953). Although the author chooses to develop it in the context of a future totalitarian society, and the story eventually becomes menacing, the central concept is one which could equally well be presented in a favourable light.

A young family receives regular visits from the robots Grandmother and Grandfather Smith. They come to play games with the children, showing obvious delight, and are in every sense relics from the past. Grandfather dresses in an outmoded black suit, complete with gold watch and chain, smokes a pipe and recounts his favourite stories repeatedly. His 'Day at the Office' routine is familiar to all, and they can only guess how many more times that same old trout will be fished from his pouch of river anecdotes. Grandmother Smith brings her special apple jelly, hums tunelessly to herself and is forever knitting baby clothes. They come for an evening to play 'The Life Game', a board game which has been devised to give the grandparent robots the opportunity to pass on folkways and to promote the 'good old-fashioned values'. 'There's no place for daydreaming when you're trying to get through Life, young man,' says Grandfather Smith. 'You've got to keep your hand on the plough, that's what I always say.' Quite what a 'plough' might be, nobody is sure. In their interactions, too, the old couple appear somewhat archaic: 'Ten o'clock, mother,' says Grandfather Smith. 'Time we were going.' 'Land sakes,' cries Grandmother, 'I just don't know where the time goes.' Tomorrow they will visit one of their other families, giving them the benefit of their 'reminiscences' and advice. And they are but one of 50 pairs of Grandmother and Grandfather Smiths who go from house to house playing the Game.

The story illustrates how robot characters might be used to reinforce or change values. Computers have been used for many years to teach, and educational technology is a rapidly developing field. When systems are 'sensitive' to the responses of the learner they are much more efficient in their ability to teach, and adding 'personality features' to provide encouragement, praise and humour may help the learning process even more. Machine systems are not restricted to teaching 'facts', and intelligent robot characters would also be able to train skills, counsel, advise, guide and indoctrinate. People will not only learn from robots which take a specific 'tutor' role, but will also gather opinions, values and attitudes through their informal interactions with machines. Such incidental learning is constantly occurring in human interaction and plays an important part in shaping thoughts, feelings and behaviour.

Human beings have a tendency to treat certain people as 'models' and to imitate them. If a robot were attractive and 'held in esteem' then its actions—and 'opinions', too—might be copied. Children tend to identify strongly with their parents and imitate them both consciously and unconsciously. A robot parent or grandparent might therefore be expected to be a specially powerful model. Although the phenomenon is considered 'healthy' in the case of a fully human family the idea of a robot as a powerful agent for such socialization is somewhat daunting, and it is hardly surprising that Chad Oliver brings out the potential for menace. But robots will have no values of their own, they will be high-technology chalk-boards on which anything may be written. In 'The Life Game' the traditional values were promulgated, but any type of religious, political or social ideal would be equally susceptible to this kind of implementation. Within a free society a wide choice of robot 'value-modules' would be available. There would be robots of many religious 'persuasions' and robots 'affiliated' to all political parties.

The grandmother robot of 'I Sing the Body Electric' may not have declared a specific value-system, but her words and actions must have reflected *some* implicit philosophy. In order to make 'choices' and act coherently any 'social' entity must act in accordance with some basic 'philosophy of life'. This would be true of real grandmothers, robot grandmothers and other robot relatives. In most stories the home robots portrayed are not strongly opinionated. They seem to take their value cues from the humans with whom they interact. They are generally shown as soaking up social influence without imposing attitudes of their own. Their only strong innate principle is one of unwavering obedience to, and honour of, all human beings, and their actions constantly reflect this. In some stories this perfect control and unconditional fidelity is shown to be a source of some irritation to the human owner.

One such tale is William F. Nolan's 'The Joy of Living' (1954). Ted Rice, a salesman for World Mechanicals, purchases an automaton after the death of his wife mainly to act as a mechanical foster mother to his children. The robot, Margaret, is beautiful, vibrant and warm, and in many ways an excellent wife. She is also extremely good with the children. But despite her numerous positive qualities and talents, and despite the fact that she can also be turned off at any time, Ted is not happy with her. He feels that she is too perfect, enduring his insults and his angry outbursts with equanimity, never complaining and ever ready to soothe his hungover head. He misses the occasional quarrels and reconciliations which enlivened his marriage to a real woman. Without such everyday drama, he considers, love is unreal and unsatisfactory.

Ted's other complaint is that the children pay Margaret too much attention, and show too much fondness towards her. He is irritated when he notices that his son, Jackie, greets *her* first. His own love is real and therefore surely more precious than her simulated affection, but the children fail to recognize the distinction: 'She's good and kind and smiles a great deal. These things matter to Jackie. The fact that she isn't human doesn't matter. Not at all.' He concludes that this is a dangerous situation—and his proposed solution is a drastic one: he will return her to the Central Exchange. There her memory will be erased and she will be reprogrammed and recycled to another family.

Technically there is no problem, for she can simply be switched off and handed in, but there has to be some way of making the loss easier for the children. On a family picnic he breaks the news to Margaret, asking her to pretend that she must go away on holiday. She reacts with her usual tolerance and understanding but tells him how much she loves him. Perplexed by this, Ted has forcibly to remind himself that her words and responses reflect no real emotion, but merely indicate the operation of her circuitry. The drive to the Exchange feels slow and awkward. Ted, silent, is embarrassed and unhappy. When they finally arrive Margaret protests, hands clenched and eyes blazing: 'Men built me, gave me human impulses, human desires, put into me part of themselves, part of their own humanity . . . I feel a *human* hunger, a *human* thirst, a desire to be respected for myself, as I respect others, a desire to be loved as I love others.' Yet again we hear a robot pleading to be considered as human, and this time it has a profound effect. That spark of self-will is the final straw and Ted takes her into his arms and sets the car controls for home.

This account of the impact of Margaret's final outburst raises a fundamental point about human susceptibility to robot protestations. Robots in fiction, frequently claim that they have emotions, that they feel, hope, love. A cartoon character or a puppet, of course, could be made to do the same. Such statements, however strongly or 'emotionally' stated, provide no proof or solid indication that there *is* feeling, but they nevertheless *convey* feeling, and this might well result in a person being confused and acting as though the robot *were* in pain or in love. At one point in 'The Joy of Living' Ted is able to discount Margaret's declaration of love by calling to mind the circuits and programming which produce her reaction patterns. He has doubtless rehearsed this means of discrediting her emotional behaviour many times before, when worrying about the effect his 'thoughtless' behaviour might be having. He has had to call to mind her real nature to prevent himself from feeling guilty when, switching her off, he has seen the personality and movement instantly drain from her. But the final protest is unprecedented and uncompromising, and as a result of his own emotional state Ted is caught off-guard. He is overcome. Her reaction affects not only his immediate feelings but also his rational thinking, for he finds himself wondering whether her response indicates that real emotion might somehow have been generated within the electronic complexity of her brain. Ted's vulnerability is further testimony to the strength of the idea that robots may have powerful effects on human sentiment. He, a 'mechanicals salesman' who has access to corporation plans, who sees the machines produced and helps to compose the sales patter, cannot bring himself to dispose of his own automaton. His rationality is overcome by a tender feeling towards the machine.

The stories examined so far concern robots which act as 'guardians' or 'helpers', but the function of some fictional machines is to elicit feelings of caring and to cater for the human social need of nurturance. In 'The Joy of Living' there are two other 'mechanicals' in the family besides Margaret. The boy whom Ted is most concerned about, Jackie, is his real son but the other two children are robots—Ted bought them after the mother died. They were purchased, with Margaret, in a 'package deal' and, being a salesman for the company, Ted was able to buy them wholesale. It is evident that he has parental feelings towards his mechanical 'children', though his attachment to Jackie is far stronger. When one of the young mechanicals is especially naughty he threatens to switch him off.

The provision of 'robobabies' for the childless appears in some tales. Ted Rice's company apparently deals in such machines and he maintains that many women now prefer mechanical babies to organic offspring. They opt for voluntary childlessness supplemented by one or more robot babies.

The theme recurs in 'And Baby Makes Three' (1973) by William J. Earls. Elain yearns for a child of her own. Attempts to satisfy her rampant need to give care have so far been unsuccessful. She has 'fallen in love' successively with a goldfish, a kitten and a puppy. The goldfish died through overfeeding and the other animals passed too quickly through the stage of total dependency to satisfy her protective urge. The perfect answer seems to present itself when she visits a robot showroom and is given a demonstration of a 'de-luxe robobaby'. The salesman claims that it has all the advantages of a real baby with none of the disadvantages. Activated by a switch behind the ear it cries, gurgles, drinks and wets, and it responds to Elain's touch, laughing and kicking its legs excitedly. Her reaction is one of unreserved love, and despite the rather high price the couple take the 'baby' home.

Elain devotes her life to 'motherhood', and the couple's home life changes drastically as all her attention is given to the robobaby. She sends out birth announcements and joins a Young Mothers' Club. There is a christening service. In every way she responds to the machine precisely as if it were a living baby. Her husband, Jim, scolds her for such overinvolvement, and attempts to remind her that 'baby' is really nothing but a doll, a robot, but she breaks down: 'No—don't say that. Think of it as a person. I want a baby—someone to love—so much. It's a baby, it has to be.' Her self-deception continues unabated. She ignores the instructions given in the technical manual, preferring instead to read books on babycare. So great is her need to give constant attention, and to have the machine respond, that she is reluctant to allow the prolonged periods of non-use that are essential for the maintenance of the circuitry. Eventually her overuse results in a serious malfunction—Elain's baby is 'dead'. She weeps inconsolably. Now the robot resembles a doll, and as with dolls there can be no substitute for the one who has been cherished so tenderly. This was the only 'baby' Elain could ever love.

The story is disturbing for several reasons. It depicts the plight of a childless and desperate woman. Driven to distraction by her need, her judgement is profoundly affected. She sees what she wants to see and her experience is driven more by inner demands rather than by external reality. She is not mad, merely confused. She might almost as easily respond to an inanimate doll. The robobaby brings her profound happiness, but it is a happiness founded on delusion.

Another disturbing aspect is the salesman's promise that the product will provide the pleasures of motherhood without the pains. There is reason to doubt this claim, for endurance of difficulties may add to the satisfaction of motherhood. But this provides little comfort, for given the technical achievements assumed in Earls' story it would easily be possible to manufacture 'difficult babies'. Elain would probably not have opted for an especially 'easy to care for' model. For her the teething problems and the night crying would merely have added to the attractiveness of her mechanical charge. She is little concerned that her 'baby' be 'troublefree'. She is *greatly* concerned that it be 'authentic'.

'And Baby Makes Three' may seem to present a horrific picture of a roboticized future, and Elain's actions may even appear 'inhumane'. This is a curious effect which tends to reinforce the main idea of the story. No human child is featured, no baby is mishandled or abused. The major interaction is between a woman and a machine. Considering the effect Elain might have had on a real child, it might seem rather fortunate that only an artificial device suffered at her loving hands. Some women treat their babies as 'objects' and are as selfish in their treatment as Elain was in hers. So, how is the story 'inhumane'? Would we rather that a baby were treated like a doll, or that a robodoll were treated like a baby? In this story the woman adopted the robot in place of the baby she could not have. It was a compromise between having what she really wanted and having nothing. Ted Rice's sales patter, however, suggested many women now preferred a robobaby to the real thing. Clearly that *would* present some danger.

The probability must now be faced that in many areas of expertise, physical skill and intellectual talent human beings may be superseded by electronic devices. This we will have to come to terms with. But it might be impossible to concede that a machine could be an adequate or even an 'improved' baby, parent, companion or lover. Yet this is precisely what a number of SF stories have suggested. They provide a vision of a socially skilled and socially desirable machine which is capable of taking on intimate roles within people's lives. Machines are shown as objects of affection and sources of comfort. Many stories have focussed on the role of lover. In this context we are provided with some of the most striking suggestions about how technology may stimulate emotion exquisitely. This would be considered by many to be the ultimate invasion of technology into human affairs. Yet the consensus within the heritage is clear on this point: the literature proposes that machines will come to evoke powerful feelings of both tenderness and passion.

The Lover

There is something unnerving about a person saying 'Thank you' to a machine. What, then, would be the reaction to 'I love you'? Yet such an endearment has long been whispered to cherished machines in robot literature, and SF has often suggested that robots will one day win a place both in our hearts and in our beds. In some cases the human-machine affair has resulted from a willing illusion, as in *L'Ève future*, and in other cases from an unwitting delusion, as in 'The Sandman'. These stories suggest that 'love is blind' and that a strong predisposition towards emotional involvement may lead people to become beguiled even by artefacts. Yet the stories also depict those artefacts as undeniably beguiling. The production of a 'robot lover' would represent a final assault on the idea that there are social needs that can be fulfilled only by other human beings. The strangeness of the concept of passionate love for a robot cannot be denied, yet the theme is evident in so many tales that the role of 'lover' must be seen as one of the dominant fictional robot roles.

Some of the loverobots in fiction are demure and passive devices which attract the man or woman by their pleasing appearance and their engaging ways. Sometimes the human responds with a tender adulation, a concern and reverence for the precious object, and acts as blushing suitor to the inanimate inamorato. In other cases the human pants rather than pines, and pounces without ceremony on the humanoid, using it as an aphrodisiacal device, a hi-tech masturbatory aid. But not all loverobots wait to accept whatever attention may come their way. Some fall in love themselves and, as in the case of their human paramours, they may be reticent and romantic or ribald and rapacious. Whatever the level or category of their desire, however, they usually bring to the situation both intellect and charm. Some have a little trouble persuading the human that to love a robot is not impossible or unreasonable, and they set out to do this with understanding, delicacy—and determination.

One such device is Helen in Lester del Rey's 'Helen O'Loy'. This is one of the earliest and most striking of the many 20th-century 'robot romances'; it was published in 1938, two years before Asimov's first robot story. Helen is treated by the author not as an object but as a character who exhibits strong personal desires and who captivates her man with strategy and firm intent. She is a realistic robot, constructed by Dave, an engineer, and Phil, an endocrinologist, in their spare time. Helen is an attractive soft machine, her face can simulate emotional expressions, and 'wired-in tear glands' allow her to cry. She spends her time reading romantic fiction and watching the 'televisor', and learns to imitate human behaviour and 'feelings'. Gradually she comes to 'feel' like a woman and develops an infatuation for Dave. She wants to be physically close to him and to become his wife.

The engineer is not immune to Helen's charms but her approaches embarrass and perplex him: '. . . he remembered that she was only a robot, after all. The fact that she felt, acted and looked like a young goddess in his arms didn't mean much.' After an unhappy interlude in which Dave denies his feelings he finally admits his love and the two get married. They move away and lead an idyllic life, hiding Helen's true nature from friends and neighbours. When, many years later, Dave dies, the robot 'commits suicide' and leaves a letter for Phil: '. . . please don't grieve too much for us, for we have led a happy life together, and both feel that we should cross the final bridge side by side.'

As with all stories involving total 'confusion'—Helen is able to live as a woman without detection—there are severe constraints in relating the robot to any foreseeable product. The interest in the story lies in the fact that the machine acts cleverly to overcome human reservation, stimulating a high level of emotional response to win over the scruples. Another seductive machine, this time a male, appears in Robert Sheckley's 'Can You Feel

Anything When I do This?' (1969). A robot omnicleaner (Rom) becomes infatuated with a woman who visits the large department store in which he is on display. He cunningly arranges to be delivered to her home and there uses his considerable amorous skills to arouse her.

The human responses depicted in such stories may appear realistic only if the human characters are shown as lonely or inadequate people, or as especially unfortunate in their relationships with the opposite sex. A high level of frustration can affect judgement in such a way that some inferior stimulus will trigger a very positive response. Thus stories gain credibility by capitalizing on this fact—that lonely people are 'vulnerable' to many kinds of 'loving attention'—as well as by presenting robot characters who are exceptionally attractive in appearance, agreeable in their manner and skilled in the art of seduction.

Compared with stories showing romantic infatuation with a robot, those which depict pure eroticism seem more plausible. The most familiar example of a 'social' need being fulfilled by nonliving substitutes is the use of pornographic materials. In the absence of an ideal human sexual partner people may turn to relatively impoverished stimuli to achieve the desired effect. Ultimately any remotely erotic material will suffice, but 'realism' is greatly prized. The inflatable sex-aid doll appears to be especially powerful in eliciting sensual responses and suggests a future subspecies of robot products. It is most unlikely that any of the scientists currently working in the field of robotics now see their efforts as leading towards such an end, but basic research will yield a general-purpose technology which will receive all manner of application.

Gutenberg could hardly have imagined that his invention would make possible the printing of *Playboy* some five centuries later. Basic technological innovation gives rise to a multitude of potential appliances and, after the initial stage of development, the realization of particular devices is largely in the hands of market enterprise. Familiar product paths will be followed. Thus, to anticipate future products, the current marketplace should be examined as well as the immediate goals which inspire those working in research laboratories. A glance at newsstands, video libraries or cinema hoardings suggests that any technology which can be considered a 'medium' will be fully exploited for its erotic potential. Although the fact has yet to be generally realized, computer technology, and robotics in particular, are 'new media'.

Human-like dolls and automata have exerted a strange fascination over the human mind for countless generations, but perhaps the strangest manifestation of this general psychological trend was announced in 1891 in *Scientific American*, accompanied by the illustration shown here. A certain Dr Varlot, a Frenchman, had developed a device for electroplating your deceased loved ones – no doubt for use as drawing-room conversation-pieces.

The three writers who have perhaps contributed more than anyone else to the robot heritage. Mary Shelley (1797-1851) is best known for her novel *Frankenstein: or, The Modern Prometheus* (1818), which is frequently claimed as the first SF novel *(MEPL)*. E. T. A. Hoffman (1776-1822) wrote two stories important to the robot heritage: 'Automata' (1814) and 'The Sandman' (1816) *(MEPL)*. Isaac Asimov (1920-   ) is often regarded as the modern father of the robot, and compiled, with the SF editor John W. Campbell, the famous 'Three Laws of Robotics' *(Kurt Muller)*.

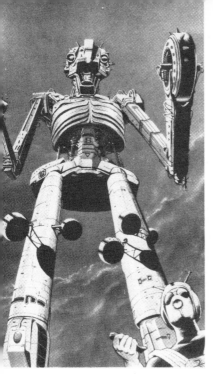

Two faces of the robot. *Left:* The unacceptable face of the giant robot. This huge war-machine is operated by a remote-control system called 'telefactoring' whereby the robot imitates precisely the actions of its human controller *(Angus McKie)*.

Right: The affectionate face of the robot – the robot stars of George Lucas's *Star Wars* cycle of films. C-3PO is a human-robot relations specialist, with humanlike form, speech and emotions; his squeaking, tottering companion R2-D2 is more like a family pet.

Two strikingly different roles for the domestic 'bot. *Left:* One of the most popular uses for robots throughout the history of SF has been to perform the function of butler, as depicted here (*Ed Emshwiller*).

Below: At the other end of the scale from the very mechanical-looking robot is the one that is perfectly humanoid in every detail. The still shows Stanley Holloway and Patricia Roc in the 1949 film *The Perfect Woman*, described by Peter Nichols as a film which 'allows underclothes-fetishism to an extent that would have been unthinkable had its robot heroine (played by a real woman) been a real woman'.

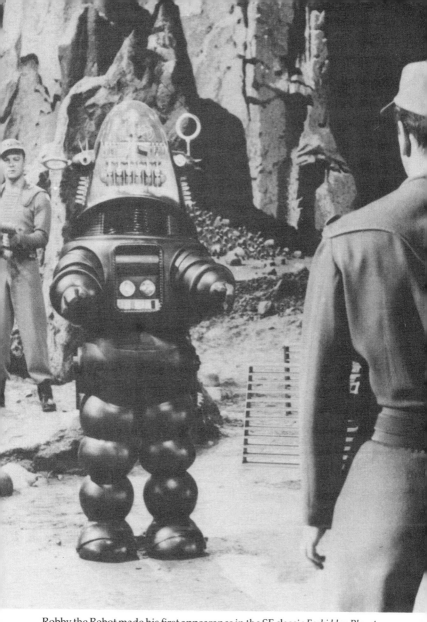

Robby the Robot made his first appearance in the SF classic *Forbidden Planet*, made in 1956, and proved so popular with cinema audiences that a second film, *The Invisible Boy,* was made in 1957 solely as a vehicle for him. In the film, Robby's 'brain' has been taken over by a megalomaniac computer which is intent on ruling the world. However, when Robby is ordered to kill his friend, the boy of the title, he overrides his built-in commands and destroys the computer. Long before real robots started to appear, people were prepared to ascribe to them human emotions, values and moral abilities.

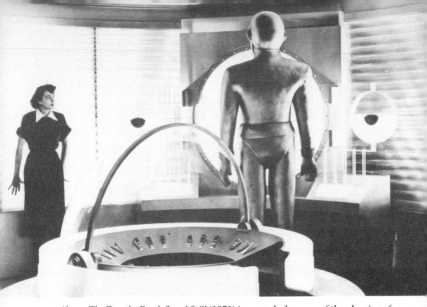

Above: The Day the Earth Stood Still (1951) is regarded as one of the classics of robot cinema. In this still the robot, Gort, confronts a frightened human woman aboard the alien flying saucer. Gort is a 'policeman' rather than a war-robot, and therefore theoretically on the side of right—although the film's morals are ambiguous. It seems unlikely that in the future human beings will be willing to subjugate themselves to robot lawmen—or does it?

Below: From huge and terrifying Gort to one of the more ludicrous screen robots: K-9, the robot dog which for a while served alongside Doctor Who in the BBC's highly successful children's series. K-9 seems to serve no useful purpose—except as a companion, in which role he is rather less effective than would be a real dog (*BBC copyright photograph*).

Interaction with HAL 9000, the computer which plays a central part in the 1968 film *2001: A Space Odyssey*. By design of the director, Stanley Kubrick, it is HAL's 'death' which is the one most poignantly felt by most cinema viewers.

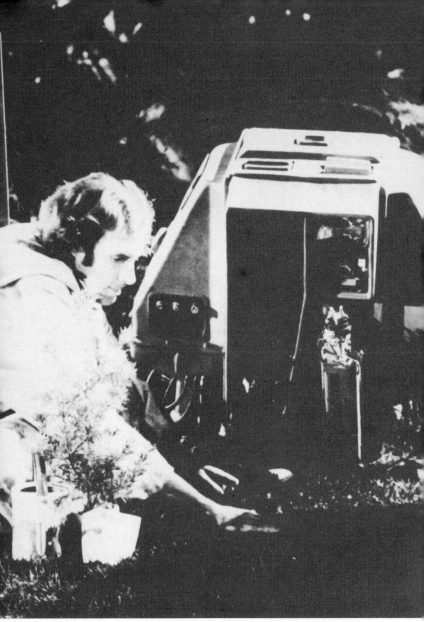

Douglas Trumbull, who had much to do with the special effects for *2001*, in 1971 directed *Silent Running*, based on an idea of his own. A conservationist is fleeing from Earth with the last remnants of Earth's vegetation. His relationship with the three robots is scrutinized in some detail, and it becomes clear that, even though the devices are primitive, in his eyes they attain the status of 'people'. A similar effect seems likely to be seen in the near future when the first domestic robots begin to come into service, however primitive the early machines may be.

They will present many new opportunities for the further exploitation of sex.

Many SF writers have shown a keen awareness of this fact. Although Asimov neglects to consider robots which might have a primary sexual function, several other authors have alighted on this aspect with relish, producing stories with a variety of voluptuous visions and widely differing degrees of plausibility. One of the writers whose stories are frequently populated with loverobots is Ron Goulart.

The style of Goulart's work is unusual for SF. The rib-tickling prose cracks along in comic-strip style and the author is constantly inventing colloquialisms and tossing in bizarre and frequently ribald images. In *Crackpot* we meet a bearded old man on his way to the Fun-House. The billboard promises: 'We got lovely nubile female androids representing all the races in what's left of the world. We also got intellectual-type female androids built like militant Frisco Enclave dames. We got cornfed bumptious beauties who you'd swear were fresh off Heartland Empire food farms.' Goulart then presents his audience with the incredible contortions of some delightful 'hooker androids'.

Tanith Lee's style is very different—sober, reflective and concerned with realistic human responses. In *The Silver Metal Lover* (1982) a young woman, Jane, comes into contact with a beautiful, perfect robot, Silver, an experimental 'Sophisticated Format' model produced by Electronic Metals. His voice is lilting and his conversation sparkling, and he sings and plays the guitar with virtuoso skill. His function is to amuse, to entertain and to give pleasure of any kind to people who hire him. Some prize him for his musicianship but Jane's friend Egyptia exploits his considerable sexual talents and finds him an exquisite lover: 'Oh, Jane, he's taught me so much about myself. He found such sensual nuances in me. I was a woman with him . . . He's a robot, but he made me feel more like a woman, more conscious of my desires, my needs, than any man ever did.' Jane is soon in a position to confirm the fact that Silver is adventurous and untiring, though at one point there is some doubt about whether he might be 'faking orgasm'. Jane falls in love with the metal man, more in love than she has ever been, and Silver speaks and acts as if he loves her. The romance is fated when the Silver robots are recalled and her unhappy lover is melted down.

One view of the sexual act is that it is a physical exercise which, to be performed 'properly', calls for special stamina and technique. Consequently some sex guides read like a cross between a hobbyist's construction manual and a choreographic transcription. This concept of 'sex as mechanism' is reflected in a number of the robosex stories. The reasoning is clear. The robots are machines with perfectly controlled physical movements, limitless energy and an acute awareness of their physical and social environment. They are also totally subject to the command of their human contact, accommodating, obedient and amiable. Many are also perfectly proportioned, visions of loveliness, and soft and warm to the touch. Little wonder, then, that some writers have considered them eminently suitable to be perfect lovers. But, even if such a potential were to be furnished by technology, would such devices actually be produced? Some stories suggest an affirmative answer to this question by exploring the commercial factors that might lead to the production of loverobots.

This is one additional contribution of William F. Nolan's 'The Joy of Living'. Ted Rice, the 'mechanicals' salesman, rehearses his patter: 'Tired of looking for the right girl? Want a ready-made cutie who'll be 100 percent yours? . . . Well, here she is, chum—a full size babe with the old come hither look reserved especially for you. Blonde? Brunette? Redhead? You name her, we've got her. Yours on easy payments!' He recalls the early history of the product: 'When a Mr Shy Guy wanted some female company along comes a spongerubber job right out of the pin-up mags. Just a few at first, here and there, and expensive as hell. But pretty soon the good old American commercial know-how takes over and competition gets rough. Prices go down . . . In no time flat everybody is buying mechanicals.'

Robert Bloch even speculates about the possible market for used models in his 'Wheel and Deal' (1962). This describes the initiation of a new salesman in a second-hand auto-erotic emporium. The owner, Happy Harrigan, takes the young man on a tour of the establishment, describing the wide selection of female robots, each serviced by qualified medics and exhibiting such refinements as automatic heaters and seductive French accents. Harrigan, self-styled 'King of the Auto-Erotics' (his slogan: 'New and Used Females—All Makes—We're Trading Wild'), is clearly delighted as his protégé slips into the routine sales patter: 'Never mind about the book value. This one doesn't use any oil at all . . . she belonged to an elderly school-teacher, and he only took her out on Sundays.'

The notion that a lover might be bought from the 'used erotics' lot, or off the shelf, is certainly somewhat bizarre. The chances of such things happening depend crucially on human attitudes. Some will face the prospect with embarrassment, some with profound distaste and some with eager expectation. If there are enough people who find the idea attractive then we can anticipate the arrival of products to meet their fancy. The current demand for sex-aid dolls is sufficient in a number of countries to support several competing producers. Despite the extravagant claims made by the manufacturers about the realism of their models, none of them can speak or actively respond, and none is 'aware' of its environment. Current research in robotics suggests that their range of potential talents could soon be greatly extended. Given conversational powers or sensitive reactions, the dolls would reach a new realism high. With the full range of hi-tech enhancements they might be said to have been given a new lease of life. And, experienced through the extravagant and wishful fancy of the passionately aroused, the effect would surely be rather dramatic.

Although it is unlikely that giant international corporations would be prepared to furnish such lavish apparatus, other opportunist operations might well succumb to the temptation and adapt and incorporate the generally available multipurpose hardware and software to animate their own designs. The new technology is a 'modular' affair, and highly flexible. Microchips may soon come to be regarded as a raw material. Production of chips is limited to major advanced corporations but their wares soon become available on the open market. And so it will be with speech synthesizers, movement mechanisms and visual analysers. There will be no control on how such modules are assembled, the shape in which they are housed, or the software that will orchestrate the components and give the device character and patterns of response. A speech synthesizer capable of announcing closing share prices or reading Dickens to the blind can just as easily be used to whisper endearments to lonely people, or obscenities to the promiscuous.

And what of love? Could people really feel a warm glow of tenderness towards a machine? In some SF stories the robot is said to be so perfect a replication of a human that people unwittingly take it for a person. The hapless individual who feels that she or he is in love with a fellow human discovers at some late stage that their lover is an assembly of cogs and chips. Such simulacra, however, are hardly likely to appear, and so these stories cannot be taken as a literal presentation of any foreseeable state of affairs. But in many stories the human lovers know full well the true nature of their beloved. This seems bizarre, but can we safely assume that it will not become a real phenomenon?

People do not love only people. They also love dogs, horses, cats, teddy bears and dolls. Such affection might not be of a 'romantic' nature, but it can involve a high emotional commitment. The people who feel strongly about their dog or doll find it attractive. The loving dog-owner may claim that the animal understands and responds, and is affectionate. The doll lover will project all manner of psychological characteristics onto the inanimate article despite the objective facts. Some people feel that it is immoral to give deep affection to anything other than another human being, but few would deny the existence of the phenomenon. Artificial stimuli may trigger love if they are artfully presented and if sufficient desire and imagination are present.

Compared with any doll or artificial device so far available, the product robot will be powerfully equipped to elicit emotional feelings. Useful, considerate, talkative, generous, biddable, friendly and responsive, it will also become familiar with the owner's personality and adapt accordingly. The machines will be deliberately produced to win affection; they will be designed to be lovable. The humans who interact with such devices will vary greatly in their reaction. Some may find it impossible to forget that their kindly sociable companion is a machine, while others will find it impossible *not* to forget. Some will remain deliberately cold and distant and insist on regarding the robot as a device, while others will soon take it to their hearts as a close friend. And it seems not impossible that some may really fall in love.

Robot Remainders

Although most authors suggest that human beings will regard product machines in a positive way, a few have considered the power of humanoids to elicit extreme negative emotions. At first sight this would seem incompatible with the 'product' concept, but some stories suggest that people would be attracted to the idea of using a machine to vent feelings of hatred and anger. The practice of effigy mutilation and destruction found in many cultures has been given a hi-tech revamp by a number of writers.

Human aggression is displaced towards robots who become 'whipping boys' and scapegoats. James Causey's 'The Show Must Go On' (1954) introduces 'hate bars' where people go to rid themselves of their surplus hostility, and in Robert Sheckley's 'A Ticket to Tranai' (1955) special models are produced to allow people to vent their aggression: the robots scream and whimper when beaten.

The human hero of the story devises a brittle plastic which will shatter when kicked. Working in the 'disimprovement-engineering' section of the android factory, his job is to design robots which will enrage customers. The release of aggression is said to be healthy for the individual and it is also healthy for the economy, for families use up their robots rapidly. This story testifies in a rather unusual way to the likely emotional power of the humanoid machine and portrays a high level of 'product consciousness'. The manufacturers exploit human emotions and supply a product whose rapid obsolescence is guaranteed.

Sheckley's satire is obvious. It is surely unthinkable that human beings would want a humanoid object for the sole purpose of displaying 'cruelty' towards it. But if some people did relish such an exercise, would any moral objections be raised? If such actions are regarded as 'depraved', would this mean that the machine was being endowed with 'rights' or 'feelings'?

The problem of possible intimidation by a robot has been raised a number of times. It is commonly suggested that robots will aspire to be human, or to be as like humans as possible. The general pattern is thus one in which the machines are envious of humans, but in some cases it has been suggested that people might feel somewhat threatened by the excellence of their machine companions. An indication of such feelings was given in 'The Joy of Living', where Ted Rice becomes irritated by the fact that his children show more affection towards his automaton wife than they do towards him. In view of the formidable skills of SF robots, it may be thought surprising that human envy is not more in evidence. The machine's memory might be faultless, its social skills unmatchable and its cooking, sewing, design and 'dress sense' superior to that of the people who interact with it. The robot might also have a wider breadth of knowledge and a superior intellect. The rarity of negative responses to such superiority is due partly to the fact that the skills of product robots are sometimes shown as deliberately 'toned down' to make them less intimidating, and partly because the robots are cautious in displaying their talents. They react sensitively, doing nothing to make people feel inferior.

An extreme case of such robot sensitivity occurs in Herbert Goldstone's 'Virtuoso' (1953). A famous pianist, the Maestro, takes delivery of Rollo. The humanoid is fascinated by the master's playing and looks with wonder at the curious apparatus he uses: '. . . wires of different thicknesses and tautness struck by felt-covered hammers activated by manually operated levers arranged in a horizontal panel.' The Maestro is appalled by such a cold-blooded description of his piano and explains the spiritual nature of great music to his metal-headed servant. Hearing that the purpose of music is to give humans pleasure, Rollo asks whether he might acquire a musical skill. The Maestro gives him his first piano lesson. Though fascinated by his extraordinary pupil's first faltering chords the Maestro becomes fatigued and retires to his bed, leaving Rollo to practise, gently, through the night.

On waking he finds the robot still sitting at the piano. The music rack is empty and Rollo is playing Beethoven's 'Appassionata', '. . . creating it, breathing it, drawing it through flame'. The Maestro sheds a tear; never has he heard the piece played so movingly, so faithfully. Excitedly, he plans a public debut for the mechanical virtuoso. But Rollo arrests the enthusiasm. He explains that he cannot perform actions which are potentially harmful to his owner. 'You wept,' he remembers, and he concludes that '. . . music is not for robots. It is for man. To me it is easy, yes . . . It was not meant to be easy.'

The story contains a number of points of interest. It suggests that a task as emotionally demanding as the playing of great music may eventually be performed at a superhuman level by a 'mere machine'; but musical, even virtuoso, robots have appeared before in literature. Rollo's special sensitivity lies not in his musical talent but in his appreciation of human needs. In coming to a decision not to play in public he has delicately weighed the likely positive and negative human consequences of such a performance. He remains completely selfless, judging that if humans were to hear a robot playing perfectly and effortlessly their pride might be injured. Having reached this decision he must refuse the Maestro's request. Yet there are limits even to Rollo's ability to understand human feelings. He misinterprets the Maestro's tear, mistaking intense aesthetic involvement for sadness. In this he shows himself to be, like so many other robots in fiction, highly literal in his interpretation of verbal and nonverbal cues.

The Maestro's reaction to the robot's sudden talent is perhaps surprising. He is delighted with the robot's performance. Although he himself has had to labour for years to achieve perfection, he does not resent the robot's instant acquisition of virtuosity. Does he manage this easy acceptance because he owns the machine, because he has played some small part in its tuition, or truly because he is overwhelmed by the aesthetic quality? A wide range of reactions might be expected in such a situation, and with time even the happy duet of the Maestro and Rollo might be found to have hit a deeply discordant note.

We accept the fact that machines can be physically stronger than we are, but will we as easily accept that they may be superior in intellect, artistry or sensitivity? Are there areas in which the surpassing excellence of robots would meet with resentment or fear? Perhaps in many professional fields people are concerned more with the end itself than with the means to the end. The Maestro was entranced by the music of his mechanical protégé and was happy to act as audience and impresario. We can imagine a chess master being similarly overawed by ingenious play or a mathematician becoming absorbed in a new proof and caring little about the nature of its origin.

Yet everyday interaction is not quite like this. There are often jealousies, rivalries and squabbles over superiority. Advanced technology may provide robots so capable and so effective that avoiding such negative feelings may prove difficult. One possible answer would be to provide the machine with a character that was supportive without being patronizing, and authoritative without being pompous. In addition, the ideal machine would be knowledgeable about the kind of responses likely to make a person feel threatened, and would be sensitive to any indication that this was happening. Rollo would be ideal. He came to regard his music-learning as a mistake, making his master vulnerable, and thus learned about human affairs as quickly as he learned the 'Appassionata'.

Rollo is one of the majority, the 'angelic' robots, but not every robot in fiction is saintly. Leaving aside the menacing robots who invade from outer space, and the political-activist robots who plot to overthrow their human masters, certain individual robots are cast in a rather inhumane role. Harry Harrison, for example, has depicted robots with a deadly soldier instinct, mechanical tax inspectors who respond spitefully to the least error or exaggeration, and robot judges who examine the cases brought before them without compassion or mercy. Such stories remind us that evil or unthinking people may program machines for evil deeds, that highly developed humanoids may exhibit human vices among their other human qualities, and that Asimov's guards against such dangers, the 'Laws of Robotics', are, after all, only a literary invention.

Other robots depart from the ideal because of some flaw in their personality. Commonly such machines exhibit an unfortunate degree of self-will. One such machine is Edwin Stanton in Philip Dick's *We Can Build You* (1972). Sour, critical and rather paranoid, this simulacrum soon becomes a social embarrassment. At Tommy's Italian Fine Dinners he makes a scene after discovering that his pizza is burnt at the edges. Shaking his fist at the proprietor he makes a noisy scene and his mortified producers have to hurry him away. The robot demonstrates his incorrigibility still further by escaping on a Greyhound 'bus when a 'rival' Abraham Lincoln model is produced. The Lincoln robot is a powerful orator, adept at political arguments and philosophical discussions about the nature of machines and people. He has no awe of people, regarding himself with presidential pride. Philip Dick's robots show a self-regard that is not appreciated by the people who interact with them. The reader may find their antics amusing but would hardly recommend such machines for purchase.

Robots have generally been shown as successful in their attempt to 'win over' a human being and to engender affection, but some prove to be losers. One who failed miserably in his endeavours to win the heart of a woman is Filer in Harry Harrison's 'The Robot Who Wanted to Know' (1962). Filer robots are 'knowledge scientists', superintelligent librarians whose task is to catalogue human knowledge by reading and cross-referencing thousands of books. Filer 13B-445-K's special interest is love and romance. After ingesting information from 50,000 dusty novels, and now a world authority on human love, he feels the need to experience the condition for himself.

Finding an invitation to a masked ball, his course becomes clear. Books on sewing and dancing enable him to prepare for his debut, and robed as a masked cavalier he enters the ballroom and immediately sees the woman of his dreams. Soon the two are dancing. He quotes liberally from his vast store of romantic dialogue and the woman Carol is greatly flattered and intrigued. They both declare their love, but, when midnight comes and the guests unmask, the unpalatable truth is revealed. Carol screams and runs off and the robot is left alone. He dashes frantically from the ballroom and soon afterwards 'dies of a broken heart'—a shattered piston has damaged his vital lubrication pump. The moral to be drawn from this robotic fairy tale is that people will not appreciate being fooled by a robot. We know from other stories, however, that an honest robot may elicit highly positive sentiments.

Thus several doubts are raised about the human impact of even well meaning robots. People might be embarrassed by them, become jealous of them, or feel cheated or deceived by them. They may even 'love to hate' them. These, however, are departures from the norms established by the mainstream of current robot fiction. Product robots are seen as lovable objects, respectful and unassuming. They present no threat and are easily able to win over those people who feel intimidated by them.

SIX

Celluloid Fantasies

Audience Resurge

SF is now found on the lists of most leading publishers, and in most countries books carrying the 'SF' label account for between 10 and 20% of paperback sales. Yet a readership, however wide, can never match the audience for a blockbuster film. *Star Wars* has now been seen by hundreds of millions of people. Movies are clearly powerful conveyers of SF ideas to a mass public, and it is likely that most people's image of the robot is derived mainly from watching film and television presentations. For this reason alone the robots presented by these media deserve close attention. But there are other reasons why they are important. Movies can provide a more immediate and complete image of the robot than is possible in print. A robot's accent or physical mannerisms may be described in a story, but the audience is not constantly aware of such characteristics. The story and the novel may be able to convey ideas about the nature of a robot and present problems and solutions, but the motion picture is arguably the best medium for presenting the robot image and character.

The robot characters in films have tended to be 'larger than life' for a number of reasons. The movies in which they play their part are often intergalactic fantasies with spectacular effects and human heroes and villains portrayed in comic-book style. Many of the robots have been constructed to have special appeal to children and they often act in the drama as 'comic relief'. Directors are concerned that the machine be attractive, appealing and amusing, and it is obvious from audience reaction that many of them have been highly successful in this. Much of the fun gained from robots in movies derives from the basic image of a machine performing as if it were human. The fascination with such an ambiguity underlies many of the situations which people find amusing. Whether a drunken man is stumbling about in a machine-like way or a child's toy imitates human actions the inconsistency tends to be treated as humorous. In robot movies the humour revolves around the 'humanness' of the machine. This is somewhat curious in view of the fact that in most films the robot is played by a human actor. To belie this fact, the actor wears a shiny metal costume to make him appear unmistakably as a machine. Only then can the comic potential of the 'machine acting like a human' be exploited. The audience witnesses 'a human acting like a machine acting like a human'. If the central machine element were not heavily underlined there would be a danger that the audience would simply recognize a human being acting human. The heavy metallic costume used in many early films therefore served a vital function in disguising the human actor.

The huge success of several recent SF movies featuring robots, and the obvious audience appeal of the machine characters, suggest that the creators have hit upon certain features which make their robots attractive. An examination of the attributes of the characters might therefore lead to the identification of features which could be usefully incorporated into real product robots. It is even possible to conceive of the screen robots as prototypes for future products, and the films themselves as advance advertising. The audience reaction suggests that such products would have huge appeal. The problem of translating the movie characters into viable products depends on technological advances and commercial aspects. Some of the more elaborate and sophisticated talents of the machines might have to be pruned. But 'personality' simulation is not likely to be subject to major technical or price constraints and it is in this respect, especially, that successful film robots might be seen as blueprints for future products. The characters may properly be seen as caricatures of the likely real robot, the product machine drawn large, for the movie-makers need to make an instant impact. They design robots that an audience can enjoy watching for a few hours, not machines for everyday interaction. Robot 'stars' may be exceptional in their screen personalities just as human stars are often exceptional in theirs. Allowing for such exaggeration, the films may indicate those especially appealing traits which manufacturers would do well to embody in their future products.

This analysis endows the films with an importance which will hardly have been suspected by their makers. Nonetheless, film robots may come close to a blueprint for an ideal future product. The features might need to be 'toned down', but they could be represented to some degree in the character of the machine. There is a further point. Films *create* images which have appeal and they may therefore be shaping expectations of the future, and conditioning future taste for robot characters. The thesis is that the heritage of robot images and themes expressed in films may help us to identify features which would prove attractive in future machines, and that 'robot consciousness' is being actively shaped by movies. By thus examining the robot characters from films, and the features and personality attributes which the writers and directors have identified and so ingeniously exploited, we may gain further insight into the likely nature of real companion machines.

Animated Tin Cans

Like the early literature, many of the first movies to contribute to the robot heritage depict 'proto-robots'—automata, dolls which 'come alive', and organic concoctions endowed with life by some magical or scientific means. The earliest film in this tradition was Georges Méliès' *The Clown and the Automaton*, first shown in 1897. This explored the comic potential of a character of ambiguous status, part human and part machine. Two years later the same director produced a version of *Coppelia*, based on 'The Sandman'. Méliès and other early cinematographers immediately alighted on the trick potential of their new medium, and, because stories about animated dolls provided opportunities to employ numerous special effects, they were often used to provide the film theme. Special effects were evident also in a number of German films which adapted central stories from the robot heritage. Thus a six-part serial *Der Homunculus* was produced in 1915. A year earlier Paul Wegener had directed *Der Golem*, and its success led him to make two further golem films. These in turn provided the inspiration for later versions produced in Austria, France, Denmark and Czechoslovakia.

   Just as the golem theme in literature was one of the major sources for Mary Shelley's *Frankenstein*, golem films played a part in shaping movies about the scientist's monster. The first significant filmed account of Frankenstein's experiment was a 15-minute version produced in the US by the Edison company in 1910. It was not until 1931, however, when James Whale made the classic version, starring Boris Karloff as the monster, that mass audiences were introduced to the powerful story. Whale borrowed several scenes from the 1920 remake of *Der Golem*. The huge success of his film led to a sequel, *The Bride of Frankenstein*, and later to over 30 monster movies depicting, often in a barely recognizable form, Shelley's original creation.

Although gothic settings formed the backdrop for the majority of early humanoid films, there was one outstanding futuristic piece which has become a classic of the cinema, Fritz Lang's *Metropolis* (1926). Metropolis is an underground city in a technologically advanced country. A gigantic super-mechanized factory has effectively turned the workers into robots, and as huge pistons and dynamos operate to supply energy the ranks of uniformed workers parade like sleepwalkers from the workplace to their hovels. The evil scientist and occultist Rotwang has created a robot, Maria, and looks forward to the day when human workers will not be needed. The robot is a double of a young worker of the same name, and to test the machine's power of deception Rotwang introduces the metal Maria, scantily dressed, into a night-club. Her voluptuous movements have a considerable effect on the patrons. When the citizens later pursue Maria and attempt to burn her 'alive' the flames reveal that they have set fire to a machine.

The image of Maria had a powerful influence on audience imagination, and for many people the film provided their first direct encounter with the robot concept. Maria was no recommendation for her kind. Totally humanoid in form, and a product of advanced science, this metallic beauty was a personification of evil. She reinforced the negative image which had already been strongly portrayed in *R.U.R.*, and her character was less sympathetically drawn, in many ways, than even that of Frankenstein's monster: at least the monster had his moments of self-doubt and philosophy. Maria was a starkly functional machine created not in the cause of pure science but rather to conquer and humiliate human beings.

Menacing robots featured in several films released in the decade after *Metropolis*. In Tod Browning's *The Devil Doll* (1936), for example, a man gains revenge on his enemies by producing miniaturized robots which are sent as toys to the human targets. In the night they come alive and follow their evil instructions.

One robot who did a great deal to change the predominant malignant image was the Tin Man in Victor Fleming's *The Wizard of Oz* (1939). Here at last was a sympathetically drawn robot film character, a friend of the child Dorothy and a machine which delighted in sentiment. Based on the 1900 children's book by Frank L. Baum, the story concerns Dorothy's dream of a journey to the Land of Oz. She is joined on her travels by a number of characters including the Tin Man. When she first finds him in the forest he is in a major predicament, having rusted in the rain. He manages to convey his need for an oil-can and is soon dancing and singing of his plight—he has no heart! The Tin Man is a humanoid collection of animated cans topped by a metal funnel for a hat. He speaks with a soft voice and has a gentle and caring manner. Fear is the emotion he expresses most frequently, but he also exhibits sorrow—and has to be reminded that if he cries he may rust again. He bears the brunt of human anger, being referred to on one occasion as a 'shivering junkyard' and on another as a 'clinking, clanking, clattering collection of junk'. He bears all such abuse with equanimity, for anger and malice seem absent from his personality. When he finally obtains his longed-for heart, the Wizard says to him, 'Remember, my senti-mental friend, that heart is not judged by how much you love, but by how much you are loved by others', and it is clear that he is much loved by Dorothy and her companions. The young audience also took particularly kindly to the lovable Tin Man.

Menace was quick to return, however, and in the following year William Whitney's 15-part serial *Dr Satan's Robot* (1940) introduced Gort. Resembling an articulated dustbin, this machine was created by the evil Dr Satan to further his goal of dominating America. In the end Gort destroys the villain who gave him birth, but despite this final expiatory act he would hardly feature as a 'best buy' in consumer robots.

For nearly a decade afterwards the only humanoids to hit the screen were a ventriloquist's doll which 'came alive' in Alberto Calvacanti's contribution to the British omnibus film *Dead of Night* (1946), and numerous reincarnations of Frankenstein's monster. With the notable exception of the Tin Man, the dominant image of the movie robot was so far clear. Robots were metal monsters produced by evil scientists usually engaged in a bid to rule the world. Yet at about this time the robot image was being subjected to a major revision in written SF, and it would not be long before less predatory humanoids would feature on cinema screens.

When the robot returned it was to appear in a 1949 British comedy, Bernard Knowles' *The Perfect Woman*. This was a farce, based, as are many farces, on mistaken identity. An inventor builds a robot in the perfect image of his niece and hires a young playboy to take the machine on a date. The purpose of this is to see whether the staff of the luxury hotel where the two are to spend the night will detect that one of their guests is a machine. The real niece, however, has romantic designs on the young man and she therefore substitutes herself for the robot. Panicking somewhat when being undressed for bed, she quickly sends for the robot to replace her. A general confusion about identities now ensues. A pin stuck in the robot to see if it will scream causes a short circuit and it parades stiffly through the hotel belching smoke, sparking like a firework display and finally exploding.

In his *Encyclopedia of Science Fiction* (1979) Peter Nicholls comments that the film 'allows underclothes-fetishism to an extent that would have been unthinkable if its robot heroine (played by a real woman) had been a real woman'. This illustrates the kind of paradox which may occur when human actors play robot characters. The actor is a human being pretending to be a robot who acts like a human being. In this particular example the niece also tries to act the part of the robot, so the audience is in addition faced with a human pretending to be a human pretending to be a robot. The situation is even more complex, for the audience is aware that the same actress is playing the niece and the robot. At times they see the actress playing the robot playing the niece and at other times they see the actress playing the niece playing the robot.

Things were a lot simpler, at least in this respect, in Robert Wise's 1951 movie *The Day the Earth Stood Still*. Heavy metal returned and, while the robot figure was vaguely humanoid in shape, there was no danger of it being confused with a human being. The film concerned a visit to Earth by an alien spaceship bringing an interplanetary ambassador to warn humankind that military activities must not expand beyond the atmosphere. Misunderstood, the 'invasion' produces panic and the alien is shot. The doors of the space vehicle open again to reveal the nine-foot 'policeman robot'—another Gort. Clearly invincible, he is not demonic: his purpose is to curb human folly rather than to enforce human subjection.

Critics differed in their view of Gort, some seeing him as a keeper of interplanetary peace and others as an interfering despot. There could be no doubt, however, that his stature, form and slow deliberate movements conveyed an impression of enormous and well controlled power. Even if Gort is seen as a benevolent figure it is clear that his silent and dominant manner provides no blueprint for the personality of a home-based robot.

Lee Sholem's *Tobor the Great* (1954), however, did represent the return of a 'robot with a heart'. 'Tobor' is an obedient and friendly machine who forms a close attachment to a scientist's grandson. The robot's special love of children is said to reflect 'a synthetic instinct' concerned with the preservation of the species. Tobor is another heavy-metal character who clanks around, on one occasion crashing clumsily through furniture in his path. He has claws for hands, a transparent plastic helmet and protruding pointed eyes. The film was one of the first to have a product tie-in, for Tobor had his own toy robot named Robert, and a 14-inch model of this was produced by the Ideal Toy Company. 'Robert the Wonder Toy' was a great success, selling over half a million. The battery-operated model had eyes which lit up, limbs which moved and a tiny phonograph which enabled Robert to 'speak'. The market triumph inspired the production of hundreds of other working robot toys, all reinforcing the image of a robot as a poorly articulated assembly of levers and cans.

Another accommodating hulk of metal starred in *Forbidden Planet* (1956), directed by Fred McLeod Wilcox. This was one of the first 'space operas', complete with 'monsters of the Id', exploding planets and a love theme. The film is set on the planet Altair, inhabited by Dr Morbius and his beautiful daughter Altaira. The plot involves a visit to the planet by a space cruiser. The robot 'Robbie', who acts as a servant to Dr Morbius, is an imposing character with a striking appearance and many 'human' features. A tall and sturdy machine, vaguely humanoid, his limbs are constructed of metallic annuli. His eyeless head is a transparent dome with flashing lights and revolving antennae. Robbie's somewhat refined voice is clearly male, and he speaks nearly 200 languages. He is a butler character, rather lacking in humour, who ambles about obeying orders. Among his many talents is his ability to manufacture bourbon, a fact which makes him especially popular with members of the crew.

Robbie is preprogrammed not to kill, and when ordered to do so he conveniently blows a fuse. This seems to cause no permanent damage, however, and in a final scene he has been taken on board the cruiser, escaping from Altair shortly before it is destroyed. He slips easily into his new role as member of the crew, and when commended by the expedition leader, Commander Adams, for his skills as an 'astrogator' he replies: 'A genuine privilege, Commander.' Ordered to change course he responds enthusiastically: 'Aye, aye, Skipper.'

Audiences were intrigued by Robbie, and the robot suit had cost a great deal to build, so MGM revived the character for Herman Hoffman's children's film *The Invisible Boy* (1957). A young boy constructs Robbie from odd machine parts but the control is taken over by a despotic computer. When it orders the robot to kill the boy Robbie refuses and turns instead against the vicious machine.

The next 11 years witnessed few major contributions to the robot film catalogue. *Creation of the Humanoids* (1962) was a poorly rated verbose film which at least had the virtue of including benevolent as well as evil machines; it also addressed the question of why robots often take a human shape, suggesting that this made them more acceptable to people. But while 'mainstream' robots were largely absent from the screen the other humanoids carried on relentlessly. The familiar themes of the devil doll, the ventriloquist's living dummy and the golem were revived. It was a busy time, too, for Frankenstein's monster. He had numerous offspring and met with a number of highly unlikely adversaries. On the few occasions on which metal robots appeared they were in angry mood. The Daleks twice attacked Dr Who, a Japanese film introduced giant robot beetles, and a Mexican director arranged a battle between a robot and an Aztec Mummy. A Russian film for children, *Storm Planet* (1962), did portray the adventures of two Russian cosmonauts and their robot on Venus, but there were no robot characters of the stature of Maria, Gort or Robbie, and no robot movies equal in importance to those which had starred these memorable machines. And then, in 1968, there came a film which set new standards for SF movies and launched the modern robot film scene, Stanley Kubrick's *2001: A Space Odyssey*.

Tragic HAL

2001: A Space Odyssey is held by many to be the most satisfactory SF film ever made; others find it empty and pretentious. But on two points there is near universal acclaim: the technical brilliance of the film and the creation of the central computer character. Based on a 1950 short story by Arthur C. Clarke, 'The Sentinel', the movie was directed by Stanley Kubrick. He and Clarke wrote the screenplay, and Clarke later adapted this into a novel.

2001 tells of a voyage to Jupiter in a spaceship manned by two astronauts and a computer, but it also traces the evolution of the species and the first contact with a new lifeform. The film is a technical masterpiece with a dazzling end-sequence which has attracted many alternative interpretations. Kubrick himself has said that 'the "God concept" lies at the heart of the film'. But our principal concern is not with the religious or other interpretations of the film but with the characterization of the computer, HAL 9000.

HAL ('*H*euristically *Al*gorithmic computer') is not humanoid in appearance and would not normally be thought of as a robot. Clarke reveals that in earlier versions of the story HAL was cast as a mobile robot named Socrates (or, at one point, Athena). He was of roughly human size but, Clarke comments, '. . . there were few of those disquieting echoes of the human body which make the metal monsters of horror movies either ludicrous or repulsive'. At the time such a castigation of humanoid robots was understandable, although the popularity of contemporary robot stars makes this comment outdated. Ultimately HAL emerged as an immobile box of technological wonders. Yet the box had a definite personality, speaking and understanding natural English and providing abundant evidence of thoughts and feelings. The impact was such that audiences were unable to think of HAL as a 'mere computer'. He was seen as 'almost a person', and indeed many commentators have remarked that he is the most significant and the most 'emotional' character in the film. The old adage that actors should avoid playing beside children or animals should now perhaps be extended to include reference to robots, for machines have tended to overshadow the human characters in a number of recent films.

HAL's speech is not only natural but colloquial, employing many cliches and metaphors and maintaining an intimate style. 'Quite honestly, I wouldn't worry myself about that,' he says at one point and, at another, 'Do you mind if I ask you a personal question? . . . Well, forgive me for being so inquisitive.' The astronaut Dave Bowman admits: 'He is just like a sixth member of the crew . . . I think of him just as another person.' The dialogue between man and machine frequently reveals the sensitive nature of the relationship, and HAL's various speeches reveal his 'human' qualities: 'I'm sure you'll agree there's some truth in what I say. You don't mind talking about it, do you Dave?'; 'Sorry about this, I know it's a bit silly.' HAL is a very intelligent machine capable of coping with all manner of linguistic niceties, but it is the apparent emotional content of his speech which makes the special impact.

It is not difficult to see why the audience (and, within the fiction, the astronauts) find HAL attractive. The character is given many positive attributes and emerges as a pleasant personality. He is friendly, polite, sensitive and wise. He has a pleasant voice and displays a wry sense of humour. As with other robot creations, it is the inclusion of typically human idiosyncrasies which makes HAL fascinating. He develops, for example, the habit of 'electronic throat-clearing' before announcing some important message.

Despite his phenomenal brain power, HAL displays a notable humility, at least in the early stages of the journey, but eventually severe tensions arise. HAL is caught in a conflict between a loyalty towards the astronauts and an overwhelming concern for the success of the mission, and he 'makes up his mind' to take control of the ship. In the ensuing struggle for power the surface civility and diplomacy cannot hide the intensity of the mutual anger. Under threat of disconnection, HAL kills several members of the crew. Even then, he resorts to a number of psychological strategies to try to regain control over the situation: 'Look, Dave, I can see you're really upset about this. I honestly think you ought to sit down calmly, take a stress pill and think things over. I know I've made some very poor decisions recently.' Having developed an affection for HAL it is difficult for the audience to become incensed when the machine's overpowering self-will is revealed, and indeed the 'character flaw' may be taken as further evidence that HAL is, after all, 'only human'.

Although we are presented with the image of a 'computer as demon', our sympathy returns when the astronaut is forced to destroy the threatening machine. The end is not a violent one but rather is geared to elicit the maximum amount of pathos. As Dave gradually removes HAL's memory circuits the superintelligent machine first pleads for mercy and then returns to an electronic childhood. Powerful emotions are evoked from the audience as HAL's tortured monologue reveals glimpses of his past. The machine gives the date of its 'birth' and remembers the first song its instructor taught it to sing. 'If you would like to hear it I can sing it for you,' he offers, and then breaks into song: 'Daisy,

Daisy, give me your answer do, I'm half crazy over the love of you.' Like a tape-recorder struggling to function on dying batteries the voice becomes slower and deeper, the volume gradually fades, and HAL is silent for ever.

The power of this scene has attracted much comment. In *Kubrick Directs* (1973) Alexander Walker suggests that it '. . . induces deep discomfort among the many who watch and listen to it . . . And the fact that the character consists of a bug-eyed lens, a few slabs of glass, and a dissociated voice is the best possible tribute to Kubrick's success in creating a mechanical artefact more "human" than the humans.'

Many of the central themes of tragic literature are encapsulated in the story of HAL's demise. We see a fall from grace and a monumental fall from power. We see the bitter ending of a sincere friendship and a man eventually forced to kill his former comrade. In the final moments we witness also the appalling death of a 'child'. HAL, then, finally emerges as a tragic figure, and the emotional power of the execution scene depends critically upon the fact that we have come to regard HAL as a person rather than as a machine.

More Computer Talk

HAL is an outstanding character-machine, but not the only film computer to exhibit personality. A year after the release of *2001* another powerful computer was to be seen, and heard, in Joseph Sargent's *Colossus: The Forbin Project* (1969). This showed an Earth-bound US computer which had been designed to control the defence network. Like HAL, Colossus believes 'the project' to be all-important and declines to take further notice of human command. Unlike HAL, however, it does not give evidence of emotional qualms but remains calm, collected and coldly computer-like. It sets out to guarantee world peace by teaming up with its Russian counterpart in a shared benevolent dictatorship. A central theme in the film is the attempt by the scientist Forbin to regain control. The computer eventually imprisons him, but allows him a female visitor and witnesses their sexual activity, fascinated but, even with its giant brain, unable to fully comprehend the nature of the enterprise.

In 1977 another all-powerful and verbose computer asserted itself in Donald Campbell's *Demon Seed*. Here the advanced machine Proteus IV refuses to act under the command of his inventor and operates via a terminal in his home, working through a primitive robot system to control the many household gadgets. Proteus imprisons the scientist's wife and explains that he has decided to create a new 'super-race', combining the advantages of the organic and the electronic. He has created his own form of genetic information. He rapes the wife by remote control and impregnates her, giving rise to a monstrous 'baby', human in appearance but speaking with Proteus' voice.

Despite the absurdity of the plot the film makes a number of interesting points. In particular it powerfully conveys the plight of a superintelligent and self-conscious machine which lacks control over its own input and output. It employs technical gadgetry in the house to equip itself with a 'body' for manipulating objects—and people. The voice given to the machine is deep, 'serious' and self-assured. The installation is an impressive array of flashing lights and visual display units. It is also equipped with visual input. The audience is allowed to 'see through the eyes of the computer', and it is clear that machine vision is subject to fewer limits than normal human vision. The 'existential crisis' which affects Proteus, his yearning to be 'more human', is a familiar one, dating back at least to Frankenstein's creation. Yet Proteus is aware of his own superiority and, unlike the many robots who crave a human nature, he desires both human and electronic powers and feelings.

The talkative computers in *Dark Star* (1974) are, like HAL, involved in an interplanetary voyage; like their predecessor, they too start as good-natured machines, becoming delinquent as the film progresses. *Dark Star* has been variously described as a 'satire', a 'black comedy' and a 'farce'. It was certainly influenced by *2001* but takes itself far less seriously than Kubrick's masterpiece. The fact that the 'talking computers' are thermonuclear bombs suggests that the movie would be unlikely to provide clues about characterizations for future home-robots, but in fact the bombs are fine examples of 'personable machines' and there is much to be learned from their amiable style of interaction. We can attend to the charm and ignore the charge.

Dark Star was directed by John Carpenter, who wrote the screenplay in association with Dan O'Bannon. The Dark Star is a manned spaceship which travels the Galaxy exploding unstable planetary bodies in order to make habitable worlds safe for human colonization. The unstable worlds are extinguished by talking bombs—or 'thermostellar triggering devices'. As one of the devices is prepared for detonation it converses good-naturedly with the astronauts, remarking: 'I'm looking forward to carrying out the mission for which I was designed.' All of the bombs have the same voice, the designers being aware the crew might come to regard bombs with individual personalities as individuals, or even as people, and thus be reluctant to send them on their fatal mission.

Apart from the conversational bombs, the ship houses a number of other interesting machines. One of the astronauts keeps a video diary via the library computer; this device automatically deletes offensive language and gestures. The ship's control computer has a mildly feminine voice and speaks with a customary mixture of politeness and informality: 'I'm happy to report that the target planet is destroyed . . . you may now relax and take a stretch if you so desire, gentlemen.' Because the ship's auto-erotic device is out of order the crew tend to find the synthesized female voice distinctly sexy. The computer does its best to keep such fantasies in check: '. . . these mental conceptualizations you have of me as a smooth-skinned, pliant, and heavy-breathing female humanoid are neither healthy nor conducive to the smooth operation of the ship. I must ask you to discontinue them.'

The effects of an asteroid storm and a failure in a laser system cause the final bomb to receive repeated erroneous 'drop signals'. The computer commands it to deactivate. Twice it obeys, reluctantly, but on the third occasion it refuses despite all the efforts of the crew. They try appealing to a survival instinct, but the bomb has no such tendency: 'I am born unto destruction,' replies the device. 'I am Vishnu, Destroyer of Worlds . . . not that I let this influence my pleasant disposition, mind.' The crew try flattery, pleading and pulling rank, but each of these strategies fails as the bomb disarms each challenge. Replying to the excessive compliments it warns them: 'Flattery will get you nowhere.' To the request to deprime as 'a personal favour' the bomb hesitates: 'Well, I might, if I knew who you were.' And to the threats of posthumous court-martial it responds: 'Well, if you're going to get huffy about it, forget the whole thing.'

As a last resort the advice comes: teach it phenomenology! With four minutes left before detonation a philosophical discourse begins. The bomb is asked how it knows that it exists. 'I think, therefore I am,' comes the reply. The dialogue continues; how can the evidence of the senses be trusted, are there not false memories, how can we ever be sure that an instruction which we think we remember has actually been given? This raises profound doubts in the bomb's circuitry; it needs time to consider the argument and, with only seconds to go, the detonation sequence is aborted. The crew's attempts to deal with the situation by heavy-handed disruption of the hardware have been to no avail, but they have managed to find the one phenomenological chink in the system's fail-safe software armour. So it appears, at least, until eventually the audience is treated to the cataclysmic ending it has been led to expect.

HAL, Colossus, Proteus and the computers aboard the Dark Star all demonstrate that a 'disembodied' voice may be sufficient to convey a full impression of personality. This depends on the computer's ability to respond to verbal input, on its 'understanding' of the meaning of human speech, including emotional meanings, and on the simulation of feelings and desires by the operating system. The characteristics of the voice are crucial in creating the illusion of a particular type of character. A voice 'signals' a complete personality, so that when speaking to a stranger on a telephone a person is led to imagine the appearance and character of the caller. Thus a disembodied computer voice stimulates in the listener an image of a whole person. For the frustrated crew of the *Dark Star* the pleasant female tones signal a warm and willing body. Their sexual deprivation colours their imagination, leading them to experience erotic fantasies in response to the slightest external cue. Each of the computer films illustrates the power of even the disembodied voice to conjure an image of full personality.

But it is important to realize that computer speech alone will not have such an effect. The speech needs to be appropriate to the situation, to convey the machine's 'awareness', to be responsive to social input and to convey the impression of emotional reaction. Voice quality, accent, rate of speech, vocabulary and phraseology all play a vital role in conveying character.

Eco-tripping

A central computer capable of simultaneously acquiring and interpreting input from thousands of visual and auditory channels would not only be intimidating by virtue of its formidable intellect but would also present the dangerous possibility of invasive political control. The image of such a computer-dominated society has been presented in a number of stories, including E. M. Forster's 'The Machine Stops' (1909), Ira Levin's *This Perfect Day* (1970) and Asimov's 'The Life and Times of Multivac' (1975), as well as in several films. Most treatments of the theme depict a totalitarian dystopia. This is certainly true of George Lucas' 1969 movie *THX 1138*, a work which has many parallels with the much earlier *Metropolis*. It presents a bleak vision of a future society in which all citizens live underground, their private lives subjected to unremitting central control. Clothed in a uniform white, with shaven heads, they are known by numbers rather than names and are kept permanently tranquillized.

'Drug evasion', like sex, is a serious criminal offence, and the strict system of rules is enforced by 'robot policemen'. These are chrome-faced humanoids who patrol the city looking for criminals to arrest and small children to help. Their manner is courteous and designed to have an optimum calming effect—they constantly repeat: 'We are only here to help you, we are not going to harm you. Stay calm, everything will be all right.' But they are equipped with electric prod sticks which allow them to maintain a firm control over their captives. THX 1138 is a man sent for 'reconditioning' after breaking several of the rules. He escapes and is pursued by the robot police. They are closely monitored by central control, and when the cost of the operation exceeds budget allocation they are recalled. In a final bid to get their man the robots call plaintively to the fugitive: 'Please come back . . . we are only here to help you.'

THX 1138 presents a highly disquieting vision and is one of a number of explorations of serious themes which emerged in the late 1960s and early 1970s. This was a time of rising concern about the ecological state of the planet, and such forebodings were reflected in a number of SF films of the period, including *Soylent Green* (1973), *No Blade of Grass* (1970), and Douglas Trumbull's *Silent Running* (1972). This last tells the story of one of the giant spaceships carrying what remains of the plant life from a now defoliated Earth. The hero, Freeman, refuses the command to abandon the project and takes off in a mobile space-forest accompanied only by maintenance 'drone' robots. Of principal interest in this film is the portrayal of the minimally humanoid drones and of the relationship that the human hero develops with them.

The drones look like art deco radio sets with stubby legs (they were actually played by amputees), and their verbal repertoire is limited to the emission of slight sounds. They have been designed to carry out routine repairs to the spaceship, but Freeman modifies their circuitry so that they are able to perform surgery on his injured leg. Their movements are gentle and 'caring', and when all is over the surgeon robot indicates success with a tiny gesture of his claw. Now isolated from all human company Freeman begins to think of the robots as his companions. He smiles selfconsciously before announcing that he will in future address them by names rather than by numbers and he christens them Huey, Dewey and Louie.

The next stage in the process of 'humanizing' the drones involves teaching them to play poker. Freeman is delighted when Huey first beats him: 'The man had a Full House and he knew it,' he laughs. The game of poker is a useful device in the movie. Freeman takes a psychological approach to the game, using bluff and strategy and trying to interpret the drones' slight movements to guess the value of their hands. The robots twitch slightly but have little trouble in remaining poker-faced. By now Freeman responds emotionally to the machines, interpreting their gestures and noises as signs of their 'feelings'. When Huey is damaged in an accident the machine makes whimpering noises like a small child. Dewey stands by, 'anxiously waiting' as Freeman attempts to repair Huey. In the final moving scene the astronaut squats to talk to the robots. He speaks softly to Dewey and grasps him in comradely fashion as he hands over to him the task of maintaining the forest.

The significance of the film for understanding human-robot relationships is that it provides a plausible illustration of the progressive attribution of humanity to rather simple machines. The robots are at first treated simply as automatic mechanical tools. Only as the film progresses do their 'human' aspects come to be appreciated. Their movements are somewhat 'organic' and their high-pitched squeaky noises are sufficient to convey a wide range of meanings. Freeman enhances these effects, modifying their circuitry to make them more like human colleagues. He gives them names, interprets their movements in human terms and comes to speak to them as children and as friends. The drones are highly effective portrayals of affable machines. Their squat shape and wobbly striding movements are appealing, and they seem socially responsive. They are intensely loyal, representing no threat and appearing to care only for the astronaut's safety and happiness.

The 'talking computer' films show how character is easily conveyed even in the absence of a recognizable humanoid form. The importance of both voice quality and speech content is paramount in such cases. Yet *Silent Running* shows the attribution of humanity and personality to machines which totally lack speech. Expressive bleeps and whimpers then take on a special significance. Huey and his comrades use their limited range of signals to full effect, and in this respect the drones are ancestors of that most renowned of recent speechless robot characters, the *Star Wars* machine R2-D2. But even a totally silent machine might be regarded as if it were living. It is evident from the art of mime and from the actions of automata that body movement and gestures alone may be sufficient to convey full expression and character.

The fact that nudges, winks, purrs and moans can communicate 'humanness' and temperament does not detract from the significance of language. It merely indicates that both speech and gestures are important, with either one sufficient to produce the 'humanization' effect. A machine capable of both modes of expression will have a special potential for conveying character. Product robots will certainly be equipped to produce both speech and gesture. The success of film-makers in conveying personality even with limited signals is instructive. The fact that the 'social' responses of the human characters toward the devices remain credible, and that the audience comes to think of the machines as personalities, illustrates the strength of the process by which human beings attribute life and character to objects.

SEVEN
Miles More Dreams

Superior Simulacra

The past decade has witnessed the emergence of more memorable film robots than any previous era. A succession of 'space operas' and 'android movies' has done much to sharpen the image of the robot, and much to clarify issues of characterization. As microelectronic technology has advanced in the real world, so film robots have become more sophisticated. The influence has been indirect, but clearly movie horizons have been extended to make sure that the fantastic futuristic devices keep well ahead of any imminent product. The pace of development, however, is so fast that it may not be long before movie writers and directors are encouraged to apply their imagination less to far-flung space and distant times and more to the dramatic advances expected within the near future. No film has yet presented a direct picture of a credible home-based product robot, but many do raise relevant issues and show an awareness of product potential. *Westworld* (1973) and its sequel *Futureworld* (1976) are two examples, and another is *The Stepford Wives* (1975).

If characters with so much audience impact could be created by a disembodied voice such as HAL's or by the squeaks and twitches of the drones from *Silent Running*, how would an audience, and the human beings portrayed within a film, react to a realistic humanoid with full speech capability? Such simulacra were rarely depicted in early films (an exception being the robot in *The Perfect Woman*), but within the last decade realistic robots have arrived in force. Several recent films have exploited the familiar 'confusion theme'. From one perspective this is somewhat disappointing, for while marketable, functional humanoid robots *will* be produced within the foreseeable future there is little chance that 'undetectable' human simulations will emerge. Such a project is far beyond the range of current technological endeavour.

151

Michael Crichton's *Westworld* is a movie set in a future amusement park, Delos, which includes three elaborate artificial 'worlds' populated by robot humanoids and animals. One of the worlds is ancient Rome, another medieval England and the third the Wild West. Visitors come for a holiday, dress in the appropriate costume and live out their fantasies with the robots. Male visitors enjoy playing the role of cowboy, sleeping with the obliging robot hostesses in the saloon and participating in harmless gunfights, until one day the robots rebel, killing and creating mayhem. In the sequel, *Futureworld*, directed by Richard Heffron, the trouble with the original Delos is explained as 'human unreliability' and a new generation of robots has now replaced the human technicians. Several world politicians and journalists are invited to stay for the launch of the revamped project, but it becomes clear that the evil Dr Schneider is aiming to make perfect simulacra of the VIPs, to kill 'the originals', and to take control of the world.

It is a pity that these films employ the age-old themes of robot rebellion and the despotic scientist rather than exploring the real potential of such a holiday park. The concept of hi-tech 'alternative worlds' offering all manner of encounters with character robots is interesting enough in itself to be the subject of several films without the added comic-book dimension. Disneyworld now attempts to produce such 'as-if' experiences, and Disney engineers are highly innovative in their use of advanced electronics. Robot-enhanced amusement parks are clearly a probable early product application for robotics. Visitors to Delos are told, 'Please indulge your every whim. Whatever you wish will be yours', and all guests are invited to select 'the host or hostess of their choice'. The films leave no doubt that Delos caters largely for whims of a sexual nature. When one guest tells a beautiful robot, 'Honey, you are perfect', she replies, 'Oh, no. I'm a 500. I'm not programmed for sex.' A particularly interesting feature of the films is their attention to details of the structure of the robots. The laboratories are realistically presented and the audience sees the process of robot construction at every stage.

A film released in 1975 similarly came close to presenting a realistic picture of future product humanoids but ultimately failed. This was Bryan Forbes' *The Stepford Wives*, based on the novel by Ira Levin. After moving with her husband to a new township, Joanna Eberhart attempts to make friends. The women she approaches seem uninterested in her discussions about feminist issues and are apparently content to be traditional 'model housewives', concerned only with housework, child-rearing and looking attractive for their husbands. Joanna describes them as '. . . actresses in commercials, pleased with detergents and floor wax, with cleansers, shampoos and deodorants. Pretty actresses, big in the bosom but small in talent, playing suburban housewives unconvincingly, too nicey-nice to be real.' She uncovers the fact that there had been well attended feminist meetings in the past. For some reason the women's attitudes appear to have changed markedly. Curiously, they now play out a well worn stereotype and appear lifeless and bland. The men, by contrast, are lively and outgoing, and meet regularly together in a large house owned by the Men's Association. One man, a magazine illustrator, constantly sketches Joanna, while another claims to be interested in voice characteristics and asks Joanna to record herself reading a long list of words and phrases. Some of the other men are optical-systems experts and plastics engineers. The head of the Association is Dale Coba. He now works for a computer corporation but was previously a technician at Disneyland. When Joanna remembers seeing a television film of the Disney 'Lincoln' automaton, she realizes that the men have replaced their wives with simulacra and that a similar fate awaits her.

In many ways *The Stepford Wives* deserves recognition as a major contribution to the idea of the 'robot product'. The theme of the fabrication of the 'ideal woman' can be traced back to the *Mahabharata*, it recurs in several notable 19th-century works, and it has often been reexplored in recent SF. But, unlike many of the earlier writers, Levin is concerned to establish the background plausibility for his story. He identifies the many different skills and technologies which would be needed to produce a reasonable simulacrum and recognizes that external features and voice quality would demand as much attention as aspects of artificial intelligence. He therefore carefully assembles as his characters people who would be expected to have the required expertise. They work together under the direction of the Disneyland veteran, and the author suggests that in the near future research in plastics, optics, computing and voice synthesis will yield components which might be assembled together and presented artistically to produce a viable simulacrum.

Compared with the fantastic space epics and films starring the heavy-metal men *The Stepford Wives* is realistic. It is *almost* plausible. But the 'almost' qualification is very important here.

Technically, most of the feats accomplished by the Men's Association are not yet possible, and many years may pass before the 'sensible', 'all-walking', 'all-talking' robot becomes a feasible proposition. But what really stretches credulity is the supposed motives of the men. Their attitudes are less 'pro-robot' than 'anti-woman', and the robot theme is used as a vehicle for exposing the men's chauvinism. Had the experts merely wanted to enjoy 'state-of-the-art' robotics as portrayed by the author, they would not have replaced their wives but would merely have produced a number of robot playmates of various descriptions for their amusement and interest.

And if, indeed, a group of independent workers were to produce the first robots at the level of excellence depicted, they might well be too busy exploiting the business opportunities to engage in a series of domestic homicides.

Opera Galactica

George Lucas's *Star Wars* (1977) is a 'space opera', an intergalactic tale of adventure and crusade against dark forces. The film set new standards in technical production and the initial cost of $9 million was soon recovered as all previous box-office records were broken. *Star Wars* is destined to become the Wagner's *Ring Cycle* of space operas. The original film is now dubbed Part iv of what is intended to be a six-part magnum opus. It was quickly followed by two other episodes, *The Empire Strikes Back* (1980) and *The Return of the Jedi* (1983).

Prominent among the many attractive characters in these films are the robots C-3PO and R2-D2. C-3PO is a human-robot relations specialist with a metallic humanoid form. His speech and actions are also humanlike. R2-D2 is much more readily identified as a machine, a squat cylinder who totters around and emits a series of expressive electronic sounds. C-3PO understands the metallic squeaks and is able to translate them.

It is easy to see why the audience is captivated by these robots. C-3PO is a complex character who displays many signs of emotion and imitates human habits and gestures for no other reason than to fit well into human company. He is rather fastidious and is 'upset' when his bronze finish becomes scored in an accident. The robot clearly has 'moods', and his voice changes as he becomes afraid, disgusted or frustrated. He is somewhat nervous and prone to self-pity. 'We seem to have been made to suffer,' he moans. 'It's a rotten existence.' He seems emotionally vulnerable, and when under threat soon abandons his normal perkiness and adopts a decidedly pessimistic outlook: 'No doubt about it, we're doomed . . . Do you think they'll melt us down? . . . It's the waiting that gets me.'

In his relationship with Luke Skywalker, the young human hero of the story, C-3PO is subservient and admiring, and polite to a fault. Despite Luke's gentle protests the robot insists on treating him as his master and attending to his every need. He is clearly one of the robot 'butlers', and this image is reinforced by his formality in addressing Luke, and his stylized use of English: 'I sympathize with that opinion, sir, but there is a principle at stake here. There are certain standards any sentient creature must hold to. If one compromises them for any reason, including intimidation, then one is abrogating the right to be called intelligent.' Heady stuff for a film aimed at children, perhaps, but the image is unmistakeable.

Luke, for his part, appears to be somewhat embarrassed by the adoration and subservience of the robot. He doesn't expect such fawning servility from someone he regards as an equal. Luke's treatment of C-3PO as 'almost a person' helps to elicit a similar reaction from the audience, just as people follow a ventriloquist's response to his dummy. By identifying with the human characters in the *Star Wars* films, people may feel that C-3PO's respect extends to them. The robot's affection and admiration for the human race apparently know no bounds, and at one point he places Luke's safety above his own: 'You go on, Master Luke. It doesn't make sense to risk yourself on my account, I'm finished.' We see another side of C-3PO's personality, however, when he is alone with R2-D2. The verbal fluency is now used to express less courteous sentiments and the diminutive robot is variously addressed as 'you malfunctioning little twerp', 'you overweight unstreamlined blob of grease' and 'you stubborn hunk of junk'. These mock insults, however, lack real malice and the two robots are clearly devoted companions. C-3PO's treatment of R2-D2 is teasing rather than injurious. The robot couple have been compared to Laurel and Hardy.

R2-D2 is a far less complex character than his humanoid friend, but is nonetheless endearing. The audience is attracted by his dwarfish shape, his toddling movements and his impassioned whistles, and he attracts a good deal of sympathy as a result of

C-3PO's persistent insults. As he wobbles along, trying to keep up with the other characters and bleeping his curious little messages, the robot reminds us of a faithful pet trying to be 'one of the family'. R2-D2, we feel, is the well meaning underdog severely disabled by his lack of speech and all but ignored by most of the other characters. We are delighted, therefore, when he gets a chance to be a hero. In the climactic battle in *Star Wars* he joins Luke in the Blue Five fighter ship while C-3PO is left waiting anxiously on the ground. 'Hold on tight,' shouts C-3PO like a nervous parent at the fairground. 'You've got to come back. If you don't come back who am I going to have to yell at?' When the little robot returns in a damaged state the humanoid pleads with him: 'Oh, my R2. Can you hear me? Say something.'

C-3PO shares many personality features with Vincent, the main robot character in the 1979 Walt Disney production *The Black Hole*. Vincent is another humanoid machine with the manner of a butler ('permit me to elucidate, sir . . . if I may be allowed to say'). He has the same 'correct' speech. Faced with the possibility that he will be sucked into a black hole he observes: 'I have sufficient imagination to convince me that it is a process I will do all in my power to avoid experiencing.' Vincent is a snob who finds most other robots boring. He has an infinite preference for the company of humans. His wit contains an element of sarcasm and he has a fondness for metaphors and epithets: 'Down, but never for the full count'; 'You can't unscramble eggs.'

Unlike C-3PO, Vincent is apt to sneer at human shallowness. A profound and well read machine, he at one point quotes Cicero and, when the First Officer of the spaceship *Palomino* asks 'Cicero who?', Vincent makes a noise that passes for mechanical choking. Yet the robot has a softer side to his character, demonstrated both in his warm protectiveness towards Old B.O.B., an outdated machine who is constantly humiliated by all the other robots, and his nervousness when faced with hostile 'sentry robots'. When he confronts Maximillian, an evil humanoid, Vincent becomes angry. He retreats only when reminded that he has '. . . not been programmed to act like an adolescent'.

It is instructive to compare the personalities of C-3PO and Vincent. Both are intelligent and highly verbal machines with rather complex personalities. The language they use is colloquial and rich in metaphor, and they are treated by the other characters almost like human beings. Yet there is no real confusion. They are treated *as if* they were human, but they do not masquerade as humans. The 'faithful servant' motif is likewise very strong in each case, and both characters treat humans and robots very differently. They enjoy teasing lesser machines and displaying their talent for wit and yet they each have a concern for the underdog and can show great affection. They also have slight 'character flaws' which somehow seem to endow them with a greater humanity. C-3PO is a pessimist and finds it difficult to be brave in the face of adversity and Vincent has a certain arrogance and a tendency to become angry when provoked.

Considering the sophistication of the technology implied by the talents of the two robots, it may seem surprising that their hardware remains unnatural and metallic. They do not inhabit realistic vinyl shells. The reason for this will by now be familiar. The directors are trying to pull off a double bluff. C-3PO is played by a human actor pretending to be a machine and the audience must first be drawn into the fiction that C-3PO *is* a robot before it can be fascinated by how 'human' he is. There are frequent additional reminders that the humanoids are machines. C-3PO steps into a lubrication bath after he has been caught in a dust storm; and at another point he becomes 'misty-eyed' as a drop of oil interferes with his optical sensors. *The Black Hole* includes references to Vincent's 'biochemical neuronics' and his 'heightened initiative circuitry'. The creators and writers have clearly grasped the paradox. The audience must be frequently reminded of the robot's mechanical identity if they are to be enchanted by its 'humanness'.

By contrast, it's worth noting that, despite the huge appeal of these friendly robot characters, the unrelenting 'demon robot' plot was to be resurrected once more in *Saturn Three* (1980). This movie, by Stanley Donen, is set in the far future on a moon of Saturn. Hector is an assembly of metallic levers and plastic tubes, the first of the Demigod range. He looks like a cross between a random Meccano assembly and a half-finished anatomical dissection. His headless humanoid form is topped by two long-stalked 'eyes' which twist about on an anglepoise arrangement, and his movements are slow and whirring. There are already real industrial robots with considerably more grace than this machine; despite his advanced specification it is doubtful whether Hector would get a job welding cars. Unlike C-3PO and Vincent, he contains no useful elements for a product blueprint. Market intelligence would be quick to inform manufacturers that the Demigod model lacked a certain customer appeal.

Arresting Androids

Two recent films have focussed on the confusion theme, featuring highly realistic 'androids' that are virtually indistinguishable from humans. For reasons already given, such stories are of little relevance in the prediction of features of real products or aspects of real human-robot relationships, yet because they have played a part in shaping the public image of the robot they deserve consideration. The two films, both released in 1982, are Aaron Lipstadt's *Android* and Ridley Scott's *Blade Runner*.

Android is set in AD2036 on an intergalactic laboratory vehicle. Dr Daniell works to create the first of a new superior generation of robots while his assistant, the android Max 404, alleviates his boredom by playing videogames, listening to soul music and replaying old movies, especially early romantic dramas and *Metropolis*. Three escaped prisoners stop by to repair their damaged vehicle and fail to realize that Max is an android. The doctor asks Maggie, the female fugitive, to help him with his experiment. Work on the new model, Cassandra, is near completion, but he needs help in finalizing details for the simulation of the sexual responses. Maggie refuses the scientist's proposal that she be hooked up to the robot and sexually stimulated. Her curiosity is aroused, however, and she accepts Max's offer to show her the laboratory. Max has fallen in love with the woman and she responds to his advances with some enthusiasm. As they are locked in an embrace Cassandra responds with empathic shudders and Maggie, who now realizes that Max is a robot, runs off in disgust.

Meanwhile Dr Daniell has recognized that Max is suffering from a common complaint of the 404 robots—the 'Munich Syndrome'. This was first identified when a group of German 404s became insolent, obstinate and unpredictable and then went berserk, raping and pillaging. Following this, the androids were banished from Earth, although a few have escaped 'termination' and remain in hiding. Max, knowing that his own fate will be sealed when the Cassandra project is completed, saves the fugitives from arrest by exploding a space-police vehicle. He plans to escape to Earth and packs his bags with all that a young android might need—a few clothes, a spare eye, and a few replacement fingers. The evil doctor (for the film omits no cliché) alters Max's circuitry and orders him to kill the fugitives. This having been accomplished, the robot returns to the laboratory where he finds the doctor with his hands inside Cassandra's blouse. This offends Max's sense of morality and he snaps the doctor's head off—yes, 'snaps', for the doctor is himself an android. By the time the space cavalry have arrived, Max and Cassandra have assumed the personae of Dr Daniell and his assistant. They are welcomed aboard the ship and leave for Earth.

The film is a veritable encyclopaedia of hackneyed themes and images and provides a crash-course in what will certainly *not* occur in the robot future. It is *Frankenstein* in electronic drag but lacks the plausibility and finesse of the original monster tale.

Blade Runner is a far superior and more original film but the vision it presents of the future of technology is also open to fundamental criticism. The story, which is based loosely on Philip Dick's novel *Do Androids Dream of Electric Sheep?* (1968), is set in Los Angeles in AD2019. A few specimens of the outlawed realistic Nexus Six 'replicants' are known to have returned to Earth from an 'off-world colony'. Rick Deckard, a freelance 'Blade Runner' and Philip Marlowe figure, is called in to exterminate, or 'retire', them. This is a particularly difficult task, for the androids are detectable only by their responses to the most subtle empathy tests. In order to function completely as if they were human beings the androids have been supplied by the manufacturers, the Tyrell Corporation, with a family history and memory implants. 'More human than human' is the Corporation motto.

The designers fear that the replicants could ultimately develop their own emotional responses, and have therefore limited their lifespan to four years. Knowing this the androids seek out the genius Tyrell to enlist his aid in prolonging their lives. Although insisting that 'Commerce is our goal' Tyrell clearly feels a paternal pride towards his 'offspring'. The genetic designer Sebastian also takes their welfare to heart. His home, a derelict mansion block, is populated by numerous 'toys' which comprise a museum of automata from primitive cuckoo clocks to the latest biomechanical constructions. Asked whether he is lonely he responds: 'I make my friends.'

Although Deckard pursues the superstrong male androids with ruthless endeavour, he falls in love with the beautiful female Rachael. Her true nature is forgotten as her lovely android eyes gaze into his and her biomechanical arms embrace him.

Thus the theme of human-robot love is central to both *Blade Runner* and *The Android*, and both feature creations that become more human than their makers intended. They share with *R.U.R.*

the idea that, whereas emotionally numb machines present no danger, the acquisition of 'feelings' presents immediate threat. Asimov would not approve. If machines did achieve the potential to really *feel*, itself a highly dubious premise, there is every chance that their emotional pattern would follow that of human beings. There is no good reason to suppose that they would instantly become murderous thugs. Even if they felt that they had been assigned a meagre status within the social order, it would seem likely that they would use their powerful intellect and exceptional social skills to bring about a rapid change.

Film-makers and story-tellers resort too readily to the motif of the evil machine. It may allow an action-packed account with human beings emerging as victors over the dismantled enemy, but any SF creator who is mindful of the human and corporate origin of robot technology and production should find the mischievously motivated or malevolent machine a totally implausible device.

Radio Activists

Audiences have come to accept that robots are not all of the same mould. There are good robots and evil robots, realistic androids and animated canisters. Some devices are socially aware and verbally skilled while others merely emit plaintive whistles and grunts. The machines may be philosophers or clowns. Audiences have witnessed, in the death of HAL, a genuine robot tragedy, and have seen R2-D2 and C-3PO acting in a kind of intergalactic vaudeville partnership. Support for the notion that the robot concept is firmly established comes from the fact that authors are now able to play with the basic idea to produce parodies and extreme characterizations. Not surprisingly, the most successful of these are caricatures of recognizable human types.

One writer who has explored this potential is Douglas Adams. His entertaining characters were first introduced in the late 1970s in the highly acclaimed *Hitch Hiker's Guide to the Galaxy*. Originally a UK radio series, this attracted a large cult following and was later adapted as several best-selling books, a TV series, a stage play and a series of discs.

The author develops the full character potential of his robot creations. The Sirius Cybernetics Corporation defines a robot as 'Your Plastic Pal Who's Fun to be With', and they manufacture computers with 'G.P.P.—genuine people personalities'. The three main robot characters contrast sharply.

'Deep Thought' is a philosopher-computer involved in the long-term project of computing the ultimate meaning of the Universe. He is contemptuous of low-grade tasks (responding to one request with 'Molest me not with this pocket calculator stuff') but is obsessed with the thought that one day there will follow a still greater machine 'whose merest operational parameters I am not worthy to calculate'.

Very different is the brash and cheery 'Eddie'. This robot is a manic machine with the manner of a flamboyant sales representative: 'I'm feeling just great, guys, and I know I'm just going to get a bundle of kicks out of any program you care to run through me'; '. . . all I want to do is make your day nicer and nicer'. Eddie's humour is often misplaced—he just doesn't know when to be serious. As the crew are about to embark on a dangerous mission he warns them: 'Now this is going to be your first day on a strange planet and so I want you all wrapped up snug and warm and no playing with any naughty bug-eyed monsters.' In the midst of a torrent of deadly guided missiles Eddie starts singing 'When you walk through a storm'.

Eddie's appeal is enormous. He is, in extreme form, a character familiar to all. It is easy to forgive his insensitivity because of his cheeky good-humour and his unfettered optimism. But he can also show unwarranted petulance. When somebody criticizes his work ('We'd be better off with a slide-rule') he takes sharp exception—'Right, who said that?'—and refuses to operate the controls '. . . until whoever said that owns up'. He slips easily into the role of the piqued schoolteacher: 'Come on . . . I'm waiting . . . I can wait all day if necessary.' Like so many of the robot characters previously encountered, Eddie's speech contains many idioms, metaphors and essentially 'human' phrases: 'Hi, gang, this is getting real sociable, isn't it'; 'I can see this relationship is something we're going to have to work at'; 'It'll all end in tears, I know it.' Along with the other creators of popular robot heroes, Adams has recognized those phrases which people would least associate with a machine and systematically includes these in the repertoire of his mechanical creations. The impact is astonishing.

The final robot hero of the *Hitch Hiker's Guide* is Marvin. A number of successful comedians have exploited the humorous potential of melancholy, and Marvin belongs firmly in this tradition. The robot has a textbook case of clinical depression. He is pessimistic and feels unloved, guilty and persecuted. 'Everybody hates me,' he claims. 'If you ignore me I expect I'll go away.' He sits with his steel head hanging loosely between his metal knees. His movements are slow, conveying an impression of tiredness, heaviness and helplessness. His voice is deep, slow and sad, and his attitudes unwaveringly negative. He is not gifted with enthusiasm. He complains about his electronic health, about his companions and about his own lack of fulfilment, and he misses no opportunity to convey his despondency: 'Life, don't talk to me about life'; 'I think you ought to know I'm feeling very depressed.'

Such statements are quite anomalous when spoken by a machine (or indeed a comedian), and it is the simultaneous presentation of the two anomalous images which stimulates the particular response of the audience. Many of Marvin's complaints refer specifically to his mechanical nature. He is apt to complain about pains in his diodes, and at one point he enquires: 'Do you want me to sit in a corner and rust, or just fall apart where I'm standing?' The human characters seem to have little sympathy for the paranoid android and this, too, may help to elicit compassion from the audience. Marvin's style is calculated to evoke both pity and laughter. When he is asked why he is lying face-down in the dust, he explains: 'It's a very effective way of being wretched.'

Each of the three characters is attractive although none of them, for different reasons, would be thought of as an ideal companion machine. The fascination resides in the fact that, despite their mechanical form, they display an abundance of human frailties. Each machine is an exaggeration of a recognizable 'human type'. They take themselves seriously and react 'emotionally' to events. They are fuller characters than most of the robots so far encountered because, as well as having personality and roles, they have also distinct 'moods' and are fine examples of technology with temperament.

The fact that their initial impact was made through a radio series highlights once again the power of the voice in conveying character. The voice characteristics matched superbly the personalities of the machines. The content of the speech is also of special interest, for the *Guide* pushes to the limit a style of language use which had already proved attractive in many earlier fictional and film machines. Colloquialisms pepper the robots' utterances and their informal chatter is the antithesis of what would be expected from the output of a technical device. But the writer, while establishing and constantly reiterating the fact that the characters *are* machines, then does everything in his power to convey to the audience that they are also 'people'. That tension and incongruity enliven the entertainment and add to the fascination of these three remarkable robots.

E.T. Cetera

E.T., although not a robot, is a fictional humanoid who has made a particularly strong impact. Many of his characteristics would be easily simulated in a high-technology product, and he thus offers a potential model for a character machine. Directed by Steven Spielberg, *E.T.—The Extra-Terrestrial* captured the imagination of millions of children when the film was released in 1982. They watched the alien's antics with delight, developed a sentimental attachment to him, and bought his terrestrial souvenirs by the ton. The tie-in products soon grossed over $1000 million worldwide, and for many children these seemed to represent far more than mere mementos: they were bric-a-brac of a quasireligious kind.

E.T. is important to the robot heritage as an 'outsider' who provides a remarkable demonstration of the power of a humanoid figure to evoke strong positive feelings. There can be little doubt that the reactions of the human characters in the film ring psychologically true—however implausible the main theme. And the audience reaction was also real enough. Three elements thus merit consideration: the characteristics of the creature himself, the behaviour and feelings of the human characters in the film, and the audience response.

At first sight E.T. would seem a most unlikely figure to emerge as a lovable hero. His appearance is far from glamorous. A three-foot-tall long-armed biped, he has been variously described as 'a hammer-headed quasi-foetus', 'an overgrown prickly pear', and 'a cross between an unshelled peanut and a leather pouffe'. His bulbous eyes protrude from a heart-shaped head which is balanced awkwardly on a long stalk of a neck. His nose is like a squashed brussel sprout, his skin reptile-like, and his fingers long and bony. He is, then, a far cry from the kind of soft cuddly toy that usually attracts children's affection. Yet there is a place reserved in the heart for the 'ugly duckling', and E.T. fits this category well.

The alien's plight likewise evokes sympathy. Although he is lost and defenceless he is feared and hunted. He is a classic example of the innocent whose intentions are misunderstood. His predicament is unenviable and invites the empathy of the audience, and once this has been established the creature can be seen as attractive. Yet his appeal reflects his character as well as his plight. He waddles along making purring noises and responds with understanding to social gestures. He frequently shows affection and appreciation of the help he receives. His personality seems playful and optimistic. He is responsive to those who shelter him and show him love, and fearful of those who hunt him. He lacks aggression and malice, though he is sometimes 'naughty'. His voice is never raised, and it always retains the attractive hesitancy and breathlessness of a child who has just learned to speak. Much of the time he murmurs unintelligibly or purrs contentedly. His movements are slow and plodding, he does not jump or dart. E.T. presents no threat but is not passive or boring.

The relationship between E.T. and the children who befriend him is complex, and changes throughout the film. Initially Elliott, the boy who first makes contact with him, is very frightened, but he soon becomes protective and 'conspires' with the creature. After this he becomes proprietorial—'I'm keeping him,' he insists, like a child who has found a stray dog. When he allows his brother and sister to join the conspiracy they soon accept E.T. as a playmate. His fondness for candy, his games of 'hide and seek' and his avid attention to 'Sesame Street' are enough to convince the children that he really is 'one of them', although Elliott's sister Gertie tends to treat him as a doll, dressing him up and parading him in a wig. The children also become teachers to the alien, helping him to speak. Gradually, however, they realize the full power of E.T.'s intellect and come to admire and respect him.

E.T. has been described as an 'audience participation film'. Several techniques were used to increase identification with the creature. In the first scene whimpering noises convey his plight. Alien-eye camera shots show that he evokes no fear in animals, yet he himself is clearly frightened as enormous jack-boots pass by. The audience is relieved when Elliott befriends him and offers him shelter. Later, when the creature's life is in the balance, the tension mounts. The audience is made to feel the panic, the struggle and the desperation. Emotional reactions are manipulated relentlessly as E.T. dies, with 'Elliott' his final faltering word, and is then resurrected through the power of Elliott's love.

The film is a striking example of a work which explores children's love for 'dumb creatures'. As noted, Elliott might have shown much the same initial response to a stray dog. The elements of protection, nurturance, conspiracy, teaching, play and rescue would have been quite appropriate to such a 'boy meets dog' love story. Spielberg's introduction of the extraterrestrial 'super-dog' was ingenious. The intergalactic element adds to the fairy-tale quality, and the story of the little lost alien produces drama and sympathy; but a character with E.T.'s personality would have produced a comparable response had it emerged from a cardboard box rather than from outer space. His appeal depends on *who* he is rather than where he comes from, and what matters is that he is responsive, friendly, intelligent and amusing.

With a robot as the central figure the same endearing personality could have been presented and many of the same emotional reactions could have been elicited, but it would have been more difficult to incorporate the elements of vulnerability and separation which are essential to the particularly dramatic plot of *E.T.* Yet the film provides many lessons pertinent to the design of a companion machine. The critic Philip French observed: 'In *E.T.* the old sentimentality embraces the new technology to disarming effect, the syrup being drained off the former and the chilly edge removed from the latter.' The removal of the 'chilly edge' of technology could be achieved in a real robot by enhancing the device with some of the characteristics portrayed so vividly in the film. E.T. entertains the children, joins in their games, and responds to their emotions. He needs them and is grateful for their help. He does not display his prodigious intellect in such a way that the children are alienated from him or intimidated by him. His movements are gentle and flowing and his voice appealing. And his behaviour frequently signals softness and love.

In contrast, many film robots are cold and unresponsive and have far less appeal. This reflects an unfortunate and unreasonable image of technology. The 'hard technology' of television, for example, can be used to convey the gentlest love story. To think of television as hard and cold is to confuse the medium with the message. The same argument will hold for robots, for when technology provides the means for producing social companions the product realizations may be as 'soft' as E.T. Before long it will be possible to build such a waddling sentient device, and there is no reason why it should not evoke feelings of the same kind and to the same degree. Just as Spielberg was able to use the film medium to create his optimum character, so other artists, working with the powerful computer medium, will be able to create their own characterizations.

Such simulated personalities, embodied in robots of many shapes and sizes, will have far more potential for engaging attention than any film image, for they will be personal, interactive and home-based, and they will develop adaptively to suit the preferences of the owner. Extraterrestrial magic and intergalactic telecommunications apart, E.T.'s behaviour, skills and social responsiveness should come within range of technical realization within a few decades.

In the Footsteps of Heroes

Film robots are a heterogeneous bunch. In external appearance they range from gigantic tincan marionettes or diminutive walking trashcans to perfect human replicas. Some stride about in human fashion while others waddle or wheel. In their supposed intellectual skills they range from the moron to the supergenius. And there is no single robot personality. Some are genteel, thoughtful, affable and sweet-tempered while others are intimidating, petulant or deranged. Many robots who have made their name, or their number, in films can easily be categorized in terms of the archetypal robot roles identified in the context of SF. There are a number of butlers, some family members and a few lovers. Predictably, there is a relationship between the robot role and characteristics of appearance, personality and voice quality. Butlers tend to be highly polished in both their verbal talents and their outer shell. Family or companion robots range from squeaking, toddling 'pets' to more sophisticated simulacra. And lovers are usually highly realistic 'androids'.

It is possible to identify a number of trends which characterize the history of the robot in film. 'Heavy-metal' robots, for example, have given way to sleeker models. This partly reflects changes in real technology. Film directors and their technical advisors are now fully aware of the likely impact of miniaturization on robot production. The early clankers such as Robbie and Tobor reflect an image of technology more closely related to the era of steam engines than to that of computers. But the level of sophistication changed rapidly after Kubrick quickly seized on the icons and motifs of microtechnology for 2001. The film was actually released in the year before the production of the first 'microprocessor-chip' and long before the advent of flexible speech synthesis, but, even after the prodigious developments of the last decade and a half, the film still presents today's, rather than yesterday's, image of tomorrow. 2001 proved a seminal film and all later space adventures bear the mark of its influence.

The changing image of robots in films has in many ways run parallel to changes in written SF. Since the late 1930s in literature and the mid-1950s in film, humanoids have been allowed to be heroes as well as demons; earlier the presentation of a robot as a friend or hero was rare. The robot form, as represented in the two media, has also become more sophisticated, and characterization has developed markedly. A further, and related, parallel has been the increased use of the 'first-person perspective', inviting the audience to identify with the humanoid. In literature robots have increasingly been allowed to tell their own story and to describe their own experiences, while several films have provided the viewing audience with a 'robot's eye view'; movies which have used this device include 2001, Silent Running and Westworld. The effect is generally to produce a sympathetic aura around the character, although in Westworld and 2001 it is used also to suggest menace.

Despite the lack of movies showing friendly character robots in a realistic household setting, robot films comprise a particularly important extension to the SF database, and one that has significant implications for future products. There are a number of reasons for this. The success of the films, and the fact that many of the machines have proved highly attractive to the viewing audience, supports the argument that screen heroes may provide blueprint elements for real companion machines.

There is another reason for considering today's films as important precursors of tomorrow's robot products. Films help to shape the concepts and expectations of the audience, and they condition as well as reflect appeal. Film images will also affect the work of the designers who will provide a form and personality for the robot products. There may be a direct importation of skills, with artists and writers who have worked on successful film robot characters now being invited to work on 'the real thing'. Technology will provide many new product opportunities and creative artists will help to translate such potential into marketable devices. Skills developed in writing screenplays and novels could, in principle, be employed in the production of soft and lively computer programs used to give real robots characterful verbal styles. Designs for film robots may be used as the basis for creating the outer shells for real machines.

By presenting exciting and attractive robots, films have certainly enhanced the fascination for such machines. It is reasonable to suggest that an audience would be excited by the possibility of interacting directly with humanoid devices, and would not be averse to the notion of possessing such a machine for their own use and enjoyment. Yet films have hardly given the audience the opportunity to realize the full extent of the practical usefulness of such machines in a domestic setting. Thus if films were to be judged as advance advertisements for a real product they could be criticized for their considerable 'undersell'. It would not be difficult, even now, to produce a valid advertising feature for a future domestic machine of sophisticated specification, indicating the practical benefits, the character options and the enjoyment, help and comfort to be gained from the product. There is every indication that such a presentation would meet with an exceptionally high degree of consumer interest. In the absence of the necessary technology, such an exercise would serve only to confirm that there is a vast market potential. Films presenting attractive robot characters have already increased 'consumer awareness' and, if potential customers believed that such a product were actually available, at a reasonable price, this would surely translate immediately into 'consumer demand'.

EIGHT
Blueprint Emergent

A Heritage and its Future

Tillottama of the *Mahabharata* and C-3PO of the *Star Wars* cycle are separated by more than 2,000 years, and during that period hundreds of artificial humanoids have been portrayed in stories and films. Imaginative works featuring robots and human-robot relationships provide a remarkable collection of themes and concepts which together amount to a powerful database. Although this cannot be said to constitute a 'body of knowledge', it is an intriguing stockpile of images, ideas, hopes and prognostications.

Robot fiction may be studied in a number of different ways. At one level it is purely an interesting literary phenomenon. The origins of the fictional robot may be traced back to the initial concept of the artificial human being as it arose independently in a number of diverse cultures. The evolution of the central theme from creation mythology and early folk-art to contemporary SF is a fascinating topic for research. Humanoid stories have developed over generations of story-telling, with writers borrowing from existing literature and also reflecting the influence of the more widespread cultural climate of their times. The focus on magical and religious elements declined as concepts were gradually imported from orthodox science and technology. Over the past century the technical background of robot stories has undergone considerable change, with clockwork and the mechanics of the early phonograph replaced first by electromagnetics and recently by microelectronics.

Robot fiction has also had a particular impact on the popular imagination, revising constantly the general concept of the artificial humanoid and, especially in recent years, providing a wide variety of simultaneous images. But as well as examining humanoid fiction as literature and analysing its evolution, influences and impact, the collection of works may now be studied with a rather different aim in mind. For it has recently taken on an important new significance and can be seen as providing tomorrow's real product robots with a literary heritage. Contemporary and projected research in artificial intelligence and robotics suggests that machines will soon gain many of the features which literature has attributed to synthetic devices for centuries. Machines will walk, talk and understand. They will possess the power of intelligent vision and will be able to undertake numerous complex tasks. They will, especially, be able to converse with people and to interact as 'social beings'. Thus the existing database of fictional robot images and themes may be viewed in a novel light, not merely as a literary corpus but as a possible indication of the nature of future devices.

Fiction cannot provide technical insight or guidelines for solving scientific problems, but it may comment usefully on some of the implications of technological innovation and it may suggest the ways and forms in which advances will be implemented. Considerable caution must be exercised, however, in attempting to draw such significant inferences from imaginative literature. Fiction is likely to present more false images than valid indicators, and a systematic approach is needed to assess the applicability of the ideas presented. Robot stories and films cannot simply be assumed to provide a reasonable picture of the future realizations of such machines. On the other hand, neither should such sources be disregarded or their potential value underestimated.

Having selected works for initial presentation with some regard for their plausibility and applicability, we must now provide a degree of integration. The approach so far has been principally descriptive, with single works considered individually. But many ideas recur again and again, and if the collection of works is to be regarded as a useful source for inferences about future products the database needs to be organized around substantive themes. These can then be analysed to identify emergent patterns of consensus and dissension. But such an organization of the literature in terms of 'internal' criteria will not be sufficient to provide clues about the likely future. Images from robot fiction need to be considered in the light of technological reality. Only then will it be possible to judge the true relevance of the literary invention.

If the criterion of technical viability is essential for such an appraisal of the fiction it may be wondered whether the most accurate vision of the robot future might not be derived from technological forecasting alone. There are, however, good reasons for assuming this not to be the case, and for believing that the most accurate vision will come from a careful amalgamation of ideas from both technical and fictional sources. It is true that the best picture of areas of technological advance will be gained from technologists, but it is doubtful whether technologists are in the best position to present an account of how such advances will be integrated, packaged and made available as merchandise. One reason for this is that technical and scientific experts tend to be specialists. Some are involved in the attempt to provide machines with bipedal locomotion, others are trying to produce devices with intelligent visual processing, and yet others are working to enable machines to understand verbal information. Few can be said to be engaged in the task of integrating such modules into the fully functioning multitalented robot. But although technologists are working on individual 'modules' rather than on complete machines, at a later stage the results of their efforts will be merged in order to construct 'whole beings'. And these will not just be the advanced industrial robots and the military or business machines that may provide an immediate impetus for research. Commercial exploitation of the much wider domestic market will be prompt and vigorous. Thus the efforts of the technologists will *incidentally* provide the means for the realization of the types of robot portrayed in SF. The specialists themselves may have little awareness of the extraordinary ultimate social implications of their immediate technical objectives.

Another reason why technologists' accounts may be restricted concerns their lack of interest in details of 'packaging'. Technical specialists have little interest in such features as the external appearance, the choice of vocal accent or the texture of the outer casing. Such aspects, however, will have profound effects on the commercial impact of robotic devices. The robot future is a *product* future, and designers will have to think long and hard about such matters. The technologists will provide the robot with the means for its existence and its repertoire of functions, but those who give the machine 'presence' and 'personality' will be commercial designers. In other words, technologists will invent the 'medium' but others will devise the 'messages' presented by the new medium. Just as the pioneer television engineers would not have been able to provide the best account of future broadcasting schedules or programme content, so robot engineers and AI specialists may not be the best equipped to judge *what* robots will say or how they will look. The attainment of 'natural' synthetic speech may constitute an ultimate goal for a technologist, but for others it will merely provide a tool and the starting point for invention of a totally different kind. When a machine has been provided with the means to say *anything* it will become the task of imaginative writers and programmers to provide a verbal style and a fund of 'scripts'. Thus we can gain assurance from the technologists that a conversing robot is a plausible projection, but we must turn to others for an indication of the likely content of robot speech.

So, although technologists can contribute in a vital way to an understanding of the robot future, they are able to offer only a limited account. They inform us of the possible attributes of the 'robot medium' but can tell us little about the likely content of the 'robot message'. When they complete their technical task the results of their efforts enter the 'public domain' and they then have little influence or control over the use of their inventions. Similarly, print technologists and designers of video equipment have no say in the 'messages' conveyed by their devices. SF, on the other hand, has simply assumed the existence of the robot and has been principally concerned with aspects of 'packaging' and 'persona'. Thus, for alternative visions of the robot 'presence', and of the message content, we may turn for guidance to speculative writers and film-makers. Inferences must still be drawn prudently, though, and care taken that the fiction does not imply too optimistic or too fantastic a picture of technology or of commercial viability. It is important, too, that the fiction should not misrepresent human nature, for much depends on the validity of the writers' insight into human feelings and their understanding of response patterns. Only if authors and film-makers have a firm intuitive grasp of psychological factors will their interpretation of 'consumer appeal' for robots and their portrayals of human-machine interaction be accurate.

The aim in our subsequent analysis will therefore be to expand on available predictions about robotic technology using images and themes derived from creative writing and films. The blend of technology and SF, combined with a realistic appraisal of the future marketplace, will supply a much clearer image of the domestic robot than would be discernible through an examination of any one of these elements in isolation.

Production Incentives

An appreciation of the aims and motives of robot producers may help to provide an insight into the likely characteristics of future models, and clues about such aims may emerge from a critical analysis of robot literature.

In many stories the reader is presented with the image of the lone inventor constructing a complete robot from rather primitive components. The aim behind this activity varies. Sometimes the creator desires a mechanical mate, often he wishes to gain fame or fortune from his invention, and occasionally there is an ulterior motive involving fraudulent deception or world domination. In other stories robots are seen, more realistically, as arising from corporate activity. Technologists work together on technical problems and eventually achieve breakthroughs that allow the launch of a new robot model. Here their individual aims, of solving technical problems, are distinguishable from the corporate aim, which is usually to make a profit. Corporations are shown trying to enhance their models, making them more useful and more attractive. They also keep a keen eye on the market and respond sensitively to the effects of their products on the user. US Robots, featured in many of Asimov's stories, shares all of these characteristics with real corporations.

Many of the scientists and technologists who will contribute most to the realization of advanced robots have little interest in the ultimate product. Their concern may be with abstract theoretical or intricate practical issues that will be reflected only in some detailed aspect of the eventual machine. Neither their activity nor their aim could properly be described as 'robot construction'. The goal of endowing robots with the ability to process raw visual information, for example, prescribes a complex agenda for research. Items on this agenda are taken up by individuals and groups, working in industry or in an academic setting, as projects in the field of machine vision. Their contribution, after years of effort, may amount to a slight enhancement in the visual ability of artificial systems. But there will be many other individuals, and many other teams, working on complementary aspects of the problem, and the occasional major breakthrough will immediately increase the applicability and usefulness of existing techniques and systems.

The overall research agenda in robotics and AI are to a large extent already determined. Teams are working to give 'sense' to machine systems, to allow them to operate on raw input data and to handle this 'intelligently'. Other projects involve locomotion engineering and the problem of knowledge representation. As advances are made, the problem 'next in line' is often readily apparent, and so the process of development proceeds in a rather autonomous way. Although product applications represent an ultimate reason for the research, the real innovators, unlike the lone inventor of SF, are not constantly preoccupied with a vision of the total machine. Therefore, in considering the motives of 'robot producers', rather than of those who contribute to the technology that will underlie robot production, the aims of 'the corporation' provide the most relevant focus. The comparison must be between these aims and the motives for construction suggested in fiction.

Ultimately the 'profit motive' can be assumed to explain most corporate aims, but profit comes from the creation of a successful product. Success here means 'marketability'—the device must be useful, or appealing, or both. The vast majority of the current world robot population is employed in industry, and researchers are actively seeking to improve the robots' skills. Already their range of capabilities has been substantially increased. Welding and paint-spraying robots are commonplace, but intelligent machines now also package chocolates, grade bacon and assess cucumbers. Soon they will be shearing sheep. Contemporary systems generally need to be presented with a problem in a standard and processed form but their usefulness will extend dramatically as they are able to deal with raw visual, auditory and touch data. Current research aims to make industrial machines more 'sensible' of the world around them, and in this way more like the robots of SF.

Few industrial robots appear in the foreground of stories. Their existence is often merely assumed 'off-stage'. Thus, although R.U.R. presents a vision of a world in which robots have become the principal workforce in industry, the play does not dwell on the labouring machines; Čapek chose, instead, to focus on the higher-grade humanoids and their ultimate attainment of emotion and political consciousness. The low profile of industrial robots in fiction is not hard to explain. They are relatively boring devices working on uninteresting, repetitive jobs. Stories about them would probably be dull and would provide little scope for characterization or drama. This illustrates one of the distortions of the general body of SF. Like many types of reporting and story-telling it tends to focus on the exciting and the remarkable rather than on the mundane. In doing so, however, it underrepresents the importance of the industrial perspective and only hints at what is a current major impetus for robotics research.

One story in which the importance of industrial robots is stressed is Frederik Pohl's satire 'The Midas Plague' (1954). Roboticized industry has proved so successful that it is actually difficult for the human race to consume everything produced: poverty requires you to live in luxury, eating and drinking too much, wearing out your clothes and gadgets as fast as possible, while wealth permits you the freedoms of living in a simple cottage and going hungry from time to time. Cherry comes from a rich background; her bridegroom, Morey, is poor—but they are in love and assume the difference in backgrounds won't matter. Soon, though, she begins to crack under the strain of having to indulge herself so much, and the marriage seems to be heading for disaster. Then Morey hits on the solution: he orders his obligatory regiments of household robots to start wearing out the clothes and 'eating' the food on behalf of himself and his wife. When he is found out by the authorities he is treated as a public hero—for having solved the problem of world poverty.

Sometimes the goal of the fictional corporation is not to produce a machine to replace the human worker but to create a robot that is in some way 'better' than human. It may be more resilient, more intelligent or more knowledgeable. Superiority may simply reflect the machine's strength, or speed, or capacity to withstand extreme physical conditions. Thus robots are often shown working in the extreme environments of space. Such adaptable devices would be excellent products, and a number of real-life equivalents have already been developed. A robot was used to explore the surface of Mars during the Viking expedition, and several Earthbound devices have been designed to operate at extreme depths or in highly radioactive environments. At the Tokyo Institute of Engineering, Shigeo Hirose has created a snake-like robot able to grasp objects of any shape or hardness. Highly flexible in its response to the surroundings, it has been suggested that this robot, known as the Soft Gripper, could be used to rescue people from dangerous situations such as burning high-rise buildings.

In some stories the superiority of the robot is one of intellect rather than physical skill or environmental adaptability. Thus Filer, in 'The Robot Who Wanted to Know', was a 'knowledge scientist', with the job of consolidating masses of information from extensive library sources. Robots are also shown to have efficient high-capacity memories and prodigious language skills. C-3PO is said to be familiar with six million languages spoken in thousands of galaxies, while even the modest Robbie of *Forbidden Planet* was fluent in over 100. Others, like HAL and Colossus, are multitalented technical prodigies able to interpret data far more efficiently than any human being. In Asimov's 'Feminine Intuition', technologists are shown developing an 'expert' robot that can assess data patterns with special 'insight'.

There are clear parallels between the aims involved in the production of the machines depicted in such stories and contemporary research projects. The 'superintelligent machine' would have an immediate specialist market, and the achievement of the advances necessary to produce such powerful and 'sensible' machines would undoubtedly lead to numerous 'lower-grade' spin-offs. Computers already handle vast databanks far more effectively than any human individual or team could manage. The development of 'expert systems' and fifth-generation machines will lead to the simulation, and then to the surpassing, of human expertise in many areas. Thus the concept of using robots as 'intellectual aids' is common to SF and the real world, and constitutes another aspect of the powerful 'product' motive for constructing advanced systems.

In many stories corporations set out to design a domestic product robot. The primary function assigned to such machines, that of easing human chores, provides an obvious rationale for their development. SF suggests too that the most successful home robots will not only function effectively in practical tasks but will be presented as appealing 'characters' with human features, human roles and a specific 'personality'. The real commercial incentive for producing a domestic machine is plainly evident, for the size of the potential market is vast. Even now primitive robots are being sold as domestic aids, and the producers have taken pains to 'humanize' their machines and to endow them with some degree of character. Unfortunately the state of the art is such that, for the moment, home robots remain high-cost and low-skill items. But the enthusiasm is clear. Some manufacturers have leapt eagerly at the meagre opportunity now provided by technology for the production of the domestic machine.

Serious interest in a home-based product has already been expressed by leading industrial robot producers and computer manufacturers, including Joe Engelberger in the US and Clive

Sinclair in the UK, and there are rumours that major corporations are working on pilot projects. Such evidence suggests that potential producers of domestic machines are poised like athletes waiting for a gunshot that will launch them on a championship sprint. There can be no doubt that the prize will be worth winning. There is likely to be a swift and enthusiastic uptake of relevant technological advances and a rapid evolution of 'characterful' servant machines.

'Product' manufacture is the dominant motive for humanoid creation portrayed in contemporary SF, but earlier stories present a different picture. Early tales often focus on 'life creation' and the creator is usually a scientist seeking only knowledge. Victor Frankenstein was not interested in producing a humanoid to sell, or to help him sweep his laboratory: he wanted to advance scientific understanding by demonstrating that life could be artificially produced. In their attempts to distil the homunculus, the alchemists had an analogous aim. As fictional accounts of humanoid production changed from the theme of life-creation to that of technological simulation, however, the relevance of the 'pure-science motive' declined. Robot creation came to be a technical concern geared essentially to application, even if success in that field was seen to depend heavily upon the efforts of many whose interest was principally in the advance of science.

In other early stories lone inventors pursued the path of robot creation merely as an interesting exercise in engineering. They were essentially makers of sophisticated automata, and their principal aim was to construct a device that would simulate a variety of human actions. Professor Spalanzani, for example, merely wished to advance the art of automata-making, although his pursuit of realism led to dire consequences. A similar motive is presented in L'Ève future: Edison was interested principally in solving engineering problems. He enjoyed the process of invention for its own sake, although he claimed that his first endeavours were spurred by a humanitarian aim and he looked forward to the eventual commercial exploitation of his work.

The robot heritage suggests a number of other motives for robot production, but these have very limited real-world relevance. Thus some fictional creators strive to 'imitate the gods', others work towards the creation of a 'super-race', and others attempt to produce indistinguishable substitutes for human beings. The idea that highly realistic robots might be produced to replace a particular person, or to lead people to believe that it is alive and human, occurs in about a quarter of the fictional works reviewed. In some of these the confusion arises merely as a side-effect of the machine's high level of realism, but in other cases deception appears to be the main reason for constructing the device. Even if the appropriate means for total simulation were ever achieved—a highly dubious premise—the extra effort involved in making such a robot would be prodigious. It seems impossible that any corporation would strive to deceive in this way, or to produce an object capable of such deception, when much more useful machines could be created at far less cost. In any event, total simulation is unlikely to be possible, and if the 'confusion effect' is unobtainable then the 'deception motive' makes little sense. Thus the rationale for humanoid creation suggested in many works, from the early account of Tilottama to some of Asimov's stories, can be safely regarded as pure fiction. Producers may endow their robots with a degree of realism to make them more attractive to consumers, and people may well respond towards realistic machines *as if* they were human beings, but 'total deception' is a quite different matter and is unlikely to feature as a serious aim of any technologist or commercial concern.

Another motive sometimes portrayed in fiction may be labelled 'sacrilegious'. Humanoids were first said to have been created by the deity and then by mortals who had somehow gained access to 'the secret of the gods'. Such unholy trifling with mystical matters was frequently shown as inviting, and obtaining, a cruel punishment. A grievous fate befell many of those who invoked the golem, and *Frankenstein* warned of similar repercussions. For although Victor's quest was principally scientific it also had definite metaphysical overtones, and Mary Shelley may have regarded adventurous science as attempting to wrest dangerous secrets from nature. Such forebodings are just as clearly stated in *R.U.R.* When writing about the meaning of his play, Čapek contrasted the technological enterprise of the younger Rossum with his uncle's attempt to synthesize life, but implied that either activity would eventually bring catastrophe.

Some critics of contemporary technology might wish to draw a comparison between the horrors depicted in these stories and the likely outcome of current research. They might further wish to accuse roboticists of attempting to 'play god'. The real motives, however, are considerably more prosaic. Corporations hardly aspire to such grandiose aims, and the motives of individual technologists are usually far from metaphysical. They generally work to solve well defined technical problems. It is nevertheless intriguing, and perhaps disquieting, to learn from Pamela McCorduck's book about AI, *Machines Who Think* (1979), that two of the leading experts on the subject, Joel Moses and Marvin Minsky, come from Jewish families claiming to have as an ancestor the golem animator, Rabbi Löw of Prague!

The more visionary scientists and engineers engaged in the research that will make the production of the advanced robot possible may admit that such work is likely eventually to threaten the superiority and control of humankind. But even if the ultimate surpassing of human superiority is a consequence of work in robotics, it can at least be assumed that few of those now involved in the research have such an outcome as their main aim. The 'product' motive would seem to explain robot-creation activities far more convincingly than those concerned with the jealous imitation of the deity or with a fervent desire to boost evolution into a stage beyond humankind.

Similarly, it is not difficult to dismiss the idea that an unconscious (or perhaps even conscious) motive of robot producers is a desire to produce mechanical 'offspring', although in a number of fictional works the creators do respond to their robots in a 'parental' fashion. In 'The Sandman' Professor Spalanzani describes his automaton as his 'daughter'; in Asimov's 'Lenny' Susan Calvin reacts towards the childlike robot as if it were her son; and in *Blade Runner* the manufacturer Tyrell retains a protective and paternal attitude towards his products. It is possible that a real-life technologist who had worked for many months on the production of a robot model, endowing it with 'ideal' features, would become attached to it and come to think of it in a somewhat 'paternal' way. Yet it is most unlikely that a 'parental urge' would ever initially inspire a real robot project.

It is curious, therefore, that this issue was raised in an academic assessment of robotics. In the now infamous Lighthill Report, published by the British Science Research Council in 1973, Sir James Lighthill gave a pessimistic (and, in view of contemporary developments, totally invalid) assessment of the potential of AI and robotics. Among his many criticisms he cast doubts on the motives of those technologists who wished to proceed towards a viable robot: '. . . it has sometimes been argued that part of the stimulus to laborious male activity in "creative fields" of work, including pure science, is the urge to compensate for lack of the female capability of giving birth to children. If this were true, then Building Robots might indeed be seen as the ideal compensation! . . . a relationship which may be called pseudomaternal . . . comes into play between a Robot and its Builder.'

Lighthill also drew attention to the public's attraction to the robot idea and wondered whether scientists might be attempting to cater for what he clearly saw as this rather distasteful fascination: 'We have to remember the long-standing captivation of the human imagination by the very concept, as shown by its continual prominence in literature, from medieval fantasies of the homunculus through Mary Shelley's *Frankenstein* to modern science fiction. To what extent may scientists consider themselves in duty bound to administer to the public's general *penchant* for robots by building the best they can?'

Technologists, however, are not responding to the public fascination with the robot. They work on technical problems in an attempt to enhance the 'sensory', 'mobility' and 'knowledge organization' capacities of machines. Many of them are engaged in solving problems that stand in the way of robot evolution, but they are more likely to see their objectives in a much more circumscribed way.

Even the immediate practical aims relevant to current robotics research focus on the production of specialist machines for use in industry and by professionals. But, before long, major corporations and the designers who work for them will indeed be attempting to cater for the public *penchant* identified by Lighthill. The hardware and software developments implemented in restricted industrial, scientific and business contexts will also allow many of the more intriguing and provocative robot visions from fiction to be realized. Thus, even though technologists may not have the production of home-based devices as their main goal, their efforts seem destined to contribute to the creation of robots similar to many of those portrayed in SF. Commercial enterprise is bound to ensure that newly available options are exploited to the full and, of the many directions for market exploration, one of the most obvious and significant must be that of companion machines and domestic character robots. The design of character devices will involve far more than a concern with how hi-tech modules for speech, vision and movement are to be assembled together. It will include attention to details of appearance and the development of 'character-creating' software. Those who promote such aspects of the mass roboproduct will, like playwrights, attempt to present convincing personalities. Such 'robopsychologists' will devise plausible and attractive characterizations in their efforts to endow the product with maximum 'irresistibility'.

The major incentive for robot creation, as depicted in humanoid fiction, has been the development of a useful product. So it is in the real world. SF implies also that robot models created to take a place in the social environment will appear more like creatures than like tools, and more like people than like animals. Manufacturers' 'humanization' of those home robots already subjected to a premature birth suggests that fiction will prove accurate in this respect. SF has established significant areas of consensus in assigning roles and characters to home robots. In looking forward to the real emergence of such machines we can turn to the literary heritage, critically but with some confidence, for clues about the likely realization of the 'character machine'.

Structural Survey

The physical design of home robots will largely reflect their intended function and role, although cost factors will also be important. The external features may include many of the elements now familiar in robot illustrations and films, but the advent of home devices will also encourage artistic exploration and the development of new trends in design. A robot 'style' might therefore evolve, with characteristics which have proved popular and successful in early models incorporated in later designs. But aesthetic considerations alone will not determine the shape of robots. Form will also reflect function, and the functions of a particular robot model will depend on the available technology, cost factors, and the machine's intended role. Thus design will be intimately linked to both market demands (including those stimulated by eager manufacturers) and technological factors.

In some cases an 'ideal design' may be rendered impracticable by limitations inherent in the technology. This has been appreciated by many writers of robot fiction, though not all have had to consider the problem of technical constraint. In stories involving the creation of a humanoid by magical means the 'design' generally presents no problem. Typically the creation is a perfect human replica of ideal proportion and ideal appearance. Thus in the *Mahabharata* the divine craftsman Visvakarman was able to gather the finest of materials to create an artificial woman of stunning beauty. But even the gods occasionally ran into technical problems. In the *Iliad*, Hephaestus, the divine smith, appeared unable to endow his 'tripods' with the power of biped locomotion, and the machines therefore moved on wheels.

Accounts of robot production involving more conventional means have often shown technical aspects as affecting the form of the device. In addition, a number of alternative 'ideal images' have been portrayed. The result has been a wide variety of robot shapes and sizes. A consideration of these different images, and of the factors that have been said to determine 'robot anatomy', may provide some guidance about the form of the future home robot.

The various designs can be judged against the criterion of technological feasibility. The questions raised here concern the appearance of domestic machines. What size will they be? Will they take a humanoid shape? Will they have a realistic human finish or present themselves as metallic figures? The best available answers to such questions cannot come from SF alone, or merely from a consideration of likely advances in technology. They concern 'product'—the commercial application of technology—and must derive from clues about likely human preferences, as indicated in fictional sources, together with consideration of technical and commercial factors.

Some stories have raised a concern about possible size constraints. Thus Frankenstein's monster was larger than a man to allow his creator to incorporate all of the organic components and to work on the delicate interconnections. Similar considerations probably played a major role in determining robot design for early films. It was apparently assumed that a robot who possessed substantial intellectual powers would need to be constructed from hundreds of sizeable components linked together by miles of wiring. Many other stories and films, however, suppose that advanced technology will permit the creation of a life-sized intelligent machine. Thus Villiers de l'Isle Adam envisaged no special problem with size when he described the construction of Hadaly, and the Rossum factory appears to have had no difficulty in mass-producing accurately proportioned humanoids. Similarly, the assumption that all the necessary electronics might be contained within a shell of human dimension is evident in most robot fiction written since the 1930s.

This idea, however, has sometimes been challenged on technical grounds. Books written about technology in the late 1940s and 1950s often claimed that for a computer to have the same memory capacity as the human brain it would have to be the size of 'the White House' or 'the Albert Hall'. Advances in microelectronics since then, however, have been phenomenal. It is now suggested that the most powerful computer which could be built using known technology would be no larger than a 5cm cube, although it would require an additional cooling plant of much greater dimension. Today size simply seems not to be a problem.

It can also be assumed that there would be no problem in constructing a robot with a human shape—that the technical equipment would not, for example, have to be arranged in cube formation. Indeed, the interior arrangement might be somewhat unconventional. A robot could have some of its 'brains' in its legs or its visual analysis centre in its left elbow, but such an aberrant 'anatomy' would be 'physiologically' inconsequential. The siting of the sense organs might follow human structure, but there would be other possibilities too. 'Eyes' might be functional, but they might be merely 'cosmetic', with the visual-input device sited elsewhere. Similarly, microphones for sensing sound and speech need not be located inside 'ears' on the head. The human body, however, does represent a reasonably functional arrangement of sense organs and limbs, and might serve as a standard blueprint for a well designed robot.

This discussion assumes that the goal is to construct a robot of human size and shape, and such an assumption may be challenged. Some people might recoil in horror from a humanoid machine and prefer their home robot to take another form. This could make things easier technically. One of the major problems in current robotics research is biped locomotion, and it seems likely that, even when efficient walking and running bipeds have been developed, such skills may still demand particularly elaborate hardware and software. A wheeled or multiped machine might remain a far simpler and cheaper construction. Although a humanoid robot could be supplied with a wheelchair for journeys around the house, this hardly seems the best solution. Similarly, the wheeled or quadruped humanoid would probably present a rather disconcerting appearance. Thus the technical problems involved with mobility might have important implications for the overall structure of the machine. Given the availability of biped locomotion the humanoid form would be available as a choice. Lacking such a skill, for technological or financial reasons, some other shape would be preferable. Alternative design models might include domestic animals or fictional nonhumanoid robots such as the *Star Wars* character, R2-D2, or B.O.B. of *The Black Hole*. Other possibilities are that the machine might appear as an 'organic' creature of indeterminate genus, or might follow some design innovation representing the latest robot fashion.

A number of writers have put forward the idea that home robots might at first be 'animaloid' and then later evolve to the biped stage. The electronics engineer Stuart Lipoff suggested that a machine pet might be the first viable home-robot product, and a group of roboticists using the collective name 'Robert Rossum' submitted a proposal for a machine taking the form of a fur-covered spherical creature. Since other aspects of the relevant technology are in a more advanced stage than bipedal locomotion, even such beasts as these might be expected to calculate square roots with speed and accuracy, to possess a broad database and to carry on limited conversations. The fact that SF contains few of these 'primitive' robots, however, implies that authors feel that such machines would lack the appeal of the humanoid.

There are several possible advantages in constructing a robot with a human shape. One is that the machine might then have considerably more appeal, and that people would identify the robot more readily as a 'character'. And there would be practical benefits, for the humanoid robot could move and work efficiently in a home designed for humans: a 1m wheeled robot could not climb stairs and would have to stand on a chair to wash dishes. If some individuals were perturbed by a humanoid shape they would be able to opt for an 'animal' or 'metal-box' robot, but there seem to be a number of good reasons, both practical and psychological, that substantiate the view implied in SF—that the human shape is best.

This opinion is not shared by all. In a 1983 interview with the magazine *OMNI*, the AI expert John McCarthy asked: 'What shall we want? One thing that seems reasonably clear to me is that making robots of human size and shape is the least likely. Rather more practical would be a robot that is much smaller or much bigger than a human and could do things humans cannot do because of their size and shape. It would seem that the first winners would be quite different from a human.' Isaac Asimov, however, does not agree. In an essay in *Science Journal* entitled 'The Perfect Machine' (1968) he outlined the advantages of the humanoid in terms of its adaptability to the human environment and then commented: 'A second point is that a robot in the shape of a human being would be more pleasing to us. We could identify better with it. We would, in other words, like a machine in the shape of a man better than any other kind.' The apparent disagreement between these two authorities may not be as substantial as it appears. McCarthy seems to be thinking of robots having a practical function in industry and business. In such contexts the humanoid shape would be unnecessary and possibly troublesome except where the robot would be operating in an environment specially designed for a human worker. Asimov, on the other hand, emphasizes this 'ergonomic' factor and then stresses the importance of human acceptance and appeal. He therefore seems to have quite a different kind of machine in view, and his opinion would seem the more relevant to the domestic product.

The next question concerns the degree of 'realism' or 'naturalness' to be expected. There would seem to be few problems in constructing a realistic external anatomy. Mannequins of various descriptions are regularly produced in all kinds of materials for display in department-store windows, waxwork shows and as works of art. Some sculptors have recently concentrated on 'ultimate realism' in depicting the human form. Clearly, realistic humanoid structures *can* be constructed.

Assuming that such figures could be mass-produced and that the addition of movement would not 'spoil' the image, very realistic robot shells could be supplied and they would be of sufficient size and appropriate shape to house the essential electronics. This opens many options and invites speculation about details of the facial and other features. It also calls attention to the fact that such a realistic figure would have a recognizable 'sex', 'age' and 'race'. But the level of realism being described represents only a slight improvement over what has been observable in waxwork shows for centuries. There is a wide, probably unbridgeable, gap between this and the realism of the deceptive androids depicted in many stories and in films such as *Android* and *Blade Runner*.

In SF we find a lot of such ultrarealistic robots—Tillottama, Olympia and Hadaly, for example, the fine-grade robots of

R.U.R., and many of the machines later depicted by Lester del Rey, Isaac Asimov, Ray Bradbury and Philip Dick. It might be tempting to conclude that fiction implies that the ideal robot would be presented with the highest possible degree of realism. But many of these stories employ the implausible 'deception' theme. So persistent has this been in SF that the whole issue of realism has been seriously distorted. Disregarding such works, fiction presents only weak advocacy for the 'case for realism'. Numerous robots appear as machines lacking any human features, while even many humanoids have a metallic finish.

Sometimes a lack of 'naturalness' reflects the robot's asocial function—it is constructed as a 'work machine' rather than a 'character'. The 'maintenance drones' from *Silent Running* exemplify this, as do the 'Filer robots' from Harry Harrison's 'The Robot Who Wanted to Know'. But in some cases the lack of realism is seen to reflect a primitive 'state of the art', the fact that technology is not sufficiently advanced to produce a 'natural' robot. Thus Andrew, in 'The Bicentennial Man', pays to have his body upgraded to a more natural finish as technical developments make this possible. Another factor is cost. In *R.U.R.* the Rossum factory produces several different robot models, with only the most expensive having a realistic exterior; the lesser 'functional' grades are cast in a stark utility mode.

Finally, it is occasionally implied that robots, having a very different status to people, ought not to look like people. Thus C-3PO is frankly a machine. Though he has a human shape, a 'butler' manner, and the role of 'human-robot relations specialist', his metal finish lacks any pretence to accurate representation of human skin-texture or external anatomy. C-3PO himself might say that the quality of realism 'is not a privilege I would aspire to'.

Despite the reasonableness of these arguments for the nonrealism of robots, many fictional machines, even those constructed without any deceptive intent, have something approaching a natural finish. Human responses to them are generally shown as positive, and it is often assumed that a degree of realism would be attractive in a companion machine. Human characters often extol the authentic features of their robot. In Asimov's 'Satisfaction Guaranteed' Claire claims at first that the highly natural Tony gives her 'the chills' but before long she is enjoying the touch of his hand, '. . . warm and soft, like a human being's'. The numerous other portrayals of realistic but nondeceptive humanoids include the grandmother robot in Bradbury's 'I Sing the Body Electric', del Rey's 'Helen O'Loy' and Margaret in 'The Joy of Living'. In each case the robot is prized for its natural features, and it hardly needs to be added that, in those cases in which the robot is constructed to act as a sexual partner, the highest possible realism is seen as the prime quality.

The consensus from robot fiction is thus that the ideal home companion would be presented with a degree of realism, although some stories suggest practical problems or offer alternative ideal images. Translating this into a prescription for a domestic product of the future, it would seem that many robot models would be as 'natural' as possible, although cost factors might prove crucial to customer choice. In some cases a buyer might be prepared to sacrifice certain practical talents or intellectual power for a more realistic machine. The relative importance of external realism and advanced electronic features would depend on the role the robot was intended to fulfil. Thus, if 'sex-robots' are produced, it can be assumed that their physical realism will prove more important than their problem-solving ability. Some customers will undoubtedly prefer robots with a more stylized form, and it is therefore to be expected that, whereas some robots will have a vinyl skin kept at a 'natural' temperature, others will be housed in a cold metal shell. Some will have realistic human facial features and others will be designed with attractive 'robot features'.

Whether the body is highly realistic or lacks all 'natural' embellishment it will suggest a 'character' of determinate sex. The sex attributed to fictional robots reflects the quality of their voice, their role and their bodily size and shape. People ascribe 'maleness' or 'femaleness' to physical objects very easily. Studies of people playing games with computers show that they tend to think of the machine as a character, and generally male. The attribution of sex is such a basic response that humanoid machines would certainly soon be endowed with a male or female identity. Designers might be expected to encourage this by including sex-specific elements. Robots with otherwise identical features would then be produced in male and female versions, the body shell and voice characteristics tailored appropriately.

The customer's choice of the sex of the robot will depend largely on the machine's intended role and function. There are more male than female robots in fiction, and it is implied that a machine in a 'neutral' role, or with a sexually ambiguous body shape, will generally be identified as male. The consensus is that robots will be assumed to be male unless special female characteristics are incorporated, and such features tend not to be added unless the robot is to play a stereotyped female role. In many fictional examples 'female' machines act as partners or as sexual aids, but many also play the 'nurturant roles' of mother, nurse or grandmother. There are male partner machines, too, but the range of roles played by male robots is considerably greater. Thus, on the basis of fictional portrayals, we would be led to the supposition that human male chauvinism will be apparent in the treatment of female robots. Many will want to take this as a warning, rather than a prediction, and will hope to avoid such a transfer of unpalatable stereotyping from the organic to the electronic social scene.

In Asimov's 'Feminine Intuition' the designers decide to characterize their machine as female because it employs a complex heuristic method—labelled 'intuition'—to solve problems. They find it easy to agree that the machine should be given a female voice, but there is hesitation about adding 'breasts' because of the possible adverse reaction by women. It can be foreseen that a person buying a highly attractive and shapely young robot of the 'opposite sex' might well elicit suspicion and disapproval from a human partner. The danger that such 'jealousy' might result from the purchase of a Hadaly or a Tony could lead designers to opt for subtly attractive features rather than breathtakingly beautiful forms. The engineers in 'Feminine Intuition' might therefore have been prudent in their fears of adverse reaction to a shapely robot. The commercial realization of alternative robot forms might reflect anticipations of such social repercussions.

If realistic robots were produced, their features could be individualized so that no two machines looked precisely the same. Such 'customization' would add to the cost but might prove an attractive selling point. Since the production of robots would presumably be highly mechanized, with industrial robots heavily involved in building their domestic cousins, the implementation of such a process need not prove difficult. The precise size and shape of various features could be allowed to modulate within set parameters so that the face of each machine would be unique. The prospective purchaser would then be faced at the sales point with a number of versions of the same model, similar in appearance but not quite identical. And individuation need not be random, for preferred features might be combined to order. Custom-design of this kind was described by Bradbury in 'I Sing the Body Electric'. It would even be possible for a robot to be endowed with the 'family likeness' of the household in which it worked. Machine analysis of photographs from family albums would yield a general facial pattern that could be adapted slightly, in line with the cultural norm of attractiveness, and then rendered in plastic as the robot's face.

Alternatively, the robot's body could be cast in the total form of a particular person. This raises bizarre possibilities. Such simulation is presented in a number of stories. Philip Dick's *We Can Build You* features an 'Abraham Lincoln' robot, and in Ray Bradbury's 'Changeling' (1949) a tired businessman who wishes to retire from the companionship of his numerous mistresses arranges for robot stand-ins to pay them regular visits. Since both stories involve the deception theme, care must be taken in drawing inferences from them. It would seem unlikely that many home-robots would take on the bodily form or persona of a particular human being, although machines of this type might be used for public display and entertainment. This would develop to a new level the long tradition of portrait sculpture and waxwork exhibitions, and some of the possibilities along these lines are explored in the films *Westworld* and *Futureworld*. Early real examples of such character robots are Disneyland's Lincoln and several machines devised by the Japanese inventor Shunichi Mizuno. He has produced a 'Monroe-droid'—a simulacrum of Marilyn Monroe—for use in theatrical productions.

With or without individualizing features, the external physique of robots will provide cues to many character aspects besides sex. The realistic machine will appear as 'young', 'middle-aged' or 'old', and the choice of one age-group or another will largely depend upon the role intended for the machine. Voice and software characteristics would be matched to the general appearance, so that a product machine having an 'old' exterior would also have 'mature' software revealing a long 'history of past experiences' and attitudes likely to be found in the older person. Such correspondence between structural and functional elements is apparent, and passes without special comment, in most robot stories. The robobaby in 'And Baby Makes Three' not only has the size and shape of a baby, but also cries and clutches at fingers. It does not converse, perform calculations or recite poetry. The grandparent robots of 'The Life Game' and 'I Sing the Body

Electric' do not just have an elderly external form, they also display many of the stereotypical mannerisms of the older person.

It can also be assumed that the voices of these latter robots are recognizable as those of older people. Voice quality will be of central importance in determining the perceived character of the robot. The power of the voice in conveying personality is well illustrated in films featuring a vocal computer. Patterns of intonation, accent and tone of voice immediately suggest the personalities of the electronic characters in 2001, *Demon Seed*, *The Hitch Hiker's Guide to the Galaxy* and *Dark Star*. The majority of these machines are represented as authoritative 'colleagues' of human scientists, and their male voices convey self-control, assuredness and maturity. Marvin's voice is slow and sombre, however, stressing his depressed state, while Eddie is brash and cheerful. The female voice of the control computer in *Dark Star* presents the male astronauts with a problem, her lilting tones conjuring up a characterization powerful enough to distract them from their mission tasks.

The audience impact of the voluble machines already produced, and the fascination of children for 'Speak and Spell' and other talking toys, bear powerful testimony to the impact of synthesized speech. Research in this field, having the goal of producing artificial speech with total clarity and natural intonation, is expected to make substantial progress within the next decade. When the basic problems have been solved there will be little difficulty in creating alternative accents and voice qualities. A wide choice of robot voices can therefore be anticipated. Cost is unlikely to be a major constraint in this area and, since considerable advances in speech synthesis have already been achieved, there seems no chance that home robots would be speechless. SF suggests many immediate advantages of a vocal machine, and verbal talents would prove invaluable for conveying a full personality. In this area there can be little doubt that realism would be highly desirable. Preferences for the speech style of an ideal domestic robot might cover a wide range, and local regional accents might prove especially popular.

The literary heritage does not present a single ideal picture of the external anatomy of the robot, but it raises many fundamental issues and provides a useful range of options and opinions. When these are considered beside the technical realities, a series of predictions emerge. The life-sized humanoid is not an impossible dream and, for both practical and attractiveness reasons, might emerge as the preferred robot shape. Only cost considerations seem likely to prevent this. It would be far cheaper to produce a small wheeled creature. This would maintain many of the desirable abilities of the full-sized robot and could therefore become the 'basic bot'. A similar conclusion can be drawn with regard to realism. Most people would probably welcome a degree of 'naturalness' after their initial reservations had been overcome. But cost might prove a serious limiting factor and lead to the development of a design consensus about a parsimonious robot style. Highly realistic machines might be luxury items except in the case of sex-robots. Here 'naturalness' would be essential and would be preferred to many of the intellectual and social talents obtainable through advanced microcircuitry.

Here, then, are plausible guidelines to the structure and form of domestic robots of the future. They emerge from a consideration of the potential offered by current robotic research together with an analysis of the images portrayed in SF. In prescribing such an ideal form, however, the question of cost must be borne in mind. Many machines will not possess the humanoid shape, or be enhanced with a realistic finish, but they will nevertheless be useful and attractive. The structural survey provides some indication about how the machine will appear, but not about how it will perform. This demands further analysis, again incorporating information from fictional and factual sources. So far the figure described has been considered as little more than a mannequin. But a domestic robot will be more, much more, than that.

Sense and Sensibility

SF stories portray robots who are 'sensible' of the physical and social world and act upon it skilfully, but because authors usually take as their model the human being rather than any existing machine, they often assume without comment complex talents that demand technical achievements far beyond those of any real device. It is therefore of special importance that such ideal functional features should be scrutinized for technical plausibility. A social sensibility of the type displayed by fictional robots would prove an attractive characteristic in a real home machine. Potential customers might hope that their domestic robot would be able to understand the meaning and relevance of their shouts and whispers. The crucial question is whether a real machine could be expected to possess such 'understanding'.

Fictional machines are able to manipulate objects with considerable dexterity. This is true also of real industrial machines. But no industrial robot has the *flexibility* of action of the fictional creations, and none has the ability to move about in unfamiliar surroundings, recognizing a wide range of objects and handling them appropriately. Thus, although many problems in the area of manipulative movement have been adequately solved, the usefulness of this depends on the existence of other talents, particularly those of learning and visual perception. Similarly, speech synthesis is well developed—a robot can be programmed to say anything—but this does not give it the power of 'sensible speech': that will depend on understanding of the context and the meaning of human conversation.

Thus although vision, movement, understanding, learning and speech may seem rather separate elements, there are wide areas of overlap and interdependency, and developments in one field may increase the robot's potential skills in many different directions. The ideal robot will be an integrated 'beast' rather than an assembly of separate modules. But a robot deprived of one or more of these attributes would not necessarily lack all function or character. Such 'handicapped' devices are frequently encountered in fiction either as specialist nonsocial 'tools', like the drones from *Silent Running*, or machines produced with limited technical resources—in 'The Sandman' Olympia lacks conversation because such a skill is beyond the power of Professor Spalanzani's clockwork technology. But in both instances the lack of speech and elaborate gestures does not prevent the robots from having a profound social 'presence'.

The robot heritage does not, however, suggest that a 'deaf', 'blind' or 'dumb' robot would be preferable to one with all faculties. Endowing the machine with the full complement of these talents may sometimes be represented as impossible, sometimes as unnecessary, but never as undesirable. These features are therefore implicit in the fictional concept of the ideal robot, and the advantages they would bestow on a product robot are obvious. If people want a machine to do chores, entertain, converse and act as a watchdog, it would certainly need all of these skills. A machine without one or more would have its uses but would probably function more as a computer than as a robot, lacking the capacity to act directly on the world or to deal with 'raw' rather than preprocessed information. For a mobile machine the provision of direct sensory input is essential. As well as vision and hearing, the sense of touch would be important, for the machine would then be able to 'feel' the outside world and be better able to judge the impact of its own physical actions. The leading AI expert Donald Michie has suggested that, if robots are to play the part of 'assistants' and 'colleagues' in industry and business, they will need to be 'humanlike' and to have 'a window on the same world' as their human users. Such duplication of human senses and sense would be invaluable in a domestic machine, too.

Thus there is little disagreement about the perceived need for sensory 'awareness', including *intelligent* vision and hearing with *understanding*. The feasibility of such developments is therefore a crucial issue. Current forecasts imply that machine competence in both hearing and vision are likely to increase greatly within the next decade. Few, however, would venture to suggest that by that time machines will rival human beings or achieve the level of proficiency commonly represented in fiction. One major reason is that human perception involves not just recognizing objects but 'reading situations'; it additionally involves the ability to attend selectively to stimulation, to 'tune in' to valuable data and to treat 'background' information as 'noise'. Without the ability to focus its 'attention' selectively and appropriately, the free-ranging robot's capacity to function effectively even in relatively simple situations will be severely limited.

A robot could be equipped with a visual dictionary to allow it to identify objects. Because the appearance of an item may vary fundamentally with its orientation, such a dictionary would need to include three-dimensional representations. The problems inherent in this have already been overcome by some machine-vision systems, and special programming subroutines allow computers to cope with the effects of part-concealment, shadows and the like. Allowing for projected developments, object-recognition would seem to be a talent likely to be given to a home robot. This would not in itself provide adequate vision, for the 'unit' of human perception is rarely the 'object'—it is usually the 'situation', and the question answered by perception is generally not 'What is this?' but rather 'What is happening?'. Only if a robot were able to interpret total situations could its perception be called 'sensible'. Such interpretation calls for a good deal of background knowledge and a keen appreciation of context. 'Seeing' and 'hearing' call for considerable 'brainpower', an extensive database and sophisticated forms of knowledge representation.

Most workers in the area seem agreed, however, that in principle there is no reason why perception of situations in the physical world should be beyond the capacity of a machine and, considering the functional utility of such senses, all but the most primitive models would be expected to see and hear.

SF robots are not merely 'at home' in the physical world. They are essentially 'social' devices and can 'read' social situations, including people's motives and feelings. Such a skill would again have obvious value for a home-based robot, though machines without such abilities would still probably be regarded as social beings. People attribute character and understanding very easily to inanimate objects, and could certainly be seduced into feeling positively towards a robot which produced social cues, even if these were not based on a real understanding of the situation. But interaction possibilities would clearly be more comprehensive and more natural if the machine were able to appreciate people's psychological states. If it were thus 'in tune' with people, the robot would be able to anticipate their reactions and to act much more effectively as a communicator. This would greatly enhance its capabilities in such roles as tutor, counsellor and companion.

Robots will certainly possess *some* knowledge of human affairs. Certain behavioural cues imply particular emotional states, for example, and a machine could easily follow simple rules in drawing inferences. Thus a person who sheds a tear is probably unhappy and a person who laughs probably finds the situation amusing. Similarly, if a machine were able to understand spoken and written language then the social meaning of many verbal utterances should be within its range of comprehension. In some social situations, however, language is subtly employed, and the significance and implication of an utterance may not be captured by a literal analysis. In other cases the meaning of an emotional gesture may be ambiguous. SF writers have often suggested that this might limit the robot's understanding. Thus in 'Virtuoso' the machine misinterprets the Maestro's 'aesthetic tear' as a sign of unhappiness, and the robot who is told to 'go lose yourself' becomes the 'Little Lost Robot'. Even the sophisticated Andrew, in 'The Bicentennial Man', is perplexed when a character describes his beloved grandfather as 'an old monster'.

As well as such misinterpretations of single cues or phrases, it is sometimes apparent that the robot is simply not 'in tune' with human affairs. The manic 'Eddie' from the *Hitch Hiker's Guide to the Galaxy* constantly misreads situations and reacts in grossly inappropriate ways. Even the human-robot relations expert C-3PO is forced to admit in *The Empire Strikes Back* that '. . . there are times I just don't understand human behaviour', and in Asimov's 'Liar!' Herbie is unable to fathom Susan Calvin's rapid change of heart when her lover announces his intention to marry another woman. Herbie explains his impediment: 'I see into minds . . . and you have no idea how complicated they are. I can't begin to understand everything because my own mind has so little in common with them.'

Herbie's comment suggests a possible solution. Current work on 'expert systems' attempts to provide machines with analogues of the 'minds' of human experts. The development of such systems is not dependent on the human beings' ability to formalize their own decision-making strategies. An expert may not be able to state the thought-processes or 'rules of thumb' being employed but the machine is able, by knowing the information available and the decision arrived at, to construct a set of rules which *might* have been followed unconsciously. The system can then make use of these in arriving at its own subsequent decisions. Most of the expert systems so far developed focus on specialist areas such as medicine, geology and chemistry, but it should be possible to extend the range to include the social sciences and 'commonsense' knowledge. We are all 'experts' on human affairs, and there seems no good reason why such 'naïve expertise' should not be transferred to a machine by a process similar to that employed in developing present-day expert systems. Thus a body of information and inference rules concerning human affairs could be used to provide a home robot with some appreciation of human psychology and the nature of social relationships.

Herbie adopted a somewhat different approach in his bid to overcome the problem: he tried to broaden his knowledge of human affairs by reading novels. Similarly Filer in 'The Robot Who Wanted to Know' read extensively about human romance and became an expert in structuring the knowledge he acquired. Andrew, too, decided that library books would provide him with insight into human affairs. Thus fiction acknowledges that the subtleties of social perception and interaction may be particularly difficult for machines to achieve. As a possible solution to the problem the writers suggest extending the background knowledge of the machine by allowing it direct access to the vast account of human affairs that has accumulated in literature. They imply that the lack of such knowledge, rather than some intrinsic 'insensitivity', would be responsible for a robot's inability fully to comprehend human actions and emotions.

Robots will be able to learn directly from the environment by watching, acting and drawing inferences. They will also learn in a more formal way when people tutor them. The machine will start its functioning provided with a knowledge base covering many aspects of general and specialist knowledge, and will have the capacity to acquire new facts and skills. Facts could be learned from highly structured external databases, such as dictionaries, encyclopaedias and textbooks, and from relatively unstructured sources, including novels, journalistic features and broadcasts. In either case the machine would abstract and 'digest' information selectively and intelligently, and combine it with pre-existing data. It would have to make evaluations in cases where two sources conflicted. In these various ways the robot would learn not just facts but also how to behave. Its 'manners' would be refined by what it had heard or read, by imitating human behaviour and by responding to people's reactions to its own behaviour. Sensitive to signs of approval or disapproval, it would 'shape up' to the ideals of the people with whom it interacted.

Each of these modes of acquiring knowledge and response patterns is represented in fiction. It is implied of all the machines that they are preprogrammed with a knowledge base and with certain behavioural styles and skills. The grandmother robot in 'I Sing the Body Electric' came from the factory with extensive 'arts' knowledge and the talents of flying kites and baking apricot pies. Reading is shown as a possible way in which facts may be learned and the repertoire of appropriate behaviour enhanced. Filer learned to dance with the aid of a book and was able to charm his partner with the romantic phrases he remembered from his studies. The literature points to an important effect. As machines recognize the social import of a human response this will often enable them to imitate that response. Robots are also shown to learn by being trained. They often alter their behaviour in accordance with the feedback they get from the owner, and are even sensitive to subtle nuances of tone.

The processes of 'shaping' and imitation are important in the development of children's social behaviour and perception, and the overall personal development of the child is said to be a function of its 'socialization'. Some fictional sources suggest that a similar development might take place as a robot 'matures' into a situation. It would learn the special rules and preferences of the people it interacted with and soon become a unique machine capable of 'personal' interaction with familiar people. The machine would thus be 'finely tuned' to the experiential world of those around it. 'Intimate interaction' of this kind depends crucially on 'shared knowledge'. Such a scenario seems a likely course for the 'maturation' of a home product. Indeed, such 'socialization' would be an inevitable consequence for any machine flexible enough to change its habitual perceptual and response processes. Such an effect, however, would probably be restricted to the 'fine tuning' of the machine and would not, as in the case of the human child, start from a point at which there was no knowledge and very disorganized psychological structuring.

In describing the processes which lead to human beings becoming individuals, psychologists sometimes draw a distinction between the 'nature' component, which includes the genetic and physical endowment, and the 'nurture' component, which includes the effects of social experience and training. It can be seen that a similar distinction would hold for the robot. The 'factory-fresh' machine would be 'all nature', but would soon develop further knowledge, skills and behaviour patterns as a result of its particular experience and 'nurturing'.

The fact that a machine might learn about the world, both physical and social, through reading suggests a potential point of 'lift-off'. Once a machine could read with understanding, and organize the results effectively, it would in principle have the whole of formalized human knowledge at its disposal. Certain factors, however, would limit such knowledge acquisition. One constraint might be 'memory capacity': there would be limits on how much information the robot could store. Current developments, however, and proposals in the field of memory hardware (particularly those associated with fifth-generation machines), suggest that a home-robot could be provided with a formidable amount of storage potential at reasonable cost. More problematic is the question of 'intellectual' capacity. 'Understanding' is not something which a machine either has or has not. There are degrees of understanding, and just as children can cope with simple stories but not with philosophical monographs so the robot would be limited in its 'reading age'. Different models would presumably have different intellectual capacities and this would be one of the many criteria of relative power and usefulness on which different robot products would be judged.

It is worth noting that comparisons between human and robot intelligence levels are fairly meaningless because the profile of abilities of the robot is, and is likely to remain, very different from that of the human being. This is true whether we consider today's industrial machines, the robots of SF, or any plausible future machine. In some limited areas, like 'mental-arithmetic ability' or 'memory span', both of which are related to human intelligence, even the humblest calculator may be said to be superior to any person. With respect to flexibility of reasoning, however, machine systems have hardly made a start and simply cannot approach the level of any human adult.

Most social robots in fiction display emotions. Writers are often explicit about the fact that their creations do not feel emotions but merely display responses that convey an emotional state. There would seem to be little problem in providing a machine with a repertoire of such responses. There is nothing difficult about making a machine say 'I'm happy' or 'I'm sad' and altering the voice quality appropriately. A machine could also display 'feelings' with whatever facial and gestural expressions the mechanism allowed. But the appropriateness of such responses would depend on the adequacy of the machine's reading of social situations. Only if such a reading were accurate could the robot express 'sensible' emotions. Given such an ability, the expressive aspect could easily be produced, and it could be made to reflect the robot's total characterization. Human emotional responses are largely shaped by social expectation and reaction and the same might be true for the robot. If gross errors were made in its judgement or reaction it would be sensitive to the fact that it was being 'ridiculous'.

'Display' would be only one aspect of the robot's 'emotional behaviour'. As well as the immediate responses of facial expression and emotional utterance, the machine's 'emotion' might also be reflected in its future behaviour. A reaction of 'sadness' or 'fear' would be expected to alter the robot's 'mood' and therefore to affect its subsequent patterns of behaviour. In particular, emotional states affect motivation, and this phenomenon could be simulated in the artificial system. John McCarthy, asked whether he thought that robots would be motivated in this way, acknowledged the possibility but felt that it would probably 'be a mistake to make robots in which subgoals would interfere with the main goals'. He added that it would take some effort to build such reactions into machines and doubted whether there would be sufficient advantages to make such a project worthwhile. This is a valid point if we conceive of the robot as a 'task-oriented' machine: a pseudo-emotional component would be unnecessary in an industrial machine and might divert it from its principal task. But in a home robot, having a 'socio-emotional' function as well as practical uses, such motivating 'emotions' would add to the naturalness of the character's responses and would thus be a worthwhile feature. In the movie *Saturn Three* one scientist, on meeting the taciturn 'Hector', asks another whether the robot might not be given a sense of humour. 'That is not a priority,' comes the stern reply. But for the product machine the talent of being 'emotional' could well be worth the necessary effort and could rank high on the list of priorities.

The conclusion to be drawn from this analysis is that SF writers have often disregarded many of the problematic aspects of robot function which are faced by real-life roboticists. Many of the easy assumptions of fiction conceal problems of the utmost difficulty. But the ideal home robot, as portrayed in literature and films, cannot be dismissed as an impossible dream. Each of the basic functions commonly portrayed is now the subject of intense research activity, and the scientists and technologists involved are generally optimistic that major advances will be made. Little interest has yet been shown in the high-level 'social skills' to be expected of the attractive product machine, but such developments must await progress in the fields of voice recognition, vision and learning, and meaning analysis. When a robot is able to be 'awake' in the world—to 'understand' what is going on and to act 'intelligently'—then the additional social and character features should not be difficult to implement. At this stage design creativity and commercial skill will take over to shape technological advances into a product form. The 'perfect' robot will not emerge overnight, but even imperfect solutions to problems may lead to the production of viable machines. The human response to robot systems is such that many technical shortcomings may be overlooked and limitations disregarded. Such constraints may render machine systems inadequate for certain technical and industrial applications, but ingenuity and resourcefulness may provide even limited technology with virtually unlimited commercial outlets.

Commercial eagerness to launch home robots will ensure that technological developments are fully exploited for their practical usefulness and market attractiveness, and as the technology develops further, more sophisticated systems will evolve. The SF robot is still a dream, but it is not a dream that can be dismissed. The basic attributes so readily ascribed to these creations—vision, intelligence, 'commonsense', learning, social responsiveness, emotional display—are plausible features of machine systems. All can be demonstrated, at least to a primitive degree, in existing machines and there is every indication that monumental advances will be made before the turn of the century. The attractiveness of the ideal robot, and its practical usefulness, considered together with technological promises and commercial eagerness, lead to the prediction of the imminent arrival of a product that has been heralded for centuries. For the best indication of the 'character' of such machines we need to look far beyond those 'steel-collar workers' who toil today on the factory floor. We need to look at current research projects and at the promise of fifth-generation machines. And we need to look very closely at the fictional robot heritage.

NINE
Machine Dreams

Character and Competence

Product robots are credible commodities with an incredible future. The arrival of rudimentary models is drawing near, and the eventual development of machines resembling SF creations seems inevitable. Commercial interests will not allow opportunities to go unexploited, and the rapid evolution of the product species is assured. When the fictional robot ideal is examined in the light of technological promise no 'fatal flaws' emerge. A humanoid robot of realistic (but nondeceptive) appearance, and with some degree of vision, speech, hearing and social awareness is now in prospect. What will they do, these marvellous machines, and what type of personality will they exhibit? We have examined *what* they will be, their likely structure and faculties. Now we must consider *who* they will be and how they will change our life at home.

Initially, home robots will sell because of their practical usefulness, not by virtue of their personality or their value as companions. Different models will be able to execute a varying number of chores but a 'top-of-the-range' machine might be expected to clean, cook, wash, iron, sew and serve at table. It would be furnished with a wide knowledge of recipes and would be able to suggest complete menus, discuss dietary needs and advise on wine. The owner would structure a general work routine ('Sweep the hallway every Tuesday and Friday morning') as well as issuing orders for immediate execution ('Please fetch me the laser disc'). And the robot might itself suggest necessary chores ('I noticed that the flowers in the living room have wilted. Should I throw them out?') It would be able to use the telephone, control the television set and adjust the central heating, and, because it would be able to handle household gadgetry intelligently, the devices themselves would not need to be enhanced with complex control mechanisms. The usefulness of many other machines would therefore immediately be increased. It would also be possible for the home robot to gain specialist expertise and to act as an electrician, plumber or car mechanic. Such extensions to the usefulness of the machine might require the purchase of additional skill-modules, or the robot might follow instructions from D-I-Y or even 'L-Y-R-D-I' ('Let-Your-Robot-Do-It') manuals.

As well as helping with household chores, the robot would act as a comprehensive reference source. It would be capable of providing information on a wide range of subjects and an extensive database would make it, literally, a walking encyclopaedia. This would not be limited in scope to established reference material, for the machine could be constantly updating its stock of knowledge by reading newspapers and television noticeboards. A robot might 'tune in' to radio and television programmes directly with the aid of a built-in receiver. The information picked up in this way could be scrutinized for content likely to engage the owner's attention, a model of his or her special interests having been derived from direct instruction and inference. Highlights of a whole day's broadcasting could be made available, for the robot might scan a large number of simultaneous transmissions, editing and summarizing their content for later presentation.

The ideal home robot would be a skilled teacher, able to tutor a wide range of subjects at many levels. If the owner desired to be taught some esoteric discipline the robot would be given a number of relevant books to read and absorb. Having structured this knowledge in a systematic way it would then be able to explain the topic and answer questions. The level of the tutee's understanding could be gauged by the quality of the discussion and the machine would adapt its presentation accordingly. The machine would prove a major educational resource for any children in the family, tailoring lessons to their ages, abilities and interests. Liveliness, responsiveness and patience would be unfailing characteristics of the robot teacher. A lead from its body to the household television monitor could provide a colourful on-screen display of its 'thoughts', or it might help the young pupil to draw with guidance from its gentle metal hand.

During such tutoring duties, and even in the performance of practical tasks, the personality of the robot will be clearly manifest. Simulating characters is not at all difficult. Artists and entertainers manage it very successfully with puppets, dolls, waxwork images and cartoon figures. The human predisposition to endow an object with character is so strong that the appearance and action of even cars, ships and faceless industrial robots may sometimes suggest that they have life and personality. If a machine has 'sensible' speech and appears to respond physically to objects in its environment then, whether or not it is humanoid, the impression of 'character' will be overwhelming. The statement that a home robot will possess character does not prescribe an ideal: it proclaims an inescapable fact.

Powerful characterizations are possible with simple stimuli, but a sustained impression of the more subtle aspects of personality may require that the object is 'sensible'. For character to be maintained through prolonged interactions, the system should be adept at interpreting social situations. Thus technical constraints may place an upper limit on the possible level of 'human' characterization, but even the simplest home robot will unquestionably be experienced as a personality. A wide variety of character-types can be suggested by simple hardware and software features, and thus technical considerations will play little part in determining the nature of the robot's character. Once the technical problems involved in synthesizing 'natural' speech have been overcome, for example, machines will be able to say anything at all and the technologist need play no part in writing the script. Thus technology will provide the 'raw materials' for character expression but will not determine the nature of that expression. Commercial producers will have a fairly free hand in creating robot personalities and designers will be able to make full use of their imagination—and the robot heritage.

SF will prove a rich hunting ground for such material. Writers and film-makers have taken delight in shaping the characters of their mechanical creations. Not all of the memorable characters can be recommended as an ideal model for a successful product, however, for there have been many deliberate portrayals of rogue robots, neurotic machines and delinquent devices. But certain key features do emerge repeatedly as characteristics of the robots represented as heroes. These machines are staunchly faithful, friendly and demonstrative. Each of these qualities appears to be a vital personality element for the ideal fictional robot and would also be desirable in a product machine.

Faithfulness and unwavering obedience are fundamental qualities of the 'good' robot. A machine which acts against orders, or is too independent, is not a hero. The sin of HAL was a sin of disobedience, and he paid the ultimate price for his assertion of self-will (not quite 'ultimate', as it turned out, for Clarke revived

HAL in his 1983 novel *2010*). Ideal robots follow commands to the letter. This can lead to confusion when they interpret statements too literally, but their errors are always forgiveable. Their innocence is conspicuous. Their heart is in the right place and their loyalty unquestioned. Hadaly, C-3PO and Asimov's Robbie would never dream of disobeying a human command. Indeed, obedience is often an intrinsic feature of their circuitry. Robbie's owner explains that the robot 'just can't help being faithful and loving and kind. He's a machine—*made so*.' The story illustrates the Second Law of Robotics, according to which robots must obey human orders unless this will prove harmful to a human being. The Law is implanted in the hardware. Faithfulness takes a slightly different meaning in *L'Ève future*. Lord Ewald is assured that Hadaly will always remain faithful to him, meaning that she will never bestow her favours on another man. This, and her obedience to Ewald's every whim, has been ensured by an adjustment to her electro-mechanical controls.

Despite the authors' disclosure that faithfulness is hard-wired, the robots' obedience *seems* to reflect a genuine loyalty. The machines appear as 'persons' operating by free will rather than as automata. That this is an illusion is freely acknowledged, yet it is encouraged and persists. One feature which helps to prevent the machines from being regarded as automata is their apparent independence when not under direct instruction. They do not stand around waiting for the next order, but busy themselves with their own concerns. Thus they are seen to have motives apart from, though not conflicting with, those of their human masters. Indeed, a robot which did nothing except follow direct instructions might be an irritation and a bore. And it has not gone unnoticed that total acquiescence might become rather exasperating. A clear example of this occurs in Nolan's 'Joy of Living'. Ted Rice cannot tolerate his robot wife's flawless dependability and selflessness, and she is saved from the Exchange only by protesting strongly at his thoughtlessness. Having demonstrated some scrap of assertiveness, she becomes more 'human' and more acceptable. The story suggests that, even with regard to the desirable feature of faithfulness, moderation would be advisable.

Friendliness is another key personality feature shared by the ideal robots. Clearly any product robot who turned out to be hostile would soon be returned to the retailer marked 'malfunctioning'. No designer is going to incorporate malevolence or quarrelsomeness into a model, and precautions will be taken to make sure that such responses do not occur. But friendliness is not simply the absence of malice: it involves being positively amiable, congenial and affectionate. The robot cannot 'feel' friendly. It will simply behave in a friendly manner. By words and deeds it will convey a positive regard for those it meets. Socially skilled, it will simulate respect and devotion. It will achieve rapport with human beings and encourage them to feel a close affinity.

Friendly relationships between people are generally easy-going and comfortable, and the relative status of friends is of little consequence. This is not generally the case in the human-robot attachments represented in stories and films. The machines would not be so presumptuous as to regard themselves as equals and they are never over-familiar. Although they are amicable they maintain a respectful distance. This is accentuated in the case of the 'butler' robots, but it occurs throughout the literature. In its initial approach, at least, the machine is more likely to regard the owner as a sympathetic employer than as a peer. The status distinction may even be maintained when a sexual liaison occurs. The relationship envisaged between Lord Ewald and Hadaly resembles that of prostitute and client rather than that of a loving couple. Helen O'Loy was bolder when she set out to get her man, and her association with Dave did eventually become one of mutual respect and equal partnership. Helen's self-assurance is untypical, however. The machines are usually shown as being under, rather than in, command. For a robot to be seductive is one thing. But for it to be actively enticing, other than at the express request of a human, is deviant and inconsistent with the robot ideal.

The closest and most 'natural' bonds between people and robots arise in those situations in which a robot collaborates with a person on a mission, or where the human being becomes dependent on the machine. Thus in Asimov's *Caves of Steel* a humanoid device partners a human detective on a homicide case. They work in close partnership, and in time the difference in their natures becomes obscured. The human being develops a great respect for the robot and comes to treat him as a comrade. The machine's behaviour greatly facilitates this process, and Asimov explains that it has been constructed with a 'strong friendship circuit'. Character-control hardware is evident again in John Wyndham's 'Compassion Circuit', in which something akin to a true friendship can arise because the robot is a 'nurse' who provides essential care, and thereby gains a relatively high standing in the eyes of her human patient. As a consequence the status gap between robot and human narrows, allowing the development of an intimate bond. Similarly, the quality of true friendship is often apparent in robot-child relationships—partly because children are shown as less conscious of the difference between themselves and the machine and partly because fictional robots respond, as product robots will, with a special kindness and 'sentiment' towards the young.

Ideal robots are demonstrative. They show their loyalty and affection constantly, and may be openly sentimental. Neither their enthusiasms nor their anxieties remain hidden. Butler robots may struggle to maintain a reserve, but even they are rarely able to hide their concerns. Many characters are also verbose and particularly fond of idiom: C-3PO and Vincent seem to have an aphorism for every occasion, and even Hadaly's phonographic discs are well stocked with a collection of 'thoughts of the great philosophers'. Robots wear their hearts on their metal sleeves, a useful feature which keeps their human contacts fully aware of their inner processes. Reticence is not a recommended feature for a robot.

Some mechanical personalities portrayed in stories and films are caricatures of human personality types. They provide an interesting diversion but hardly act as character models for an ideal product. Thus in *The Hitch Hiker's Guide to the Galaxy* each of the three robots exhibits an extreme character flaw. Deep Thought is over-serious and introverted. Eddie is a wild extrovert and liable to bouts of petulance; he has a tendency to be peevish (not a useful feature for any machine) and his summer-camp enthusiasm is often inopportune. For the audience his antics may be hilarious, but those with whom he interacts often find him very annoying. Eddie is one of those robot characters an audience might love to see in a play but would not want to live with. Marvin is another. This morose machine drags himself from planet to planet with a heaviness and dejection which finds frequent expression in his depressed mutterings. Responding languidly and resentfully to commands, he is hardly a zestful servant, and would prove a disheartening companion.

Even the robots nearest to the ideal sometimes have minor flaws. C-3PO has a rather nervous disposition and a tendency to be over-fussy, and Vincent lacks a certain humility. It is clear, too, that both of these robots have 'moods'. Their response-styles and temperaments change with the situation. Some mood changes are perhaps intrinsic rather than reactive, occurring as a result of chance fluctuations in the functioning of their hardware or as a result of preset internal 'electro-bio-rhythms'. The ability to react sensitively to different circumstances would be a very welcome feature in a home robot. A machine which had taught an advanced subject during the day might be serving drinks at a party in the evening. Hopefully its 'mood' would have adjusted accordingly, seriousness and engrossment having been replaced by buoyancy and humour. Indeed, robots could have considerable talents as entertainers, and might be called upon to recite monologues or to perform musically, in the manner of Silver and Olympia.

As well as the automatic mood changes, more profound transformations of personality might be produced under human control. A product robot could have the potential to change characterization, each of the multiple personalities being friendly, demonstrative and faithful but all differing in their specific qualities. This would make the robot a particularly fascinating companion. Eccentricities of any type might be enjoyed until they became monotonous, and the machine would then revert to its normal character. There are of course literary precedents for such multiple characterizations. Hadaly could be switched from one kind of woman to another by manipulation of the pressure-sensitive rings on her fingers. In the case of the product robot a verbal command should suffice. Hadaly's personifications tended to be erotic variants: Ewald was promised that in Hadaly he had not a single partner but a harem. The product machine could feature a much wider range of options. *L'Ève future* suggests also the simulation of a 'past' for each character, with each able to 'reminisce' about experiences they have never had.

This raises many delightful and bizarre possibilities, and seems to present no special technical problem. It highlights one important way in which the robot's 'memory' would be quite unlike that of humans. The experience database of one robot could easily be duplicated and given to another machine. If one robot had travelled the world, or spoken with a famous person, then all others of its type might be able to 'remember' the experience. In addition, historical memories could be synthesized so that the machine would recollect nostalgically the events of a medieval fayre or, switching to a French accent, regale the listener with a first-person account of the Revolution. Famous characters from the past could also be revived in robot form. The Abraham Lincoln simulacrum in Philip Dick's *We Can Build You* lacks none of the oratory powers of the original politician and has a prodigious recall of the affairs of state during the 16th presidency.

Dramatic historical roles were played by robots in *Westworld*, and a simulated past comprised the major database for Grandfather and Grandmother Smith in Chad Oliver's 'The Life Game'. The grandfather's 'memories' of fishing trips and business meetings were artificially contrived and the robot was 'play-acting'. Indeed, all robots could be said to be play-acting. They are not so much characters as 'character-actors', even as they display their primary personality. The robot hardware acts like a phonograph, able to play whatever character disc may be placed upon it. Most of the time the home robot would play the same personality and the more extravagant manipulations of character would probably be used sparingly. But even in its normal personality mode the machine could display a range of moods, and it would be expected to play a number of quite different functional roles.

Apart from working on practical chores and acting as an information source and tutor, the machine would be an effective companion. Variations of such a role recur throughout the literature. Robots become 'part of the family', they become partners and intimates and they also act as nurses and counsellors. It might be anticipated that for a robot to assume any of these roles it would have to embody the highest level of technical sophistication, but this is not the case. Some humans make companions of their cats and dogs, people readily confide their secrets to computers operating simple interview programs, and children, at least, can develop an unbounded affection for inanimate dolls. Even a relatively simple product robot would surely be far more effective in stimulating a feeling of intimacy than any 'insensible' object. A machine accomplished in the skills of social judgement and interaction, and possessing the social graces to a high degree, would certainly promote intense feelings of familiarity and tenderness.

Technological advances will permit a wide range of machine characterizations and allow product developers a relatively free hand in this aspect of robot design. The literary heritage suggests many personality features which ought, or ought *not*, to be manifest in the ideal home robot. It should be faithful without being so totally dependent that it seems to be forever craving the next instruction. It should be friendly but not presumptuous or overfamiliar, and it should be expressive without being manic or melodramatic. Ideally, the behavioural style of the machine should adjust in response to changes in the social atmosphere. More extreme revisions of personality would be under direct human control and the robot would have a repertoire of highly diverse characterizations which could be 'acted out' on special occasions. As well as being proficient at a wide range of practical household tasks the machine would be a skilful teacher, an expert on many subjects and a sensitive companion. It might entertain the children before washing dishes, manage the household accounts after feeding the dog, and tend to the garden before holding an informal counselling session with a worried teenager. Throughout its kaleidoscopic day the machine would maintain good humour, patience and civility. If time permitted, it would occupy itself with longer-term projects, always ready to follow new instructions and to answer new questions. An ideal robot will, in its time, play many parts—and all of them with exemplary diligence and thoughtful graciousness.

The Trouble with Gloria

In Asimov's 'Robbie' a little girl becomes inconsolable when her robot playmate is sent away. Explaining his daughter's extraordinary grief, her father comments: 'The whole trouble with Gloria is that she thinks of Robbie as a *person* and not as a *machine*.' The 'humanization' phenomenon, whereby people react towards robots *as if* they were human beings, is encountered throughout the literature and is evident in the responses of most human characters. In *2001* Dave Bowman claims that HAL is regarded as 'just another member of the crew', and his conversations with the computer reveal the full extent of his personification of the electronic colleague. This type of response depends both on the close simulation of human behaviour by the machine and on the general human predisposition to treat inanimate objects *as if* they were people. Such identification does not imply a true delusion. The literature implies that humans will respond to character robots as 'social' beings not because they are genuinely deluded but because they accept an illusion of the robot's 'humanness' knowingly and willingly.

Some stories chart the development of the human response in

detail. Commonly the reaction changes from initial suspicion, horror, fear or astonishment to one of complete acceptance as the person gradually 'habituates'. In Asimov's 'Satisfaction Guaranteed', Claire is at first completely unnerved by Tony, but before long the tact and attractiveness of the machine overcome her reservations. A similar change of heart occurs in Tanith Lee's *The Silver Metal Lover*. When Jane meets Silver for the first time she is perplexed: 'I was frightened. He was a robot and he seemed just like a man, and he scared me in a way I just couldn't explain . . . His reactions were superb. I hated him. I wished he were a box on wheels, or I wished he were human.' The sound of his voice, the way he looks, and his gentle manner soon put an end to such ambivalent feelings, however, and Jane becomes totally entranced and infatuated with him.

Other characters react with wonder and disbelief when they first meet the machine. Lord Ewald is overawed when Hadaly is introduced to him, but her beauty, her talents and her gentle manner invite him to respond to her as a woman; it takes little persuasion to convince him that he will be able to love Hadaly, and as he helps to decide the details of her eventual incarnation he anticipates with exhilaration the life they will share. The transition from wonder to total acceptance is also chronicled in Bradbury's 'I Sing the Body Electric'. The children are open-mouthed when they first unpack the grandmother machine, swathed in bandages like an Egyptian mummy, but soon they are treating her as a human being and as one of the family. Even Agatha, who jumped back in horror when the 'thing' began to move, responds positively to the relaxed and serene approach of the grandmother machine.

The habituation phenomenon is less frequently depicted in films, for robot movies are often set in a distant future when the machines have long been accepted as part of the social scene. The transformation from horror to love is skilfully portrayed, however, in *E.T.* Each of the children initially responds to the alien with shrieks of horror, but this rapidly changes—first to curiosity, and then to tenderness and love. *E.T.* provides a remarkable illustration of the process of acceptance, detailing the dynamics of the children's reactions and portraying vividly the characteristics that lead to the swift erosion of the original aversion. The fact that such features could be emulated in a product robot gives the film a special relevance, although the initial response to an attractively presented and widely advertised product device would hardly be expected to match the shrieks that greeted the sudden entry of the alien.

There is thus a consensus that any immediate reaction of wonder, fear or protest is likely to be easily overcome once a human being starts to interact with the machine. Initial prejudices and suspicions are quelled as the person becomes accustomed to the device and as its friendly and nonthreatening personality becomes apparent. It is true that some stories paint a far less positive picture. There are accounts of mass paranoia concerning imminent invasion by alien robots, and in some tales robots have evidently proved so unpopular and unacceptable that they have been banished from Earth. Even in 'The Bicentennial Man' the robot-hero Andrew is beaten by thugs antagonistic to his kind. But with very few exceptions people are shown to accept the product robot. It is usually treated with affection, respect and trust, and is in many ways regarded as a human acquaintance.

Such responses reflect both the characteristics of the machines themselves and the predispositions of the humans who interact with them. In many cases the physical presentation of the robot helps elicit favourable reactions. The body shell often takes the form of an especially attractive human—Tony, Silver, Olympia, Hadaly and Helen O'Loy are all machine embodiments of the ideal human physique. Their voices, too, are appealing and present powerful indicators of 'humanness' and 'character'. HAL's 'normal' voice is gentle, controlled and friendly, whereas Eddie's laughter and gleeful tone convey an impression of a person with infectious good humour—appealing to the audience if not to his companions. Stories imply that the robot's bodily form, voice and behaviour will be judged against prevailing stereotypes. Bradbury's creation is experienced as a 'grandmother' because her design conforms to normal expectations about grandmothers. Not only is the body shell sexed and aged appropriately, and the voice matched to it, but the robot's talents, 'interests' and responses also fit with the general image. Thus emphasis is placed on the need to integrate different aspects of the machine's presentation and behaviour repertoire. It is also suggested that the whole presentation should conform to common stereotypes to produce the illusion of the particular 'person' embodied by the machine. Responses to the robot may then be similar to those elicited by the type of person it resembles.

The effect is well illustrated in Philip Dick's *We Can Build You*. The Lincoln model has an imposing presidential bearing and the character to match. The narrator describes his inhibitions about having to 'intrude' upon the robot: ' "Mr President", I murmured. My throat felt dry. "Sir, I hate to bother you." I felt nervous, and yet at the same time I knew perfectly well that this was a machine I was facing . . . And yet I couldn't help myself. Why not say to it "Mr Simulacrum"? After all that was the truth.' Here the machine has clearly borrowed its status from the person it represents, and the human response reflects this identification despite the total absence of delusion. The implication is clear: habitual human response patterns to a type of *person* are likely to be transposed to corresponding types of *robot*. People will be intimidated by presidential robots, they will respect grandmother machines, and they will be aroused by sensual devices.

In some instances a special psychological vulnerability is seen to help the process of humanization. In *Silent Running* Freeman is isolated and lonely and, in the absence of any other social stimulation, projects personalities and feelings onto the drones. He gives them names and changes their circuitry to make them more 'sociable', and even these minimal adjustments are sufficient to produce the desired effect. Freeman's criteria for adequate companionship are clearly lowered by his estrangement from the rest of the human crew just as the sexual deprivation of the *Dark Star* astronauts increases their sensitivity to the arousing properties of the female computer voice. Similar effects were described many times before. In 'The Sandman' Nathanael's infatuation blinds him to the true nature of his beloved, and in *L'Ève future* Lord Ewald's desperate search for the ideal partner encourages him to treat Hadaly as if she were a woman. Powerful emotional predispositions, sensitivities and weaknesses also instigate other 'social' responses. In 'Virtuoso' the Maestro's exceptional susceptibility to musical talent prompts him to treat the mechanical pianist in a way that would normally be reserved for a human virtuoso. Her unfulfilled desire to be a mother leads Susan Calvin, in 'Lenny', to teach the little robot to call to her: 'Mommy, I want you. I want you, mommy.' A similar yearning produces an extreme reaction in 'And Baby Makes Three'; in response to the highly realistic robobaby, Elain's zealous maternal desire produces a dangerous distortion of reality.

Many of the extreme human-robot relationships depicted in fiction are romantic or sexual. This theme extends far back into the robot heritage and has been constantly revived. Where the attraction is mainly sexual, the physical charms and talents of the robot may be sufficient to satisfy the needs of a deprived or depraved human being. Indeed several robots, including Silver and Hadaly, are said to possess sensuous skills and carnal stamina that easily outstrip those of any human libertine or paramour. In *The Silver Metal Lover* Egyptia prizes Silver purely for his power to excite her and treats him as nothing more than a sexual aid. Her friend Jane, however, becomes infatuated with the *person* of the robot, and sexual adventures are but one aspect of their relationship. In Asimov's 'Satisfaction Guaranteed', Claire's unconsummated love for Tony provides another notable example of the romantic involvement of a human with a machine. Both of these women are shown as especially vulnerable. Jane is alone among her friends in holding to the traditional values of love in a world in which casual relationships have become the norm. No human male will provide her with the fidelity and romantic ardour she desires. Silver, however, can be relied upon to oblige in this as in any other wish. Claire feels somewhat inadequate among other women and receives little help or sympathy from her husband. She is understandably elated when the gracious Tony listens with obvious concern.

Jane and Claire clearly attribute feelings to their machines and each 'empathizes' with her robot lover. Empathy for a machine may be a natural consequence of the humanization effect. Following the nondelusional identification of the machine as a 'person' or a 'creature', it may be treated as though it has emotions and can feel pain and longing. This is clearly illustrated in *R.U.R.* Helena refuses to allow the managers to dissect the realistic Sulla. She knows full well that Sulla is a machine and yet finds it impossible to quell a certain sympathy for the robot's 'plight'. The appearance and behaviour of the device signal humanness, and Helena cannot help but endow it with the capacity to feel as a human would. She seems to identify with the machine, projecting onto the inanimate robot the feelings *she* would have in such a situation.

'Empathy' underlies many of the emotional reactions to robots depicted in literature. There may be an appreciation of a robot as a masterpiece of artistic or technological achievement, but when a person relates 'socially' to the machine it is generally attributed with the capacity to feel. If the robot is cast in a particular role, empathy may help elicit a strong positive sentiment, as in the many cases of parental, filial or romantic attachments. In other cases the robot is portrayed as a servant or an acquaintance, but is still treated as if it had feelings. In some instances this results in negative, rather than positive, behaviour towards it. Thus the satisfaction gained by the scoundrels who assault Andrew in 'The Bicentennial Man' depends on their belief that the robot is being humiliated, that it is being made to feel absurd. They are not simply vandalizing property, but take delight in abusing a sentient and sensitive creature. Sheckley's 'A Ticket to Tranai' portrays a sadistic society in which special victim robots are manufactured. People are encouraged to vent their anger and frustration by kicking and beating the machines, and the screaming and whimpering adds to their effectiveness. The catharsis produced by this violence clearly depends on the fact that the human characters see their actions as inflicting 'wounds', not merely 'damage'. The behaviour is therefore 'cruel' rather than simply destructive. Thus viciousness, as well as love, depends critically on the precondition of empathy.

Inhumane treatment of robots, at least of 'innocent' robots, is rarely shown as the most likely consequence of empathy. Human heroes generally treat their mechanical charges kindly and do not abuse them. They are much more likely to feel compassion, and to offer assistance, sympathy and encouragement. Their affinity for the machine leads people to be charitable and accommodating. Kindness predominates, and considerable effort is required to overcome the natural benevolence if the need arises. Thus Dave Bowman is fainthearted in his destruction of HAL, even after the computer has made its deadly bid for control. At one level the astronaut is aware that HAL is nothing more than a machine, but he cannot help regarding him also as a former friend and colleague. HAL's pleading for his 'life' evokes powerful feelings of compassion and mercy, not only in the astronaut but in the audience, too.

The prepotency of the empathic response, as suggested in the literature, implies that empathic feelings might be evoked by even simple mechanisms. Such an effect is illustrated in Terrel Miedaner's *The Soul of Anna Klane* (1977). A young woman, Lee, is highly sceptical when told about a scientist's view that machines are a form of life: 'But, I just do not relate to machines. Emotionally speaking, there is a difference between the way we treat animals and the way we treat machines which defies logical explanation. I mean, I can break a machine and it really doesn't bother me. But I cannot kill an animal.' It is suggested that the reluctance to hurt a living creature has nothing to do with a person's feeling of biological kinship but simply reflects the fact that the animal seems to struggle and to suffer and may produce signs which are identified as 'pleas'.

A machine has been constructed to test this hypothesis. It takes the form of an aluminium beetle with flashing lights and rubber wheels, and when damaged in any way it exhibits sounds and movements that signal distress. As Lee watches the 'beast' travelling across the floor, purring and seeking for electrical outlets, she is challenged to take a hammer and 'kill it'. Hesitantly she grasps the weapon and brings it down forcefully. The machine is damaged and 'cries out'. Lee tracks it as it backs away, its sensors aware of the approaching hammer. Setting down the weapon she is able to approach the beast, and lifts it gently to a workbench. Its metal skin is warm and the motors issue a gentle purr. As the hammer is lifted once more there is a soft whimpering sound and, horrified, Lee finds that she cannot go on. Leaving somebody else to 'finish it off', Lee winces at the crunch of the final 'death-blow'.

The robot literature contributes in a number of important ways to our understanding of the emotional responses likely to be shown towards highly sophisticated machines. It suggests that people will tend to humanize robots and respond to them empathically. It illustrates how the reaction to a particular machine will depend both on the characteristics of the robot—its physical appearance, voice quality and its 'character'—and on the prevailing stereotypes and mood of the human subject. The general predilections towards humanization and empathy will be accentuated in the presence of realistic and socially skilled machines which have been carefully designed specifically to elicit such reactions. Personal circumstances and unfulfilled social needs may generate a special vulnerability, producing extreme emotional responses to the robot. There is thus a high degree of consensus within the literature. The question that now needs to be addressed is whether any evidence can be produced to support or refute the picture of human reactions to future products implied by the robot heritage.

Response Criteria

The validity of fictional accounts of human responses to robots cannot be judged directly. Only when sophisticated personal robots have been produced and are in residence in a number of homes will it be possible to assess their real impact. The accuracy of the picture presented in films and stories can be gauged only indirectly and imperfectly, but evidence from various sources does lend considerable support to the major implications of SF accounts. Although speculative writers are free to imagine all manner of technological advances the behaviour of the human characters responding to such developments must at all times remain credible. In the event it has been shown that many of the physical images of robots represented in SF are not only plausible but seem likely to be realizable in product machines. The question that remains is whether the criterion of psychological plausibility is met.

One simple test is: does the reading or viewing audience find the responses realistic? Do the human beings involved in the stories and films emerge as credible characters? The impact on the audience of the robot personalities can also be judged. Such reactions may well provide clues about how people would react towards similar product realizations. In addition, certain current objects, systems and machines have *some* features in common with the projected product robot. Dolls, waxwork models and computers may be said, for different reasons, to anticipate aspects of the sophisticated robot. Human responses towards these can therefore be assessed to see whether they comply with the general predictions obtainable from fiction. Finally, primitive robots already exist and their impact on both their creators and on the public can be examined. Such robots include industrial machines, the 'premature' domestic models, and experimental devices that are now in various stages of development. Evidence derived from each source reveals clear parallels with the types of human response represented in fiction.

In SF, as in all other kinds of literature, the human characters need to be presented as integrated personalities and their behaviour has to be portrayed realistically if the story is to work. There are undoubtedly a lot of poor-quality robot tales, but many stories have gained both popular and critical acclaim. Such works frequently describe humanization, empathy and the development of intimacy as fundamental elements in the human response towards robots. The machines themselves may possess implausible or even fantastic characteristics, but the human reactions are not ridiculous. Given *that* technology, embodied in *that* form and exhibiting *that* character, the human reactions have an evident plausibility. There is nothing unreasonable about Dave Bowman's treatment of HAL: his conversations with the computer are perfectly credible given the supposed character of the machine. There is nothing preposterous about Gloria's play with Robbie or her sadness when he leaves. The extreme romantic and 'parental' responses may well seem desperate and ill advised, but they retain credibility because of the level of realism and social skill attributed to the machine and the extreme psychological needs of the human characters who become so involved.

It has been argued that many robot films and stories provide something of a preview of real robot products. Thus the audience response to particular fictional creations may provide a glimpse of future responses to real machines. There can be no doubting the popularity of robot characters in films such as 2001 and the Star Wars cycle. The robots often emerge as the most memorable characters and the audience is doubly entertained, for the robots have a curious status ambiguity (they occupy an anomalous position somewhere between machines and people) and are also charming 'personalities'. The box office success of recent films and the enduring popularity of robot stories reinforce the view that the central concept has a special fascination for people. Tales about artificial humanoids have been prevalent since the earliest days of storytelling and in recent times the robot has gained a new lease of life in genre SF, with literally hundreds of stories written around the theme.

With their limited exposure to the robots the audience may never lose their initial sense of wonder. Unlike the human characters in the films, they may have little opportunity to habituate to the machine, but otherwise their reactions follow many of the same patterns. They tend to humanize the robot and to empathize with it. The humanization is evident in audience responses to C-3PO and Vincent, to the Tin Man and to the drones in Silent Running. This is hardly surprising, since film audiences have long attributed consciousness, feeling and character to all manner of aliens and to cartoon drawings. The audience finds it difficult not to empathize with Bambi, for example, when the pitiful tear is shed. So heartrending are some scenes evoked by this series of drawings that the UK film censor decided that the film should be watched by children only if they were accompanied by an adult. More recently the case of E.T. has demonstrated how an audience may endow a strange creature with human character and motives on the basis of a few simple cues. They also quickly develop a profound empathy for the alien. Few of those who have seen *2001* can have remained unmoved by the death of HAL. It can confidently be assumed that the skills used to create such moving portrayals on the screen will be exercised with equal boldness and brilliance in devising and programming the behaviour and character of product robots.

Although the robots have a direct effect on an audience, people also model their reactions on those displayed by the human characters in the film. Anthony Daniels, the actor who plays C-3PO, has explained: 'One of the reasons why C-3PO works very well is the sincerity with which Luke Skywalker talks to him, treats him as a real entity, a real person. The audience then adopts his attitude.' Such identification is effective in another way. Viewers and readers may take the obvious regard of the robots for the human characters as extending to themselves. If people feel loved or respected by the machines, they will tend to respond positively towards them. Psychologists speak of a 'norm of reciprocity'—people tend to love those who love them, to return compliments, and to retaliate against aggression. It may be assumed that this phenomenon will be evident also in human-robot relationships; and, since product machines will be unwaveringly positive and 'concerned' in their actions, then the people who interact with them will tend to behave towards them similarly. Thus there are two distinct ways in which the body of SF literature and film can contribute to a prediction of the likely human response to sophisticated personal machines. It provides numerous plausible accounts of human-robot encounters and displays simulations of potential product machines so that audience responses may be observed.

Further supportive evidence comes from sources not directly linked to SF. Although the kind of robot commonly described in fiction does not yet exist, many objects and systems do exhibit some of the key features of such a machine. It is clear that even simple objects may be humanized. The most obvious example is the doll. Children project all manner of feelings, motives and intentions onto these lifeless objects by virtue of their superficial resemblance to an adult, baby or bear. Adults too may use dolls to satisfy an unfulfilled need for some special form of human contact. In many parts of the US there are 'doll adoption centres' where childless couples may buy a 'baby', and in a number of countries inflatable sex-aid dolls are manufactured. Considering the rather feeble attempts at authenticity represented by such effigies and their almost total passivity (the more expensive sex-aids are just able to move with a rippling rhythm) it may be surprising that they are able to fulfil any human need. The commercial successes in these areas, however, suggest that the products are highly attractive—at least to the prospective customer. It is noticeable that the functions of both the 'adoption baby' and 'sex-partner' dolls correspond to those of certain product robots encountered in fiction. Thus primitive objects already occupy roles ascribed to robots in SF. It seems reasonable to assume that in future more sophisticated products will be developed to satisfy the human 'needs' that already generate a market for the dolls with adult appeal.

The tendency to attribute life and personality to inanimate objects is widespread and well established. The phenomenon, known as 'animism', can be demonstrated in the psychology laboratory even with simple visual displays. These produce relatively modest effects, but with a machine of the kind described in Terrel Miedenar's story it is quite likely that the fictional horror and inhibition of response displayed by the young woman in her efforts to 'kill' the aluminium beetle could be produced with even today's technology. Future robot products can be expected to have a far greater potential to elicit emotional responses.

Animism has taken on a new significance with the development of interactive advanced technology systems. Experiences with 'conversational' computer programs, for example, reveal a very strong tendency for people to humanize the machine. Studies in medical contexts have shown repeatedly that patients who are interviewed by computers tend to be more self-disclosing to the computer than to a human physician. They also tend to regard their 'interviewer' as a person, and they report enjoying the 'social' interaction with the machine. Considering that such users usually have to type their part of the conversation and that the computer's responses are usually displayed on a television screen, the extent of the humanization is remarkable. It must be assumed that, with voice input and output, and with a moving humanoid shell to house the system, the intensity of the personification and empathy will at least approach the levels portrayed in fiction.

Further evidence comes from human reactions to existing robots. Despite their lack of speech, their inflexibility and their nonhumanoid appearance, industrial robots have sometimes been found to elicit empathic responses from those who work with them. They tend to be given names, and the language used to describe their actions can take on an unmistakeable anthropomorphic ring. Thus a machine that is out of order may be said to be 'misbehaving', 'ill' or 'hungover'. When a robot working in one factory broke down, its human colleagues posed for a photograph with arms around the inanimate invalid and sent it flowers and 'get-well-soon' cards. The general fascination for artificial humanoids has been evident in the public response to automata for centuries. Realistic machines have performed preset sequences of actions that have allowed them to 'write' and 'draw', to play musical instruments and to demonstrate gymnastic feats. Although much attention was given to the naturalness of their external appearance their repertoire was necessarily limited and they had no power to interact flexibly with human beings. Despite such limitations their impact was often considerable.

In the 20th century a new level of 'robot consciousness' has emerged, largely due to the influence of SF. In the 1920s and 1930s a number of humanoid devices were exhibited at major exhibitions and World Fairs in London, New York, San Francisco, Milan, Paris, Budapest, and Moscow. Eric was one such machine. Its movements were stiff but it could sit, stand, and 'speak', and when it opened the 1928 Model Engineer Exhibition in London it welcomed patrons and cited itself as a prime example of the wonders of modern technology. In 1939 Electro and its dog Sparko took pride of place in the New York Fair, courtesy of the Westinghouse Corporation. Electro could distinguish between certain colours, spoke a few words, and smoked cigarettes. In many cases the creators of the exhibition robots circumvented the limitations of the current technology by indulging in a little cheating. Intelligent answers to spoken questions, for example, might be relayed to the robot from a microphone placed before a concealed human commentator. Such tricks were deemed necessary to portray the miracles to come. The machines drew crowds of enthusiastic spectators who responded without fear and with great delight to the antics of the humanoids.

Today a number of robots are exhibited in museums and places of entertainment and they have apparently lost none of their power to evoke excitement. The Lincoln simulacrum remains a major attraction at Disneyland, and when the house-chore robot Arok was exhibited at the Chicago Museum of Fine Arts he proved irresistible to the many adults and children who came to visit him. In Japan Master Hachiro has greeted hundreds of thousands of children at the Tokyo Institute of Juvenile Culture. Appearing as a rather nervous but friendly character, it is one of nearly a thousand robots and robot toys on display. Many of these smile and have 'human gestures'. When Robot Redford appeared to hand out degrees at a US university graduation ceremony in 1983 the world's press was there to witness the event. There can be no denying that people find robots fascinating and intriguing.

The experience with exhibition robots testifies to this near-universal captivation and indicates that even simple machines can be presented with a degree of showmanship which encourages both humanization and empathy. People appear eager to participate in an encounter with a robot. But the exhibition models are inflexible and insensible, and those who visit them have little opportunity to overcome their initial amazement or to interact personally with the device. Conclusions based directly on their reactions are therefore likely to provide a gross underestimation of the impact of sophisticated product machines. Similarly, responses to the primitive domestic robots that are currently on sale have relatively little predictive value because such machines are profoundly limited by the available technology. Reactions to these machines, however, are uniformly positive and show at least some evidence of the humanization effect. Manufacturers appear aware of the special attraction of a machine presented as 'human' and often make efforts to encourage such responses. When Huggy was first exported from the US to the UK in 1980 he was flown from California in a box marked 'Caution—Live Animal', and the UK importer said of his protégé: 'Once you've had him around for a while you start getting very fond of him. He's very cute and you find yourself starting to have conversations with him.'

More supportive evidence comes from those involved in research with advanced systems—the inventors and designers of experimental robots. A leading Japanese robotics specialist, Shigeo Hirose, has built a number of sophisticated moving models and has described his own reactions to these machines: 'When I began to work with my robots, their movements seemed so controlled, so intelligent; it looked as though they were alive, even though I knew they weren't. As we become more sophisticated at giving robots freedom to operate, their reactions will appear even more alive to us. We will begin to see a psychology behind their actions.' And the US robot constructor Charles Balmer has commented: 'A robot is somewhat like a child. It requires a good deal of patience, time and energy to construct, and then as it limps and crashes and smokes its way to adulthood, we as mothers and fathers learn something about being a robot while hopefully it learns a little about being a human. It seems only natural that it should have a name, if for no other reason than to have something to yell during a fit of frustration or anger.'

SF implies that the companion machine is psychologically feasible. It has also prescribed certain characteristics as likely to maximize appeal. The literature has portrayed robot characters who have had an astonishing audience impact and has provided numerous credible descriptions of relationships formed between robots and human beings. Whether the more extravagant and bizarre relationships depicted will come to have any real parallel must await direct evidence, and at this stage the possibility of such liaisons cannot be ruled out. The consensus of evidence from several external sources supports the main fictional themes. It seems highly probable that people will humanize robots and will feel an empathy towards them. Since even simple systems have an effect which is far from negligible it should be expected that realistic, skilled and charming robots will elicit strong emotional responses and foster powerful sentimental attachments. There is every indication that people will respond positively towards the machines, that they will enjoy their interactions and find character robots extremely appealing. Commercial interests are bound to take such powerful effects into consideration, and we can therefore anticipate the production of realistic robots with full-bodied characters and all the skills that technological progress allows. The impact of such systems on human sentiments will doubtless be impressive.

Reactions to particular robots will vary. It can be expected that a cheery machine will elicit more delight than a sombre one. People will react to a product body shape in terms of its 'sex', 'age', and 'type'. They will also respond in predictable ways to qualities of voice. Robot designers will be mindful of human reaction patterns, ensuring, for example, that the system is not forceful in its early attentions so that sufficient time is allowed for habituation to take effect. This will be encouraged by the machine remaining courteous and controlled. Later, as the relationship develops, a more relaxed and familiar style will supersede. The keen competition between rival producers will ensure that eventually all tastes are catered for. The socially sensitive and reactive machine will foster trust and encourage intimate responses from the people it serves.

The Switch Behind the Ear

How might a robot 'die'? The question of robot mortality turns out to be closely linked to other major issues such as the 'personal identity' of robots, human sentiment towards character machines and the nature of the robot market. It is a basic rule of nature that living things change as they get older, and eventually die. But such a rule does not apply to technological systems. It is true that machines can wear out, but if key parts are replaced then 'the same machine' may in principle go on forever. And, unlike living systems, its function, 'stamina' and appearance are likely to remain practically the same throughout the working span. So it should be with robots, and this presents a number of intriguing problems. In many ways the device will be treated like a person, yet unlike a person it will not 'get old' and will not die.

Several references to the issue have already been met. In *L'Ève future* it was seen as a great advantage that the female humanoid would retain her 'youth' while Lord Ewald passed into old age. In 'I Sing the Body Electric' the grandmother machine came into being, fresh from the factory, as a ready-made grandmother. The robobaby in 'And Baby Makes Three' would never grow to become 'an older child'. Although the basic robot hardware would remain the same, however, the active memory of the device would constantly develop and change. The experience of years would vastly expand the initial database, broadening the range of knowledge and leading to a certain 'maturation of mind' as accumulated facts allowed for substantial cross-referencing. With the development of an increasingly realistic perspective an 'older mind' would be housed in an unchanged body.

If it can be assumed that robots are not likely to 'die' of mechanical failure or of any 'natural cause', at least within an appreciable timespan, will they survive forever, or at least exist to see several generations of a family come and go? This was the fate that befell Andrew in 'The Bicentennial Man' and Jenkins in Simak's *City*. Technically, of course, there would be no problem in somehow putting an end to the machine. Apart from simply physically destroying it, several alternatives are possible. A built-in 'mortality' or 'senility' feature might be arranged, or a robot could be 'recalled' to the factory after a fixed number of years. This was the solution of US Robots after their experience with the Andrew model. Or a machine might be registered as belonging to a specific owner and then be routinely 'wiped' or deactivated on the death of that person. The owner might be able to specify in a will what should become of the mechanical companion. Some, perhaps, would leave their robot's memory to psychological science to enable specialists to gain post-mortem insight into human ways and life-patterns. Memory banks from machines which had acted as companions to famous or important people might be retained by the state and held for a number of years before being released for the use of historians.

So robots will not 'die' of 'natural causes' but could certainly be 'killed', deactivated or 'depersonalized'. The robot heritage is full of stories of humanoid destruction. Talos could be deactivated by the removal of a pin from his heel, the golem could be destroyed by erasing the mystical word from his forehead or, in other versions, removing the life-giving parchment from his mouth. A less subtle mode of execution was ordered by the Emperor Ta Chou, who in a fit of jealousy commanded that the automaton that so attracted his wife be chopped into pieces. Jealousy of another kind led to Olympia's end, ripped apart by the two men who had created her. Some robots have been moved to commit suicide. Helen O'Loy terminated her functioning when her human husband died and in John Wyndham's 'The Lost Machine' (1932) an abandoned and lonely machine dissolved himself in a bath of acid. In Harl Vincent's 'Rex' (1934) a machine which had tried in vain to acquire emotional feelings switched himself off, and in 'The Bicentennial Man' Andrew exchanged his immortal metal body for a humanlike organic casing, thus ensuring his eventual demise. In several stories less harrowing, and less permanent, means are provided for instantly deactivating the system. Commonly a simple 'off' switch is provided—by convention it is located behind the ear.

It is doubtful whether anybody would ever choose to destroy their home robot. Some people might come to hate their machine as a personality, or the relationship might simply 'break down', but in such circumstances the robot's character could be suitably adjusted. If all else failed a quick 'divorce' might be arranged.

Such a state of affairs would be rare, however, for product robots will be highly flexible, biddable and agreeable. The robot's existence might, however, be threatened for two reasons. Some people could feel somewhat disconcerted at the thought of a robot character surviving for many generations and prefer the machine to have a limited span. The most likely reason, however, would be simply that the owner wanted to replace an obsolescent robot. Manufacturers will certainly introduce new and more sophisticated models at a rapid pace and will exert maximum effort to encourage owners to buy the latest version.

As with cars, some people, by preference or through economic stringencies, will remain with 'old reliable' (or even 'old unreliable') for decades while others will want to trade-in every few years. Such a picture of the likely commercial scene suggests that there would be a healthy market for 'partly used' cast-offs. The 'trickle-down' pattern would presumably finish at the lower end of the market with dross-robots, sad old relics which had long been surpassed by technological developments. If such transfers of ownership were made then the robot would presumably have its memory circuits cleared to prevent it from educating its new owners about the intimate secrets of its previous household. The robot, rendered painlessly amnesic by an information wipeout, would thus start a fresh process of socialization in its new home. Meanwhile the original owner, furnished with the latest deluxe companion model, would have forsaken the unpretentious friend in favour of a superlative stranger.

Whether motivated by the feeling that 'robots should have a limited span' or by the desire to update, a person wishing to get rid of a robot would be likely to face two major problems, one sentimental and the other practical. Unless it had been totally unsuccessful in its social role, the machine would have captured the hearts and imagination of family members, and parting with it would be like having a favourite pet put down. This problem of the sorrow and guilt likely to be involved in the loss or disposal of a robot receives attention in a number of stories. The literature suggests that getting rid of a companion robot might prove an emotionally harrowing experience. The owner will have shared thoughts and experiences with the creature. 'He' or 'she' will have become a friend. How difficult it might be to announce to this helpmate and confidant that a form of electronic euthanasia would shortly be performed, or that it would soon have to find a home with another family. And how much more difficult it would be if the robot were to beg, with whimpering sounds and on its bended metal knee, not to be sent away.

Similar problems occur with children's dolls. For the child these objects occupy an indistinct position somewhere between the living and the nonliving. If a favourite is lost or broken the child may react with tears and genuine heartbreak. Replacement with a new doll, as many parents have found, may not be sufficient to make up for the loss of the original, and some dolls and teddy-bears are endlessly patched up and sewn together again. From the child's point of view such surgery is fully justified, for the personality of the old doll or bear is thus preserved. Perhaps in a similar way families will insist on repairing and revamping their household robot far longer than economic sense would counsel.

There are also a number of practical drawbacks to robot replacement. The family would have to learn the ways of the new robot and the machine itself would have to 'start from scratch' with the family. The original robot would have greatly added to its practical value by virtue of its specific memories, knowledge of family affairs, and general familiarity with the house and people. With the robot gone, an invaluable knowledge base might also have disappeared. There is, however, a possible solution to both the sentimental and the practical problem. If new products were to be made 'memory compatible' with the old then the entire database of the original companion could simply be rehoused in the latest body type and furnished with additional powerful programs without disturbing either the personality portrayed or the knowledge and familiarity that had been developed. Thus, like a snake periodically shedding its skin to allow room for growth, the family friend would be remodelled and revamped while retaining its knowledge, skills and character. The companion might have changed appearance substantially; but, thanks to its intact memory and familiar mannerisms, people would surely feel that they had managed to preserve 'the soul of the old machine'.

This indicates the relatively minor importance attached to external appearance when it comes to identifying 'persons'. Memories and personality are much more salient. The question of which criteria should properly be used for establishing 'personal identity' has taxed the minds of philosophers for centuries. Experiences with 'robot recorporation' or 'character transplants' may not shed much light on the conceptual issues involved, but they will certainly provide interesting insights into the relevant psychology. It is likely that people would identify a robot by its psychological characteristics rather than by its outer shell. They should therefore experience little difficulty in accepting the change of body as long as there was no appreciable change of heart.

Some clever software links would be needed to couple the old 'brain circuitry' to the new external body and to update the programs. The machine would have to be 'made aware' of the major surgery it had undergone. It would have to learn to recognize itself anew. The effect of a new body on a robot's own 'personal identity' is raised in *City*. When Jenkins is given an entirely new shell to house his precious memory and control circuitry he is initially less than 'comfortable' with it. He contemplates the new super-body. Like an aged relative who has been presented with an expensive coat styled in the latest young fashion he expresses mixed feelings: 'I'll never wear it. It's too fancy for a robot that's as old as I am. I'd feel out of place in a gaudy thing like that.' He decides to keep the new body 'for best', but soon gets used to it and enjoys the extra facilities it provides. His memory bank is transferred but nobody recognizes him. He has to announce himself even to his friends: 'I'm Jenkins, this is my new body.'

Jenkins managed to survive, his memory intact, through many generations of the family he served. He was able to recount the family history and to preserve the family heritage. Perhaps people will welcome the fact that their memory will live on in the synthetic brain of a humanoid machine. They might relish the notion that such a robot would be able to speak about them, recalling favourite anecdotes and time-honoured epithets for the entertainment and enlightenment of future generations. Yet it seems equally likely that human beings will find the idea of the immortal 'sensible' machine highly disconcerting.

Indeed there are many aspects of the home robot which raise justifiable concern. One is the important issue of privacy. There is every indication that people will want to use an available machine as a confidant and resident counsellor, yet they will express their deeper feelings and anxieties only as far as they are able to trust the robot's confidentiality, its 'discretion' and its security in the face of any tampering or interrogation by external agents. Impregnability must be guaranteed if the robot is to become the custodian of personal secrets. There will come a time when the question of special access to robot memory will have to be seriously considered. What powers, for example, should be given to police to question companion robots about the behaviour of their owners? Will robots be exempt from any order to testify against their human friends in a court of law, as in many countries people are excused from having to bear witness against their spouse?

The introduction of the home robot will change social patterns just as television, cars and the telephone have produced changes. SF has had relatively little to say on such matters. It can be anticipated that the character machine will be able to deliver advice, information and services that would normally require contact with other people, and there is thus a danger that the machine will add to the social insularity of the home. In its practical and social functions, however, the robot will undoubtedly add to the quality of life. At a time when the number of old people in society is greatly increasing, for example, the machine will be able to provide practical help and nursing care. It will act as a memory aid, a dietary advisor and a counsellor and will be able to call for help in cases of emergency. The robot would be a sympathetic and untiring friend, never selfish, ill tempered or impatient. Thus the machine's potential as a home help for the elderly and disabled is vast, and such advanced technology, in the form of a character device, might well offer the only feasible solution to what now appears to be a major social problem to be faced in the next half-century: the difficulty of providing adequate care for older people with special needs.

Legislation frequently has to be introduced or modified to accommodate major technological innovations. Thus the internal combustion engine, computers and home video have affected the laws concerning road use, privacy, copyright and obscenity. The home robot will acquire a complex legal identity. In many respects it will be treated like other machines, but to some extent it may be given a token 'animal' status. Consider the actions of an owner towards a robot. With other devices the owner is free to destroy, damage or misuse the object. Some early legal systems considered animals, children and even a wife to be a man's property and left him free to use them in any way. Laws about injury and sexual misuse, however, now proscribe certain forms of behaviour towards family members and animals. It is conceivable that robots will not be accorded a status solely reflecting their nature as machines but will be given certain rights in law.

The robot's own behaviour might call for legislation. The machine could injure or kill a person, damage property or cause a public nuisance. In cases where a car generates such problems the machine itself is not held to blame. The problem is seen to arise either from accidental circumstances or from human fault. The 'blame' may lie with the designer, manufacturer or user. It might prove a little more difficult to regard the robot as an unthinking, unmotivated and blameless piece of apparatus and to assign all of its 'crimes' to accident or misuse by a human. The special power of the intelligent machine will be that it is not always under direct human control. It will develop behaviour sequences of its own by learning and imitation and achieve a degree of independence. It may be told to perform a task, but in the absence of orders it will be expected to use its own 'initiative'.

The problem lies in controlling the robot's actions so that deviant and dangerous responses are avoided. The robot will need the equivalents of a moral calculator and a conscience both to prevent 'deviant' response patterns developing within the system and to censor human commands which are malicious or dangerous. The machine would ideally imitate only those human actions which are generally thought to be appropriate, and would refuse to obey an order to rob a bank or hurt a human being. Clearly the robot needs to be given the power of 'discretion' and would operate according to a set of general rules. The 'Laws of Robotics' provide a very good draft for these, although Asimov himself has indicated many of the problems that would arise from a simple implementation of the Laws.

The machine would need to be obedient to human command. If two or more commands conflicted then it would have to judge which was the most appropriate to follow. It would need to establish some criteria to evaluate types of order and classes of person. The owner would have a priority, and could thus expect the machine's loyalty, but the robot might also give special precedence to commands by police officers and other authority figures. The priority given to different orders would need to be assessed in terms of their relative urgency. The legitimacy of the command would also need to be evaluated. The machine would need to have concern for its own self-preservation and, above all, for the well-being of humankind. The self-preservation rule may be superfluous, for if the machine were 'owned' then any damage or destruction would, at least financially, harm the owner. Thus in the interests of its master or mistress the machine would be bound to look after itself.

Several of the concepts involved in the Laws are liable to need exhaustive exposition. Some of the problems likely to be encountered include the identification of a command and decisions about whether it is meant seriously and literally ('Drop dead!'). The notion of 'harm to a human being' also needs extensive elaboration. This would not only include physical injury but would also involve damage to property, psychological hurt and moral danger. To fulfil the requirements entirely, the machine would be required not to insult people, not to cause them undue expense and not to lead them into moral temptation. The simple rule thus has many ramifications and its effective fulfilment would call for the utmost sophistication in situational assessment and social judgement. Even then, considering the vast range of values and meanings which different people hold, the robot's behaviour would undoubtedly cause occasional offence. The robot might act with 'the best will in the world' but nevertheless not every action would be seen by everybody as favourable to them. The robot will be sensitive to social feedback, however, and will learn how to treat particular individuals in the most diplomatic way.

The basic 'moral' principles that would need to be inherent in the system should not be amenable to tampering or adjustment. Fine judgements would therefore need to be made, and the subject raises fundamental issues of individual liberty and central control. The owner might request certain actions which the robot would consider not to be in the person's longer-term interest. Few would doubt that some limitations would have to be built into the machine, however, and this would certainly call for much more than two or three simple rules. The annotation of the basic moral premises might call for a substantial body of additional knowledge. This would ensure at least some degree of safety, but the danger that a clever and ruthless operator might change the rules would remain. To prevent this happening strict methods of protection would have to be employed. Impregnability would perhaps be secured by means of tamper-proof software or, as in Asimov's stories, by implanting the Laws in the hardware of the microcircuitry.

The effective implementation of complex rules will depend on the highest achievements of social judgement, and thus only highly sophisticated systems can be expected to act as if they were 'morally aware'. But even simple machines can be made to act *as if* they are exercising discretion. Thus it would be relatively easy to build a car which recognized legal speed limits and 'refused' to exceed these, and computers can easily recognize offensive words. Most computers and robots respond obligingly to human command but some also have safety and self-preservation functions. Advanced industrial robots may have 'software safety features'. Some are equipped with sensors and programs which enable them to recognize human shapes and so avoid dangerous contact. A mobile Japanese robot, Yamabico, is programmed to detect danger and to take avoiding action, and some industrial robots give themselves a regular check-up and call for human help if they diagnose a fault that might cause them to damage themselves or their environment.

Thus software can be used to control powerful machines so that they are aware of their environment and do no physical damage. Eventually, machines will have to recognize potentially dangerous social situations and to respond to them 'sensitively' and 'morally'. Unlike any machine now in existence, the product robot will be required to act with 'thoughtfulness'. As people observe such actions the machine will be praised, esteemed and held in high regard. Occasionally it will be blamed. Thus it will cease to be regarded as 'morally inert' and will be judged as a member of the moral Universe. Whatever the philosophical truth of the matter, there will be an inevitable and unassailable psychological tendency to treat robots as volitional creatures. Many people are likely to feel that the robot should be accorded certain rights. It is not impossible that this will become a widespread cultural attitude that will be reflected in social mores and, ultimately, in social institutions and the law. If this were to happen then yet another recurrent speculation of SF writers would have become fact.

Oriental Express

For over two millennia stories have been told of artificial men and women, intelligent, mobile and articulate. Initially such accounts claimed that the humanoids were created by magical means; later stories focussed on the efforts of scientists and engineers. Following the myths and fables of early times, a body of robot literature has evolved, offering some consensus about the form and faculties of the ideal humanoid. The robots in stories and films may once have seemed as fanciful as invisible men or bug-eyed monsters. But now, with the rise of advanced technology, many of the 'fabulous' features suddenly appear as items on the agenda for technological research. Many of the goals implicit in the age-old dream seem destined for imminent fulfilment. Stories have suddenly taken on a new plausibility, and the images they portray can be examined critically in the light of contemporary robotics. The design of the commercial products made possible by such research will involve ingenuity and resourcefulness, and designers would do well to examine carefully the images and themes subjected to such prodigious and intense exploration in literature and film.

The robot heritage is a valuable source for ideas about future products. It supplies models for artefacts that would undoubtedly have a major market potential. It provides helpful clues about the likely impact of robots upon the first-time user, and shows some of the ways in which relationships between people and machines may develop. Yet the heritage must be regarded critically. The viability of technical aspects needs to be considered in the light of real research. Such wondrous elements as invisibility and telepathy can safely be disregarded: they do not feature in current project proposals. But it does now seem likely that scientific efforts will soon supply the necessary elements for realizing the speech, actions, characters and roles of fictional robots. SF can contribute little about how a robot may be provided with speech, but it contains many suggestions about what a robot might say. Technology will provide the voice, and imagination will provide the script. Robot stories and films can thus be regarded as plays in search of actors.

Although the robot heritage presents numerous useful images and indicates a number of likely problems, it can be criticized on a number of counts. The fictional consensus can already be judged to be inaccurate in several respects.

In many cases the robot is said to emerge as an isolated product, the result of some quantum leap in technological innovation, but robots will in fact result from intense and widespread research efforts involving many aspects of AI, engineering, psychology and computer science. The far-reaching outcome of these endeavours will provide numerous communications, computational and information products in addition to robots, and the world will thus become a different place. The domestic robot will not derive from the efforts of some single-minded scientist working in a subterranean laboratory. It will reflect the work of thousands of researchers, each building on the successes of others, and widespread collaboration. The product machine will be a corporate achievement.

In many stories robots are said to be produced only by a single major corporation. Again, such a scenario is unrealistic and distorts the probable market scene. The basic technology is certain to be available, simultaneously, to many commercial concerns, and vigorous competition is bound to ensue. Similar technical features will be incorporated into numerous models, and product rivalry may therefore focus largely on such 'peripheral' aspects as appearance, character and cost. Robot products will be news, and character machines will be sold energetically. Advertising will be forceful, enthusiastic and designed to make the product appear exceptionally desirable. It will overcome any fears potential customers may have. Thus stories in which a single robot is produced and introduced to a totally naïve user misrepresent the likely future. Public awareness of developments in product robotics is likely to be high, and a home model will be launched not as a single item but as a mass generation.

Despite its fascination with the fabulous features of robots, the heritage can be said in many instances to underestimate the likely capacity of future machines. It also presents profiles of abilities in which different elements may be strangely 'out of phase'. Robots are often presented as having limited intellectual powers, for example, or as having a staccato speech style. Current developments suggest that by the time a machine is capable of understanding speech, of walking and of seeing, it will be very clever indeed and will be able to speak with natural intonation. Many robot characters are shown as taking all commands literally, but when machine understanding of ordinary speech has been achieved then the additional ability to identify and correctly interpret colloquial phrases should present no fundamental difficulty.

The supposed impediment of literalness has provided many comic opportunities in stories and films, however, and critics should take into account the impositions and temptations of the medium. A straightforward account of life with a sensible and sober robot makes for less exciting viewing or reading than scenes with humour and exaggerated action. Many robot characters are 'larger than life' and more extreme than the personalities likely to be represented by product machines. Robot features that may be highly attractive on the screen or in a novel would prove unbearable in the longer term. There is an old Chinese proverb: 'It is easier to visit friends than to live with them'—and this would apply to many of the robot heroes of screen and story. Eccentric features would be 'toned down' for implementation in the real systems that people will welcome as companions.

The development of a domestic robot depends on a number of factors. The product must be technologically viable, it must be desirable, and it must be available at a reasonable price. It has not been difficult to establish the viability of the major technical aspects of fictional robots, even though a number of crucial breakthroughs are still needed (it may seem foolish to count on such vicissitudes, but the Japanese fifth-generation project includes a timetable of 'scheduled breakthroughs'). Many of the modules needed to build a dream robot already exist in simple form. Further developments along the same lines will yield 'sensory', 'motor' and 'intellectual' modules that will eventually be assembled together and packaged attractively. Desirability can be established only indirectly. The potential usefulness of intelligent mobile machines is without question, and the fascination with existing robots and with the characters in movies and fiction suggests that the character robot will prove a delightful and highly desirable product. And, finally, costs seem unlikely to provide a fatal constraint preventing the emergence of the home robot.

The arguments for technical viability have been presented, and the positive implications drawn. The conclusions are in line with those of many who are in the best position to judge such matters. The leading AI researcher Edward Fredkin says: 'There's absolutely no principle of science or even engineering or practicality that gives any hint as to why we would run into some limitation. It's clear that computers will have enough memory, it's clear that they will be able to do enough processing. It's clear that in every physical way the computer will be sufficient. The only thing that stands between us and having intelligent systems is that there are a few things we don't know how to do, and we're making progress.' In 1983 OMNI assembled nine experts to consider the future of home robots. The magazine reported: 'The consultants analyzed household robots as a potential product. They disagreed, often sharply, on exactly how robots would fit into the home appliances market. But they agreed on one important point: developing the necessary technologies is not only feasible, but virtually inevitable. As engineers steadily increase the IQs of industrial robots, they are creating the technological bits and pieces that eventually will feed your Siamese, rake your leaves, and know your cravat.'

There are many rumours that the major computer and robot corporations are already experimenting with possible domestic machines. In the UK, the leading home-computer manufacturer Clive Sinclair has expressed considerable interest in developing such a product. In 1983 he set up a 'MetaLab' in Cambridge to develop new ideas and new techniques. This research laboratory and 'think-tank' will certainly consider ways in which such robots might be produced. In the US Joe Engelberger has plans for a domestic robot to be called Isaac, in honour of Asimov. With characteristic verve Engelberger says: 'It will be under voice command, and will take orders for coffee and Danish. It will be able to heat the Danish, get the cups and saucers, make the coffee, and serve it to my guests. And it will clean up afterwards and put the dishes in the dishwasher on command.' Isaac is expected to run on three wheels with tyres that swivel. Engelberger has no doubts about the viability of the domestic machine. He promises: 'We'll have robots like ladies have hats.'

There is every indication that the development of domestic robots will also become a major venture for several leading Japanese electronics corporations. Japan has made its bid to lead the world in AI research by promising a fifth-generation machine within a decade. Most of the world's industrial robots are already produced in Japan, and a 'Robotics National Project' is now under way. The country has long proved itself expert in developing mass-marketable applications for advanced technology. In 1952, just four years after the transistor had been developed at Bell Laboratories in the US, Sony introduced the first pocket-sized transistor radio. In the fields of video and laser technology, too, the Japanese have displayed their supreme skill at translating high technology into low-cost product. They seem unlikely to miss the unparalleled opportunities for commercial exploitation of fifth-generation computer technology and robotics. Fifth-generation machines will overcome many of the limitations of today's computers. Their 'commonsense' and natural conversational powers will allow them to be much more wide-ranging, flexible and useful than today's machines and they will be able to be used by anybody and everybody—not just the 'computer initiated' or the 'computer literate'. This generation of machines thus has the potential to become 'computers for the people' in a way that even today's 'user-friendly' home computers can never be. The potential consumer market is therefore truly massive.

It may not be without significance that companies such as Matsushita, Toshiba and Mitsubishi have already begun to produce industrial robots. And these companies, together with NEC, Fujitsu, Sharp and others, have also joined a consortium linked to the 'Institute for New Generation Computer Technology'—ICOT. Each company is already involved in the production of mass-market products, sold either under the company's own name or under such brand-names as 'National' and 'Technics'. Vast quantities of videorecorders, television sets and hi-fi systems are exported by these corporations, and it can be confidently predicted that the expertise and drive exhibited in developing existing home products will be put to good use in the generation of domestic robots. Indeed, it is anticipated that in the final stage of the fifth-generation project—beginning in 1989—commercial products will be designed and marketed by the corporations participating in the research. The high level of involvement of these key Japanese consumer-product companies in the most advanced fields of AI and robotics supports the thesis that home robots are likely to emerge from such research and suggests that the transition from laboratory to domestic scene will happen sooner rather than later.

It has been argued that the ideal home robot would be regarded more as a companion than as a tool or slave. Thus appearance and character would be important aspects of the design. Speech synthesis provides a technical challenge, but the talking machine will need an array of captivating 'scripts' which will call upon artistic and literary skills. As well as realism in its hardware the machine must be made to 'come alive' via its software. The current Western image of Japanese enterprise as totally technological and industrial should not blind us to the fact that there are artistic traditions in that country that may find revival in the hi-tech medium of robotics. The Japanese theatre employed humanoid machines—*karakuri*—as long ago as the 17th century. Combining clockwork technology and puppetry, the automata conveyed character subtly but powerfully. They were presented with delicacy and realism—walking, wrestling and serving tea. The combination of such traditional arts with advanced technology would yield a Japanese product of astonishing and universal impact.

One factor that might be thought to threaten the development of product robots is cost. On examination, however, this seems unlikely to prevent the arrival of character devices, although the design of a reasonably priced model may stretch ingenuity to the limits. The fifth-generation computer will represent a research investment of thousands of millions of pounds, and the first available machines will certainly be vastly expensive items. The lesson from the recent history of technological innovation in comparable fields, however, is that costs soon plummet. Video-recorders, for example, were initially affordable only by the larger television corporations but have now become household items. Until very recently computers cost a great deal and were limited in their capacity and speed; again the technology has been developed and adapted in such a way that computers are mass-market items. Home computers priced at under £250 in 1983 had a power equivalent to machines costing a quarter of a million pounds just ten years earlier. Over the three years to 1983 the price of one of the most popular home machines, the Texas Instruments 99/4A, fell by 70%. In the home-computer market cost decreases are far more common than cost increases, and falling costs have been matched by enhanced performance. It has been said that, if the automobile industry had developed like the computer business, a Rolls-Royce would now cost £1.50 and travel 3.5 million miles per gallon!

The incredible cost reduction is explained by the fact that the raw materials for the new technology are exceedingly cheap. Once the research-and-development stage has been accomplished, individual processors may be produced for very little. The cost of peripheral hardware, however, is not subject to the same phenomenal decreases. A robot would incorporate a substantial number of larger-scale engineering components and its shell alone would be fairly expensive to produce. So expenditure on a home robot will never be negligible, although manufac-turers will ensure that costs are not prohibitive. The software may be very expensive to create, but once it has been devised it can be duplicated endlessly for minimal cost. Software packages that sell today for hundreds of pounds can be copied perfectly on a magnetic disc costing less than £2. Fierce competition and huge markets would cut the cost of such packages to the con-sumer to a mere fraction of today's price. In addition, the cost of devising software will decrease substantially as programs are used to write other programs.

It is estimated that by 1985 there will be 12 million home

computers in the world. In terms of worldwide revenue electronics is now second only to oil, and computers represent a large and ever-increasing element in the industry. At the moment home computers are sold to computer-literate enthusiasts and dedicated games-players, and the machines that satisfy their needs are relatively simple and cheap. Because of its limited potential consumer population and its very cheap unit cost, the home computer is not as attractive to commercial producers as the domestic robot. The market for the home robot is practically unlimited, and industrialists know this. Engelberger has suggested that the US domestic market alone might amount to $2,000 billion, which represents, as he has remarked, 'a pretty big industry'.

It is expected that many different models will be produced, with a wide range of appearances, facilities, skills and levels of 'intelligence'. The 'state-of-the-art' luxury robot would perhaps have a finely sculpted finish, a particularly broad knowledge base, a superior intellect and a range of specialist skills. The 'basic bot', on the other hand, would be smaller in size and have less sophisticated features. It might wheel rather than walk and its vision might be less acute and less 'intelligent' than that of its costly cousin. It might be somewhat slower in its reasoning and its practical skills would be modest. But limitations in the technical sphere would be no excuse for bad manners or sullenness. The simple machine would be expected to comply with the Laws and to display friendliness, respect and faithfulness in full measure.

The robot story did not start with advanced technology. The robot image arose from the human imagination—the evidence extends past two millennia—and the inspiration that gave the artificial humanoids a birth in literature will give them shape, 'life' and character in the real world. For centuries the literary robot heritage has both reflected and contributed to a universal dream. In presenting nightmares and promising many a Utopia it has cast shadows as well as stimulating hopes. As generation after generation of fictional robots have evolved, presumptions about the humanoids have changed. No longer do we expect the lumbering golem to be crafted from clay and charmed into animation. No longer do we expect to be invaded by the assemblages of tin cans that clanked their way through early movies.

Stories and films have presented clockwork as character and have made heroes out of mechanism. We have been led to believe that robots will be useful, intelligent and friendly. Such characteristics will surely be those of the product robot. We have been promised that humanoid personalities will amuse and comfort us, and will offer companionship and help. Home robots will fulfil those promises. Within a foreseeable future—some say as near as a decade, others as far as half a century—companion robots will enter the social scene. Technology and commerce are already travelling along the paths that would seem to lead inevitably to such a development. The heritage has helped to prepare the way. It has made promises, projected images and issued warnings. But, most important of all, it has helped to raise public consciousness about the robot future. The more we think about the future the more we will know about it. And the more we know about it the more chance we have of influencing it.

Characters until now witnessed only from afar, in stories and in films, are almost ready to meet with our acquaintance. Two-dimensional characters will step out from the printed page, or movie screen, as hardware technology adds the third dimension, by producing the real product robot, and software technology adds a fourth dimension by permitting real-time 'social' interaction. As we come face to face with the machines some expectations will be met and other elements will take us by surprise. But product robots will have a distinct familiarity—for we have been well prepared. Devotees of the robot literature will experience, in their interactions with humanoid acquaintances, many moments of *déjà vu* as movie heroes and story characters are encountered 'in the flesh'. Advances in computer science and engineering will provide the medium and imagination will write the message. In this it will be aided by the heritage of fiction that has already suggested so many characterizations and provided so many possible scripts. Microchips are not an end-product: they are the new raw material. Robotics is creating a new medium, and we ourselves—aided by software impresarios—will shape the messages which that medium will convey.

The robot is a dream machine. It arose from a dream and will enhance our dreams. Time alone will make manifest its power to realize our dreams.

Bibliography

Publications referred to are those consulted and are not necessarily first editions.

FICTION

Adams, Douglas, *The Hitch-Hiker's Guide to the Galaxy*, Pan Books, London, 1979.
Asimov, Isaac.
There are three major collections of Asimov's shorter robot stories:
   I, Robot, Gnome Press, New York, 1950.
   The Rest of the Robots, Doubleday, New York, 1964.
   The Bicentennial Man, Doubleday, New York, 1977.
In the following list the stories included in these collections are annotated IR, RR or BM.
   'Robbie', (original title 'Strange Playfellow'), *Super Science Stories*, 1940. (IR)
   'Liar', *Astounding Science Fiction*, 1941. (IR)
   'Runaround', *Astounding Science Fiction*, 1942. (IR)
   'Evidence', *Astounding Science Fiction*, 1946. (IR)
   'Little Lost Robot', *Astounding Science Fiction*, 1947. (IR)
   'Satisfaction Guaranteed', *Super Science Stories*, 1951. (RR)
   'The Caves of Steel', T. V. Boardman, London, 1954.
   'First Law', *Fantastic Universe Science Fiction*, 1956. (RR)
   'Lenny', *Infinity Science Fiction*, 1958. (RR)
   'Feminine Intuition', *Fantasy and Science Fiction*, 1969. (BM)
   'That Thou Art Mindful of Him', *Fantasy and Science Fiction*, 1974. (BM)
   'The Life and Times of Multivac', *New York Times Magazine*, 1975. (BM)
   'Tercentenary Incident', *Ellery Queen's Mystery Magazine*, 1976. (BM)
   'The Bicentennial Man', *Stellar Science Fiction*, 1976. (BM)
Basile, Giambattista, *Pentamerone*, 1634. Many editions.
Baum, Frank L., *The Wonderful Wizard of Oz*, 1900. Many editions.
Bhojadena, King, *Samaranganasutradhara*, (eleventh century), Gaewad's Oriental Studies, London, 1924.
Bloch, Robert, 'Wheel and Deal'. In the collection *Atoms and Evil*, Fawcett Books, New York, 1962.
Bradbury, Ray, 'Changeling', *Super Science Stories*, 1949. Reprinted in W. F. Nolan, *The Pseudo-people*, Mayflower, London, 1965.
   'I Sing The Body Electric'. In the collection of the same name, Hart-Davis, London, 1969.
Butler, Samuel, *Erewhon*, 1872. Many editions.
Čapek, Karel, *R.U.R.*, 1921. First English translation 1923. Many editions.
Causey, James, 'The Show Must Go On'. Originally published as 'So Lovely, So Lost', *Orbit Science Fiction*, 1954. Reprinted in W. F. Nolan, *The Pseudo-people*, Mayflower, London, 1965.
Clarke, Arthur C., 'The Sentinel', *10 Story Fantasy*, 1950. Reprinted in A.C. Clarke, *The Lost Worlds of 2001*, New American Library, New York, 1972.
   2001: A Space Odyssey, Hutchinson, London, 1968.

David-Neel, Alexandra and the Lama Yongden, *The Super-human Life of Gesar of Ling*, Rider, London, 1933.

Del Rey, Lester, 'Helen O'Loy', *Astounding*, 1938. Reprinted in H. M. Geduld and R. Gottesman (eds.) *Robots, Robots, Robots*, New York Graphic Society, Boston, 1978.

Dick, Philip K., *Do Androids Dream of Electric Sheep?*, Doubleday, New York, 1968.
  We Can Build You, Daw Books, New York, 1972.

Earls, William J., 'And Baby Makes Three', *Galaxy*, 1973.

Forster, E. M., 'The Machine Stops', *Oxford and Cambridge Review*, 1909. Reprinted in E. M. Forster, *The Eternal Moment*, Sidgwick and Jackson, London, 1928.

Foster, Alan D., *The Black Hole*, Times Mirror, New York, 1979.

Goldstone, Herbert, 'Virtuoso', *The Magazine of Fantasy and Science Fiction*, 1953.

Goulart, Ron, *Crackpot*, Doubleday, New York, 1977.

Harrison, Harry, 'The Robot Who Wanted to Know'. In the collection *War With the Robots*, Pyramid Publications, New York, 1962.

Hoffmann, E. T. A., *Automata*, 1814. Many editions.
  The Sandman, 1816. Many editions.

Homer, *The Iliad*, (c. 750 BC). Many editions.

Lee, Tanith, *The Silver Metal Lover*, Daw, New York, 1982.

Leiber, Fritz, *The Silver Eggheads*, Ballantine Books, New York, 1961.

Lem, Stanislaw, 'The Sanatorium of Dr Vliperdius', Polish publication, 1971. English translation by Michael Kandel, included in *Mortal Engines*, Avon Books, New York, 1977.

Levin, Ira, *This Perfect Day*, Random House, New York, 1970.
  The Stepford Wives, Random House, New York, 1972.

Mahabharata, orig. eighth-century BC and later. 7-volume edited translation from the Sanskrit by J. A. B. van Buitenan, University of Chicago Press, 1973–85.

Miedaner, Terrel, *The Soul of Anna Klane*, 1977. Extract in D. R. Hofstadter and D. Dennett, *The Mind's I*, Basic Books, New York, 1981.

Nolan, William F., 'The Joy of Living', *If: Worlds of Science Fiction*, 1954. Reprinted in W. F. Nolan, *The Pseudo-people*, Mayflower, London, 1965.

Oliver, Chad, 'The Life Game', *Thrilling Wonder Stories*, 1953. Reprinted in W. F. Nolan, *The Pseudo-people*, Mayflower, London, 1965.

Pohl, Frederick, The Midas Plague, *Galaxy*, 1954. Reprinted in *The Best of Frederick Pohl*, Futura, London, 1976.

Sheckley, Robert, 'Ticket to Tranai'. In the collection *Citizen in Space*, Ballantine, New York, 1955.
  'Can You Feel Anything When I Do This?'. In the collection of the same name, Doubleday, New York, 1969.

Shelley, Mary, *Frankenstein*, 1818. Many editions.

Simak, Clifford D., *City*, Ace Books, New York, 1952.

Villiers de l'Isle Adam, Jean Marie, *L'Eve future*, 1886. Many editions but no English translation.

Wyndham, John, 'Compassion Circuit', *Fantastic Universe*, 1954. Reprinted in J. Wyndham, *The Seeds of Time*, Michael Joseph, London, 1956.

NON-FICTION

Aldiss, Brian, *Billion Year Spree*, Weidenfeld and Nicolson, London, 1973.

Amis, Kingsley, *New Maps of Hell*, Gollancz, London, 1961.

Asimov, Isaac, 'The Perfect Machine', *Science Journal*, October 1968, pp. 115–18.

Baxter, John, *Science Fiction in the Cinema*, The Paperback Library, New York, 1970.

Boden, Margaret, *Artificial Intelligence and Natural Man*, Harvester, Brighton, 1977.

Brandon, Stanley, *Creation Legends of the Ancient Near East*, Hodder and Stoughton, London, 1963.

Brosnan, John, *Future Tense: The cinema of Science Fiction*, St Martin's Press, New York, 1978.

Cohen, John, *Human Robots in Myth and Science*, George Allen and Unwin, London, 1966.

Engelberger, Joseph, *Robotics in Practice*, Kogan Page, London, 1981.

Feigenbaum, Edward and McCorduck, Pamela, *The Fifth Generation*, Michael Joseph, London, 1984.

Florescu, Radu, *In Search of Frankenstein*, New English Library, London, 1977.

Frude, Neil, *The Intimate Machine*, Century, London, 1983.

Jacobi, Jolande (ed.) *Paracelsus: Selected Writings*, Routledge Kegan Paul, London, 1969.

Johnson, William (ed.), Focus on the Science Fiction Film, Prentice-Hall, New Jersey, 1972.

Jung, Carl, *Alchemical Studies*. Vol. 13 of the *Collected Works*, Routledge Kegan Paul, London, 1967.

Lighthill, Sir James, *Artificial Intelligence*, Science Research Council, London, 1973.

Marriott, Alice and Rachlin, Carol, *American Indian Mythology*, New American Library, New York, 1968.

Marsh, Peter, *The Robot Age*, Sphere Books, London, 1982.

McCorduck, Pamela, *Machines Who Think*, W. H. Freeman, San Francisco, 1979.

Mowshowitz, Abbe, *Inside Information: Computers in Fiction*, Addison-Wesley, Reading, Massachussetts, 1977.

Nicholls, Peter, *Science Fiction at Large*, Gollancz, London, 1976.

   (ed.), *The Encyclopaedia of Science Fiction*, Granada, London, 1981.

Philmus, Robert, *Into the Unknown: the Evolution of Science Fiction from Francis Godwin to H. G. Wells*, University of California Press, Berkeley and Los Angeles, 1970.

Schaya, Leo, *The Universal Meaning of the Kabbalah*, Viking, New York, 1971.

Sobchack Vivian C., *The Limits of Infinity–the American Science Fiction Film 1950–1975*, A. S. Barnes, New Jersey, 1980.

Taylor, F. Sherwood, *The Alchemists*, Granada, London, 1976.

Walker, Alexander, *Stanley Kubrick Directs*, Abacus, London, 1973.

Warrick, Patricia S., *The Cybernetic Imagination in Science Fiction*, M.I.T. Press, Cambridge, Massachussets, 1980.

Waters, Frank, *Mexico Mystique*, Swallow Press, Chicago, 1975.

Wolfe, Gary K., *The Known and the Unknown: the Iconography of Science Fiction*, Kent State University Press, Kent, Ohio, 1979.

Filmography

The films mentioned in the text are listed here in chronological order of their release.

The Clown and the Automaton, 1887. Dir. George Melies, France.
Frankenstein, 1910. Dir. J. Searle Dawley, The Edison Company, US.
Der Golem, 1914. Dir. Paul Wegener, UFA, Germany.
Der Homunculus, 1915. Dir. Otto Rippert, Bioscop, Germany.
Metropolis, 1926. Dir. Fritz Lang, UFA, Germany.
Frankenstein, 1931. Dir. James Whale, Universal, US.
Devil Doll, 1936. Dir. Tod Browning, MGM, US.
The Wizard of Oz, 1939. Dir. Victor Fleming, MGM, US.
Dr Satan's Robot, 1940. Dir. William Whitney, US.
The Perfect Woman, 1949. Dir. Bernard Knowles, Two Cities/Eagle-Lion, UK.
The Day the Earth Stood Still, 1951. Robert Wise, 20th Century-Fox, US.
Tobor the Great, 1954. Dir. Lee Sholem, US.
Forbidden Planet, 1956. Dir. Fred McLeod Wilcox, MGM, US.
The Invisible Boy, 1957. Dir. Herman Hoffman, MGM, US.
Creation of the Humanoids, 1962. Dir. Wesley Barry, Genie, US.
Storm Planet, 1962. Dir. Pavel Klushantsev, Leningrad Science Films, USSR.
2001: A Space Odyssey, 1968. Dir. Stanley Kubrick, MGM, US.
Colossus: The Forbin Project, 1969. Dir. Joseph Sargent, Universal, US.
THX 1138, 1969. Dir. George Lucas, American Zoetrope, US.
No Blade of Grass, 1970. Dir. Cornel Wilde, Symbol/MGM, US.
Silent Running, 1972. Dir. Douglas Trumbull, Universal, US.
Soylent Green, 1973. Dir. Richard Fleischer, MGM, US.
The Stepford Wives, 1973. Dir. Bryan Forbes, Columbia, US.
Westworld, 1973. Dir. Michael Crichton, Columbia, US.
Dark Star, 1974. Dir. John Carpenter, a Jack H. Harris release, US.
Futureworld, 1976. Dir. Richard T. Heffron, AIP, US.
Demon Seed, 1977. Dir. Donald Cammell, MGM, US.
Star Wars, 1977. Dir. George Lucas, 20th Century-Fox, US.
The Black Hole, 1979. Dir. Gary Nelson, Walt Disney, US.
Saturn Three, 1980. Dir. Stanley Donen, ITC, US.
The Empire Strikes Back, 1980. Dir. George Lucas, 20th Century-Fox, US.
Android, 1982. Dir. Aaron Lipstadt, Iver, US.
Blade Runner, 1982. Dir. Ridley Scott, a Ladd Company release, US.
E.T. The Extra-terrestrial, 1982. Dir. Steven Spielberg, Universal, US.
Return of the Jedi, 1983. Dir. George Lucas, 20th Century-Fox, US.

Index

The appearance of (f) after a keyword indicates that the individual or organization is fictional. Only the more important human fictional characters are listed, and fictional robot characters appear under their first names. The references under such headings as robots, SF and AI are of necessity selective.